SO-CEY-296

Time to Wonder

Time to Wonder

Bernard J. Weiss
Lyman C. Hunt

Educational Consultants
Eloise Eskridge / Janet Sprout / Millie Moore

THE HOLT BASIC READING SYSTEM
· LEVEL 13 ·

Holt, Rinehart and Winston, Inc.
New York · Toronto · London · Sydney

Printed in the United States of America
ISBN 0-03-070905-9
89   032   98

Acknowledgments

Grateful acknowledgment is hereby made to the following authors, publishers, agents, and individuals for their special permission to reprint copyrighted material.

AMERICAN BOOK COMPANY, for "The Friendly Cricket," a Costa Rican folk song, copyright 1948.

ATHENEUM PUBLISHERS, for "Ululation," from *It Doesn't Always Have to Rhyme*, copyright © 1964 by Eve Merriam.

ATHENEUM PUBLISHERS, THE BODLEY HEAD, LTD., and ERIKA KLOPP VERLAG, for "The Would-Be Cowboy," adapted from *Grandmother Oma* by Ilse Kleberger, copyright © 1964 by Erika Klopp Verlag, Berlin; English translation copyright © 1966 by The Bodley Head, Ltd.

ATHENEUM PUBLISHERS and BRANDT & BRANDT, for "The Grasshopper," from *Cats and Bats and Things with Wings*, text copyright © 1965 by Conrad Aiken.

ATLANTIC-LITTLE, BROWN AND COMPANY, for "Books Fall Open," "The Clouds," "Pad and Pencil," "Singular Indeed," from *All Day Long* by David McCord, copyright © 1965 and 1966 by David McCord; for "Father in the Woods," "The Newt," from *Far and Few* by David McCord, copyright 1952 by David McCord; for "The Pickety Fence," from *Every Time I Climb a Tree* by David McCord, copyright 1952 by David McCord; for "Take Sky," "The Importance of Eggs," from *Take Sky* by David McCord, copyright © 1961 and 1962 by David McCord; for "I Shall Not Live in Vain," from *The Complete Poems of Emily Dickinson*, edited by Thomas H. Johnson; and for "Names for Twins," from *Ounce, Dice, Trice* by Alastair Reid, copyright © 1958 by Alastair Reid and Ben Shahn.

ATLANTIC-LITTLE, BROWN AND COMPANY and CURTIS BROWN, LTD., New York, for "Crocodile," from *Boy Blue's Book of Beasts* by William Jay Smith, copyright © 1956, 1957 by William Jay Smith.

5

6

THE WORLD PUBLISHING COMPANY, for "The Animal Parade," from *The Rainbow Book of Nature* by Donald Culross Peattie, copyright © 1957 by Donald Culross Peattie.

THE WORLD PUBLISHING COMPANY and WILLIAM COLE, as agent, for "Sarah Cynthia Sylvia Stout" by Shel Silverstein, from *Beastly Boys and Ghastly Girls*, collected by William Cole, copyright © 1964 by Shel Silverstein.

ILLUSTRATION CREDITS

(Numbers refer to pages. Credits not listed here appear with the illustrations.)

24–36   Muriel Wood
38–39   Tim and Greg Hildebrandt
40–53   Muriel Wood
55–57   Diane de Groat
58–63   Harry Schaare
64–65   Jim Spanfeller
66–89   Muriel Wood
95–101 Joseph Cellini
110–119 Tim and Greg Hildebrandt
120–136 Ted Lewin
138   Viewpoint Graphics, Inc.
139–141 Maybe Trousdell
142   Diane de Groat
143   Maybe Trousdell
144–145 Ray Cruz
146–151 Bob Pepper
152   Jerry Pinkney
153–162 Diane de Groat
163–168 Kyuzo Tsugami
169   Richard Amundsen
171–177 Joseph Cellini
179   Jerry Pinkney
187–209 Paul Giovanopoulos
210   TOP: photo by Nadar, Archives Photographiques, Paris; BOTTOM: New York Public Library
211   Diane de Groat
212–214 Jerry Lang

215   C. G. Maxwell from National Audubon Society
217   John H. Gerard from National Audubon Society
218   Jerry Lang
219   Ray Cruz
220–225 Diane de Groat
226   TOP AND CENTER: New York Public Library; BOTTOM: Scurlock Studio, Washington, D.C.
227   TOP LEFT: Dennis Brokaw; TOP RIGHT: Brown Brothers; BOTTOM: Johnson Publishers
228–244 Betty Fraser
246–247 Robert Owens
248   TOP: Courtesy of the American Museum of Natural History; CENTER AND BOTTOM: Gifts of Mrs. Walter B. James, National Gallery of Art, Washington, D.C.
249   Ethel Gold
250–253 Jerry Lang
255   Arthur Freed
262–267 Phil Smith
268   John Loengard, *Life* Magazine, © Time, Inc.
269   UNICEF
270   C.B.S.

271 Courtesy of the Dance Collection, New York Public Library
272–288 Denver Gillen
314–315 Ethel Gold
332–340 Kyuzo Tsugami
342–343 Diane de Groat
344–349 Denver Gillen
350–355 Loretta Lustig
356–357 Betty Fraser
358–371 Phil Smith
372–391 Tim and Greg Hildebrandt
392–407 Douglas Gorsline

414–428 Ted Lewin
429–430 Viewpoint Graphics, Inc.
431 Harry Schaare
436–437 Ray Cruz
438–449 Tim and Greg Hildebrandt
451 Victor Valla
452–458 Maybe Trousdell
462–468 Joseph Phelan
469–484 Colos
485 George Solonevich
COVER, CONTENTS PAGES, AND UNIT OPENERS constructed by SN Studio

9

TABLE OF CONTENTS

UNIT 1

BOOKS WILL VENTURE

10

UNIT 2

THE GIFT OF LANGUAGE

UNIT 3

THE WONDER OF LIFE

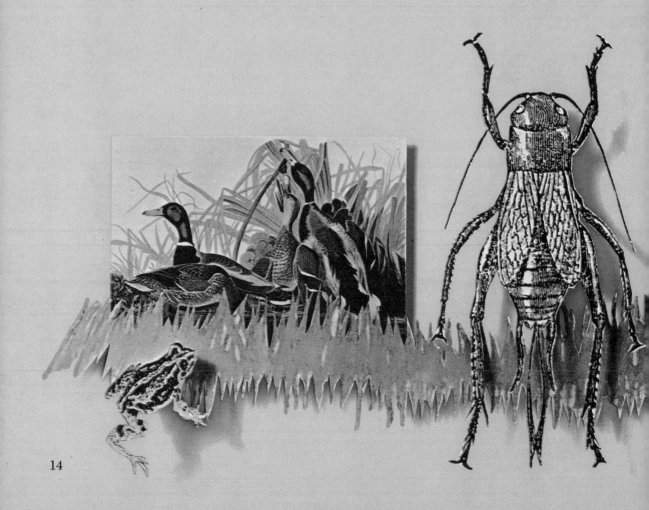

15

UNIT 4

A DIFFERENT DRUMMER

16

UNIT 6

TO CATCH THE HIGH WINDS

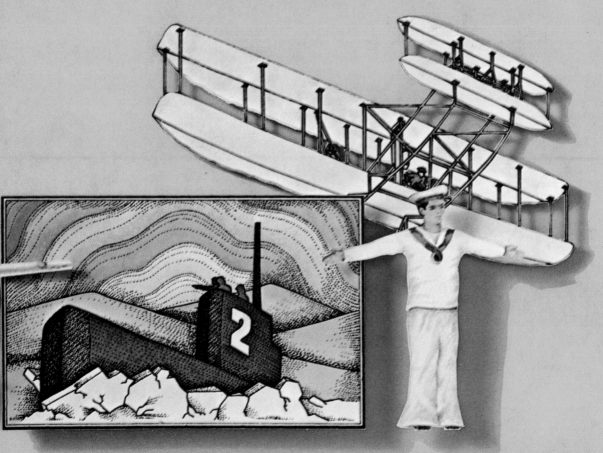

Unit 1
BOOKS WILL VENTURE

Books Fall Open

Books fall open,
you fall in,
delighted where
you've never been;
hear voices not once
heard before,
reach world on world
through door on door;
find unexpected
keys to things
locked up beyond
imaginings. . . .
True books will venture,
dare you out,
whisper secrets
maybe shout
across the gloom
to you in need,
who hanker for
a book to read.

David McCord

23

The Magnificent Brain Concocts a Recipe

CLIFFORD B. HICKS

All Flibbertyneedled

It had all started on a rainy, blustery day in March. They were alone in the house because Mrs. Fernald, Alvin's mother, was at a club meeting.

Shoie, Alvin's best friend, was there—and the Pest. Eight years old, she worshiped her big brother, Alvin, and showed it. She was Alvin's slave and shadow, bothering him all the time. This is why he'd started calling her the Pest, instead of Daphne, many years ago.

Shoie let her tag along after them because she always made him laugh. Shoie had an easygoing sense of humor. He was half a head taller than Alvin, although they were the same age within a few days of each other. Around Roosevelt School he was known as the Great Athlete because he could run faster, stand on his head longer, and throw a baseball farther than any other kid. His real name was Wilfred Shoemaker, but early in life he'd been nicknamed Shoie.

The kids sat in the living room arguing about whether Miss Hootens, who taught third grade, wore a wig, whether Shoie was a good enough ballplayer to make the major leagues, and whether, if you were trapped in a falling elevator, you should jump up and grab the light fixture.

Alvin was growing tired of the arguments. He was, as he put it, all *flibbertyneedled* inside from the long winter and the bad weather. Alvin often made up words to describe how he felt, and today *flibbertyneedled* seemed to fit just right.

He had picked up one of his mother's magazines and was turning the pages when his eye suddenly stopped at an advertisement that announced, "You can win any one of a thousand valuable prizes." He was reading the rules of the contest when Shoie glanced at him. Alvin's face was scrunched into a frown, and his eyes were glazed. It was a sure sign the Magnificent Brain was working.

"What's up?" asked Shoie, who was immediately interested.

Alvin didn't even hear him. Shoie went over and bonked him lightly on top of the head, which he knew was the only way to unplug the Magnificent Brain. Alvin's Magnificent Brain was a separate part of his mind over which he had no control. When it took over, his eyes glazed and no one could get through to him. Shoie had named it the Magnificent Brain because the phrase seemed to describe some huge computer, always flashing with new thoughts.

"What's up, Alvin?"

Alvin stood up and shook his head to clear the circuits. "We're going to win a contest. It says here that we can win any one of a thousand valuable prizes for inventing a new candy."

"Inventing a new candy," repeated the Pest. She had a habit of repeating the last few words anyone said, and a conversation with the Pest always sounded like there was an echo in the room. "We ought to put chocolate in it."

"And cinnamon," said Shoie. "Cinnamon has a good flavor."

There was a pause as they thought it over. Then they all headed for the kitchen at once.

Globbledy Gook

"Who's running the contest?" asked the Pest as she got out a big pan.

"The Kitchenmate Appliance Company," replied Alvin. "They make all kinds of ranges and refrigerators and stuff. Where's the sugar?"

"It's inside the bowl over there, but you need a little butter first." The Pest was taking charge because cooking was a girl's job, although she often complained to her parents because they had not made her a boy. She put a little butter in the pan and turned on the burner. "Now put in some milk and sugar, Alvin."

Alvin dumped in enough sugar to cover the bottom of the pan about an inch deep. He poured in a little milk.

Meanwhile Shoie had found the baking chocolate, and now he stood halfway across the room, flipping in the squares one by one as though he were tossing free throws on a basketball court.

Alvin went through the kitchen cabinets.

"Corn syrup," decided the Pest. "And a little brown sugar."

"And cinnamon," repeated Shoie.

They dumped in these ingredients, paying no attention to the amounts.

"Sometimes they put cereal in candy," suggested Shoie. He imitated the voice of the TV announcer. "'I eat Good Omens because they start off my day with a smile on my lips and a song in my heart.'"

A cup of Good Omens disappeared into the pan, followed by half a dozen marshmallows.

Alvin found an envelope half full of powder to make grape-flavored frozen suckers and tossed it to Shoie, who dumped it all in. Alvin had come across a small bottle of orange-colored liquid. "Tabasco," he read off the label. "Anybody know what it is?"

The other kids, searching for possible ingredients, were too busy to answer, so Alvin shook some of the colored liquid into the pot, which by now began to bubble. He turned down the burner, and then he shook in a few more drops of the liquid.

"It's getting kind of *globbledy,*" he reported to the others. "Maybe we ought to add some water or something."

The Pest had been exploring the refrigerator, and now she came up with half a glass of lemonade which she had stored in there the week before. She dumped it into the pot instead of water "just to give it a little better flavor."

"Cinnamon," said Shoie. "More cinnamon." Alvin shook the rest of the can of cinnamon into the pot and for good measure added something called allspice that he'd found in the cabinet.

Looking into the slowly bubbling pot, the Pest shook her head. "It's got kind of an awful purplish color, Alvin. There's some food coloring on the shelf over there. Let's see if we can make it look better."

First she tried red, but that seemed to work badly with the purple powder, turning the candy a sickening violet. Yellow helped a little, but not much.

"This stuff labeled 'Tabasco' is bright orange," said Alvin. "Maybe if we used a little more of it—" Again he shook the bottle into the pot. It didn't seem to help much. He tried adding some green food coloring. The purplish mess turned to a rather odd brown.

"How long do you suppose we ought to cook it?" Shoie asked the Pest, who was slowly stirring the bubbling contents of the pot with a wooden spoon.

"Soft-ball stage," she said. It was clear to Alvin and Shoie that she didn't know what soft-ball stage was, but it sounded good. The three kids stood around the pot watching the mess thicken.

The Pest lifted the spoon out and let a clump of the candy drop into the pot. Suddenly, as though the wooden spoon were a magic wand, the candy stopped bubbling and turned solid before their eyes. At the same moment a horrible burning smell rolled up from the pot.

"Quick, turn off the burner!" shouted Alvin.

The Pest dropped the spoon back into the pot and turned off the heat. "Now we've got to beat it," she announced brightly, "like Mom beats the fudge."

"What do you beat it for?" asked Alvin.

"To make it smooth."

"Here," said Alvin, taking charge. "Let a man do it."

When he grabbed the spoon, he found that it was stuck. He pulled harder, with no success. Finally Shoie stood on the pan while Alvin tugged upward on the spoon. There was a sudden pop, and the candy, with the spoon still stuck in it, went sailing up toward the ceiling, flew across the room, and plopped down on one of the kitchen stools.

Alvin looked at it for a long moment, then walked over and picked up the spoon. The entire stool came off the floor.

"That's the worst mess I ever saw," said Shoie. "But we ought to taste it." He got a sharp knife from a drawer, managed to saw off a piece, and popped it into his mouth.

"Arrrrrrgh! Arrrrrrrgh!" He ran for the sink and swallowed a full glass of water without stopping. "That stuff," he gasped, "is living fire!"

"Let me try some," said the Pest.

Alvin sawed off a piece for her, and she slipped it into her mouth. Trying to show off in front of the boys, she didn't run for the sink, but big tears appeared in her eyes, and she snorted in great gasps of air.

By now the sticky mess had settled a bit across the seat of the stool. Alvin knew the other two would call him chicken for weeks if he didn't try a piece himself, so he sawed off a glob, took a deep breath, put the piece in his mouth, and bit down hard.

The trouble was, as he said later, the stuff not only was burning hot, but stuck his teeth together. He stood there making choking sounds deep in his throat as he tried to pry his jaws apart. Meanwhile the Pest was hopping around on one foot with tears streaming down her face, and Shoie was fanning his open mouth with both hands.

It was at that moment that Mom walked into the kitchen.

Fernald's Fireballs

After they'd cleaned up the mess as well as they could, Shoie was sent home, and Alvin and the Pest were sent to their rooms to "think about"

ruining the kitchen stool. Alvin went to his desk, took out a pencil, and sat there staring at the contest entry form he'd taken to the room with him. He had to admit it wasn't very good candy, but maybe somebody would like it. He began filling in the form.

"Name of Candy" was the first line. Alvin sat thinking for a long time. Finally he licked the tip of the pencil and carefully printed "Fernald's Fireballs."

The next line said: "Ingredients." Here he was lost. He couldn't possibly remember everything they'd put in. He wrote down a few of the ingredients, and after each of them he wrote "one cup" or "three teaspoons" or "two pinches, to taste," which was a phrase he'd picked up from one of his mother's cookbooks. He couldn't remember the name of the orange stuff in the strange little bottle, so he left that out.

Finally, under "Cooking Instructions," he wrote: "Let simmer over low heat to soft-ball stage, stirring constantly. Then put the pan in cold water and beat it—I mean the candy, not the pan. Can be rolled into balls or wrapped around ice cream sticks." He thought for a moment, then smiled to himself and added a final line, "Either way, it has a very unusual taste."

He placed the entry form in an envelope, sealed it, and waited for Dad to come home. He knew he was in for a lecture about that stool.

Two months later, when he'd forgotten all about the contest, came the letter announcing that he'd won a prize. He stood there in the hallway with Shoie and the Pest, hardly believing what he'd read.

"Do you suppose they *really* liked that awful stuff?" he asked in a low voice.

"I can't believe it!" said Shoie.

"Can't believe it." said the Pest.

"Did you write down everything we put in?" asked Shoie.

Alvin tried to remember. "No. No, I couldn't remember everything, and besides I had to guess at the amounts." Suddenly everything clicked into place. "That's it!" he said. "I couldn't remember everything, so I must have invented a new candy right out of my head—"

"The Magnificent Brain did it again!" shouted Shoie.

"—and won a prize!" finished Alvin.

"Won a prize!" echoed the Pest.

Reflections

1. What other name might you give for the separate part of Alvin's mind called the Magnificent Brain?

2. Have you ever felt "flibbertyneedled"? What was the feeling like, and how did you get over it? How did Alvin get over it?

3. Where was Alvin's mother? Why is that fact important to the story?

4. Does the color of food make a difference as to whether you like it or not? Give examples. How do you form an opinion about food before you taste it?

5. What name would you have given the horrible candy?

6. Why did Alvin smile as he added the final line to his recipe: "Either way, it has a very unusual taste"?

Sarah Cynthia Sylvia Stout

SHELLEY SILVERSTEIN

Sarah Cynthia Sylvia Stout
would not take the garbage out!
She'd boil the water
and open the cans
and scrub the pots
and scour the pans
and grate the cheese
and shell the peas
and mash the yams
and spice the hams
and make the jams.
But though her daddy
would scream and shout,
she would not take the garbage out.
And so it piled up to the ceilings:
Coffee grounds, potato peelings,
stale bread and withered greens,
olive pits and soggy beans,
cracker boxes, chicken bones,
clamshells, eggshells, stale scones,
sour cream and soggy plums,
stale cake and cookie crumbs.

At last the garbage piled so high
that finally it reached the sky.
And none of her friends
would come to play.
And all the neighbors moved away.
And finally Sarah Cynthia Stout
said, "I'll take the garbage out!"
But then, of course, it was too late.
The garbage reached beyond the state,
from Memphis to the Golden Gate.
And Sarah met an awful fate,
which I cannot right now relate
because the hour is much too late.
But, children, think of Sarah Stout
and always take the garbage out!

The Boy Who Changed His Mind
NELLIE BURCHARDT

That Awful Reggie Thompson

The three o'clock bell clanged inside the school on First Avenue. Almost at once the boys of Mrs. Sullivan's fourth grade, which was nearest the door, burst out onto the sidewalk. As usual, Reggie Thompson was in the lead. He blinked and shaded his eyes with his hand as he came out into the June sunlight.

"Hey, Reggie," yelled a boy behind him. Reggie turned his head just in time to be hit in the face with a baseball cap.

"I'll get you for that, Joey," he yelled.

He snatched the cap from the ground and flung it back at Joey. Joey ducked when he saw it coming, and the cap hit a girl behind him.

She shrieked. "You awful Reggie Thompson! I'm going to tell Mrs. Sullivan on you."

"I should worry, I should care," chanted Reggie. "Come on, Joey."

The boys tore off at top speed along the crowded sidewalk. A group of girls scattered before them with little shrieks.

"It's that awful Reggie Thompson," said one of the girls.

"He's the worst pest in the whole school," another added.

By now Reggie and Joey had reached the next block. Down at the other end a big metal ball swung back and forth from a crane as wreckers were turning buildings into piles of rubble. At this end of the block the empty houses were still standing, with all their windows marked by big white X's.

In the next block they slowed down. Across the street was the City Housing Project, where they both lived. They started to take a shortcut through the playground.

At the entrance was a sign.

Reggie read the sign out loud. "How do they expect a guy to live around here?" he grumbled. "It's a wonder they don't make a rule against breathing."

"Yeah," agreed Joey. "What do they want us to do? Play with dolls like girls? Or play in the sandbox with the little kids there?"

Beyond the playground was Reggie's building, and there the project trees began—the only trees within blocks. In one of them was a nestful of blue jay fledglings. Two of them had just pulled themselves up to the edge of the nest, where they teetered and clutched the rim with their still-weak claws. They stretched their half-grown wings. It would still be some time before they were strong enough to fly.

"I'll bet I can hit that no-good old blue jay there," said Reggie. As no stone was handy, he picked up a crushed tin can lying beside a wastebasket and threw it at the birds.

"Missed," shrieked Joey. "Is your aim rotten today!"

One baby jay fluttered unsteadily back into the nest. The other one flapped its wings wildly, then lost its balance, and fell to the ground.

Several girls walking behind the boys screamed.

"Ha!" said Reggie. "I did not miss. I got him, all right, all right." The bird lay on the ground, its eyes closed. "I got him. I got him," bragged Reggie. He did a dance around the trunk of the tree.

"Aw-w-w. It's a baby bird," cried one of the girls.

"Reggie Thompson, you're the meanest boy in the whole school," said another. It was that silly Diane from his class. She was always screaming. Reggie couldn't stand her.

He stopped prancing around the tree. "I sure am," he said, grinning proudly. "And I've got the best aim in the whole school, too," he boasted.

"Is the bird dead?" asked Diane.

Reggie shrugged. "I guess so," he said.

"Why don't you find out?" asked Diane.

Reggie looked at her. "How?" he asked.

"Why don't you pick it up?"

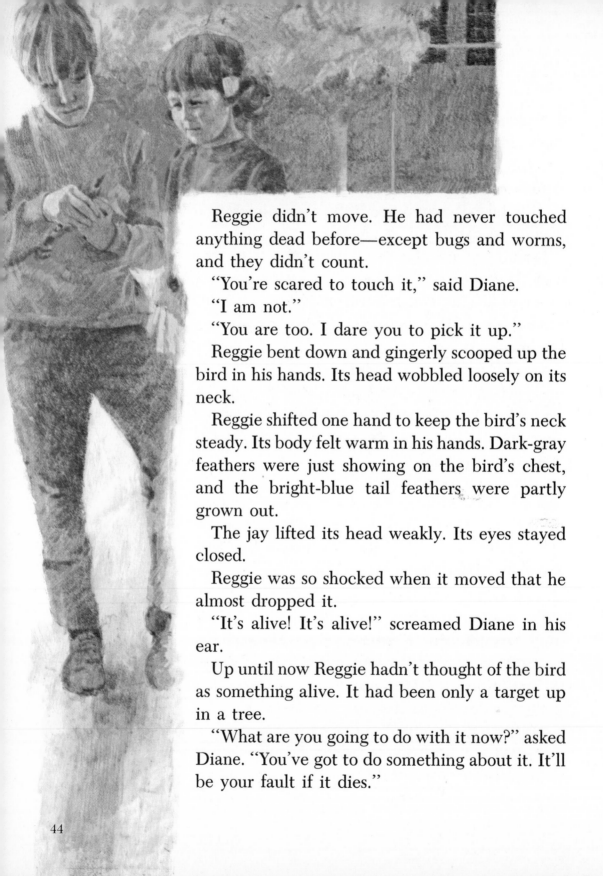

Reggie didn't move. He had never touched anything dead before—except bugs and worms, and they didn't count.

"You're scared to touch it," said Diane.

"I am not."

"You are too. I dare you to pick it up."

Reggie bent down and gingerly scooped up the bird in his hands. Its head wobbled loosely on its neck.

Reggie shifted one hand to keep the bird's neck steady. Its body felt warm in his hands. Dark-gray feathers were just showing on the bird's chest, and the bright-blue tail feathers were partly grown out.

The jay lifted its head weakly. Its eyes stayed closed.

Reggie was so shocked when it moved that he almost dropped it.

"It's alive! It's alive!" screamed Diane in his ear.

Up until now Reggie hadn't thought of the bird as something alive. It had been only a target up in a tree.

"What are you going to do with it now?" asked Diane. "You've got to do something about it. It'll be your fault if it dies."

Suddenly Reggie wished he had never heard of tin cans or blue jays—or girls either, for that matter. Why did the silly girls have to make such a fuss over an old blue jay?

"I'll take it home and take care of it," said Diane, reaching out her hand for the bird.

"You keep your hands off him. He's my bird," Reggie said.

He undid the two top buttons of his shirt and tucked the bird inside.

"What are you going to do with it?" asked Diane.

"Mind your own business," said Reggie. He turned and went up the walk toward his own building. He felt the bird stir inside his shirt. Now why on earth had he taken the bird, and what was he going to do with it? He really didn't know. He just knew he wasn't going to let any girl have his bird.

Nice for a Change

The next day all the girls in Reggie's class were talking about his blue jay. It wasn't surprising that Mrs. Sullivan, Reggie's teacher, heard them.

"So you have a blue jay, Reginald," she said. "How interesting! You must come up front and tell the class about it.

"Where did you get your blue jay, Reginald?" asked Mrs. Sullivan when Reggie had made his way to the front of the class.

"I—I found him. He fell out of his nest in one of the trees on the project," said Reggie, shifting from one foot to the other.

"Blue jays aren't very common around here," said Mrs. Sullivan. "They must have flown over from the park. What did you name your bird, Reginald?"

"Charley."

"And how old is he?"

"I'm not sure. But I know he can't fly yet. All he does is flap his wings."

"And what does your bird eat?" asked Mrs. Sullivan.

"Caterpillars and stuff like that."

The girls made a big show of shuddering.

"All right, girls," said Mrs. Sullivan, "if you were blue jays, you'd think caterpillars were delicious."

Then Reggie listened in amazement as Mrs. Sullivan said, "I do hope you'll bring Charley to school. Not many of us have seen a baby blue jay."

She smiled at him as he sat down. Reggie couldn't remember when a teacher had last smiled at him. Bringing Charley in to school might even help on his report card, he thought, and he sure could use a little help.

That afternoon Reggie and Joey asked Mr. Santino, Reggie's neighbor, to help them build a cage for Charley. Mr. Santino had been a carpenter, but since he spent most of his time at home now, he was happy to help the boys.

In a week they had finished the cage, and Reggie took Charley to school in it. The whole class crowded around to see him, and he was a big hit.

"Isn't he sweet?"

"Can I hold him?"

"Let me pat him."

"Huh, I don't see what's so great about him," said Eddie Halloran. "He can't even talk like my parrakeet can." He walked to his seat without giving Charley another glance.

Finally Mrs. Sullivan had to tell Reggie to set Charley's cage on the ledge at the back of the room so that the class could get some work done.

Suddenly Reggie heard a squawk from Charley. He turned his head just in time to see Eddie, who sat in a back seat, give Charley a poke with a pencil through the bars of his cage.

"You leave that bird alone, Eddie!" shouted Reggie. He jumped to his feet and swung at Eddie. Eddie ducked and fell out of his seat onto the floor, with Reggie on top of him.

"Stop it this instant, you two!" called Mrs. Sullivan as she pulled Eddie and Reggie apart. "That was a mean thing to do, Edward," she said. "I saw the whole thing. March right up here to a front seat for the rest of the day. I see I'll have to keep an eye on you."

Reggie was surprised that Mrs. Sullivan hadn't scolded him for trying to punch Eddie. The way the girls in the class acted was even more surprising. Even the ones who had always treated Reggie as if he had something catching were treating him like a hero. It was nice, Reggie decided, to be a hero for a change.

Reggie wasn't sure who thought of the idea, but all of a sudden everyone was promising to bring in food for Charley. Then Mrs. Sullivan found out that Reggie and Joey had helped to make the cage themselves. "To think that you made it!" she said as she looked at the cage. She kept smiling at Reggie and Joey so much that Reggie began to wonder if he shouldn't get into trouble just to feel more like himself again.

When Reggie got home that afternoon, he was feeling very happy. He went straight to his room and took Charley out of his cage. As he held him, Reggie noticed something was different about Charley. He was beginning to look just like the adult jays Reggie saw now and then outside. Only the smoky dark feathers on his face and throat and his lighter-colored beak marked Charley as a young bird. Reggie supposed he'd have to let him go soon. The only question was, would Charley know how to feed himself? Up until now he would not eat unless Reggie fed him.

All at once, the jays in the tree outside started shrieking. Both Reggie and Charley looked up at the open window. When Charley heard "Ja-ay!" from outside the window, he went wild. Sometime, long ago, that sound had meant something to him. Angrily he struck out at the hands that held him, and all at once the hands were gone. Charley hurled himself through the open window and toward the screeching "Ja-ay!" He beat his full-grown wings wildly, suddenly found his balance in the air, and was flying.

"Charley!" shrieked Reggie. "Come back here!" But he could do nothing but watch helplessly as Charley flew toward the tree where the other jays were calling. The leaves hid him as he landed somewhere among the lower branches. As long as there was any daylight left, Reggie kept watching the tree, but he saw nothing. Finally, when it grew dark, Reggie went to bed. Charley was gone.

All the Pets in the World

The next day was Saturday, and Reggie got up very early. He left some bread crumbs on the windowsill, just in case Charley did come back, and then he went outside to the playground. It was empty, and Reggie walked slowly in the direction of some cement barrels that were placed on their sides and painted with bright colors. When he was smaller, he used to crawl inside one of them to hide. He crawled inside one now.

After a while he saw a small black and white dog trotting along, sniffing at each barrel. When he got to Reggie's barrel, he began wagging his tail so hard, it almost knocked Reggie over.

"Go on! Go on home!" Reggie said. The dog gave a little bark, as if to say, "You can't fool me. I know you're only joking."

"I said, go on home! Go on! Get out of here!" shouted Reggie. He picked up a pebble and pretended to throw it at the dog. The dog walked

away slowly. Reggie put the pebble down. The dog looked so unhappy. "He's a nice little mutt," Reggie told himself. "And anyway, even if Charley is gone, it isn't the dog's fault."

"Hey!" called Reggie. "Come on back! Here, boy! Come on, boy! Good boy!"

The dog came back with joyful leaps and flung himself into the barrel and onto Reggie. Reggie covered up his face with his arms as the dog tried to lick it all over. He rubbed the dog's ears for a while. Then he said, "You'd better go now." He gave the dog a little pat, and it ran off.

Reggie started back home and met Joey on the way. He told him about Charley, and then, without saying another word, the two boys walked slowly back to Reggie's house.

In Reggie's room they went straight to the window to see if any of the food Reggie had left for Charley was gone.

"One bread crumb is gone!" Reggie cried. "Do you suppose Charley ate it?" He leaned out the window. "Charley!" he called. "Come, Charley!"

There was a great squawking in the tree. Suddenly two blue jays burst out of the thick leaves. One of the birds headed for Reggie's window.

"Charley? Charley?" called Reggie. He held out his hand as he used to for Charley to make a landing. The bird flew almost to Reggie's window, then turned and started back toward the tree. "Charley, come back!" called Reggie.

The bird circled again and started back towards
Reggie's window. "It *is* Charley! It is!" Reggie
cried. "Did you see how he turned back when
I called his name? Come on, Charley!"

The blue jay landed on Reggie's hand, teetering
only a moment to get his balance. Then he
opened his beak wide and gave his baby cry for
food. Reggie's heart sank. Hadn't Charley learned
to feed himself yet? Reggie picked up the bread
crumb from the windowsill and held it a few
inches away from Charley's beak.

"Peep—peep—peep!" cried Charley, opening
his beak even wider and begging to be fed.

"No, you great big spoiled baby!" said Reggie. "I'm not going to give it to you. You'll have to get it for yourself this time. You have to grow up sometime."

Charley stopped peeping and cocked his head on one side to look at the crumb. Then he turned his head to the other side to get a look from that eye. Suddenly the crest on top of his head shot up, and he squawked angrily. Then, faster than Reggie's eye could follow, Charley struck out and grabbed the crumb with his beak.

"You did it! You did it!" cried Reggie. "Good boy, Charley!"

When the crumb was gone, Charley looked up at Reggie for more.

"That's all," said Reggie. Charley looked at him with his head on one side. Suddenly a Japanese beetle flew past the window. Charley's head shot out, and the beetle was in his beak. Then the beetle disappeared down his throat.

"That's the boy, Charley!"said Reggie. "Now you've got the idea!"

"Ja-ay! Ja-ay!" came a call from the tree. Charley turned his head in the direction of the sound.

"Ja-ay! Ja-ay!" he answered. He took off and headed straight for the tree.

Reggie watched Charley as he went. He sighed. Charley had been a lot of trouble to feed, but he'd miss him. He remembered that first day, when he had thought Charley was going to die. He had thought then that if only he could save Charley, he would be a doctor when he grew up. Maybe he'd do better than that—maybe he'd be an animal doctor. Then, in a way, all the pets in the whole world would be his. All the dogs and cats and horses and parrakeets. And, of course, there'd be all the no-good birds he could find.

Reflections

1. At the beginning Reggie is called "the meanest boy in school." Do you think this is a good description of him? Why or why not?

2. How did Mrs. Sullivan treat Reggie after she learned about the blue jay? How had she been treating him before that?

3. In your opinion, why did Eddie Halloran act as he did when Reggie brought his blue jay to school?

4. Why do you think Reggie acted toward the little dog the way he did?

5. How did Reggie feel when he discovered Charley could feed himself? Why did he feel that way?

6. Do you think that Reggie would make a good veterinarian (animal doctor) when he grows up? Why or why not?

Crocodile

WILLIAM JAY SMITH

The Crocodile wept bitter tears,
    And when I asked him why,
He said: "I weep because the years
    Go far too quickly by!

"I weep because of oranges,
    I weep because of pears,
Because of broken door hinges,
    And dark and crooked stairs.

"I weep because of black shoestrings,
    I weep because of socks,
I weep because I can't do things
    Like dance and shadowbox.

"I weep because the deep blue sea
    Washes the sand in a pile;
I weep because, as you can see,
    I've never learned to smile!"

"To weep like that cannot be fun,
    My reptile friend," I said;
"Your nose, though long, will run and run,
    Your eyes, though wide, be red.

55

"Why must you so give way to grief?
    You *could* smile if you chose;
Here, take this pocket handkerchief
    And wipe your eyes and nose.

"Come, laugh because of oranges,
    And laugh because of pears,
Because of broken door hinges,
    And dark and crooked stairs.

"Come, laugh because of black shoestrings,
    And laugh because of socks,
And laugh because you *can* do things
    Like dance and shadowbox.

"Come, laugh because it feels so good—
    It's not against the law.
Throw open, as a reptile should,
    Your green and shining jaw!"

The Crocodile he thought awhile
    Till things seemed not so black;
He smiled, and I returned his smile,
    He smiled, and I smiled back.

He took an orange and a pear;
    He took shoestrings and socks,
And tossing them into the air,
    Began to waltz and box.

The animals came, and they were gay:
    The Bobcat danced with the Owl;
The Bat brought tea on a bamboo tray
    To the Yak and Guinea Fowl.

The Monkeys frolicked in the street;
    The Lion, with a smile,
Came proudly down the steps to greet
    The happy Crocodile!

The Fun They Had

ISAAC ASIMOV

Margie even wrote about it that night in her diary. On the page headed May 17, 2157, she wrote, "Today Tommy found a real book!"

It was a very old book. Margie's grandfather once said that when he was a little boy, *his* grandfather told him that there was a time when all stories were printed on paper.

They turned the pages, which were yellow and crinkly, and it was awfully funny to read words that stood still instead of moving the way they were supposed to—on a screen, you know. And then, when they turned back to the page before, it had the same words on it that it had had when they read it the first time.

"Gee," said Tommy, "what a waste. When you're through with the book, you just throw it away, I guess. Our television screen must have had a million books on it, and it's good for plenty more. I wouldn't throw the screen away."

"Same with mine," said Margie. She was eleven and hadn't seen as many telebooks as Tommy had. He was thirteen.

She said, "Where did you find it?"

"In my house." He pointed without looking, because he was busy reading. "In the attic."

"What's it about?"

"School."

Margie was scornful. "School? What's there to write about school? I hate school."

Margie always hated school, but now she hated it more than ever. The mechanical teacher had been giving her test after test in geography. She had been doing worse and worse until finally her mother had sent for the County Inspector.

He was a round little man with a red face and a whole box of tools with dials and wires. He smiled at Margie and gave her an apple, then took the teacher apart. Margie had hoped he wouldn't know how to put it together again, but he knew how all right. After an hour or so, there it was again, large and gray and ugly, with a big screen on which all the lessons were shown and the questions were asked. That wasn't so bad. The part Margie hated most was the slot where she

was to put homework and test papers. She always had to write them out in a punch code, which she had learned when she was six years old. The mechanical teacher calculated her mark in no time.

The Inspector had smiled after he was finished and patted Margie's head. He said to her mother, "It's not the little girl's fault, Mrs. Jones. I think the geography sector was geared a little too quick. Those things happen sometimes. I've slowed it up to an average ten-year level. Actually, her progress is quite satisfactory." And he patted Margie's head again.

Margie was disappointed. She had been hoping that they would take the teacher away altogether. They had once taken Tommy's teacher away for nearly a month because the history sector had blanked out completely.

So she said to Tommy, "Why would anyone write about school?"

Tommy looked at her with very superior eyes. "Because it's not our kind of school. This is the old kind of school that they had hundreds and hundreds of years ago." He added, proudly pronouncing the word, "*Centuries* ago."

Margie was hurt. "Well, I don't know what kind of school they had all that time ago." She read the book over his shoulder for a while, then said, "Anyway, they had a teacher."

"Sure they had a teacher, but it wasn't a *regular* teacher. It was a man."

"A man? How could a man be a teacher?"

"Well, he just told the boys and girls things and gave them homework and also asked them questions."

"A man isn't smart enough."

"Sure he is. My father knows as much as my teacher."

"He can't. A man can't know as much as a teacher."

"He knows almost as much, I betcha."

Margie wasn't prepared to dispute that. She said, "I wouldn't want a strange man in my house to teach me."

Tommy screamed with laughter. "You don't know much, Margie. The teachers didn't live in the house. They had a special building, and all of the kids went there."

"And all the kids learned the same thing?"

"Sure, if they were the same age."

"But my mother says a teacher has to be adjusted to fit the mind of each boy and girl it teaches, and that each kid has to be taught differently."

"Just the same, they didn't do it that way then. If you don't like it, you don't have to read the book."

"I didn't say I didn't like it," Margie said quickly. She wanted to read about those funny schools.

They weren't even half finished when Margie's mother called, "Margie! School!"

Margie looked up. "Not yet, Mama."

"Now!" said Mrs. Jones. "And it's probably time for Tommy, too."

Margie said to Tommy, "May I read the book some more with you after school?"

"Maybe," he said. He walked away whistling, the dusty old book tucked beneath his arm.

Margie went into the schoolroom. It was right next to her bedroom, and the mechanical teacher was on and waiting for her. It was always on at the same time every day except Saturday and Sunday, because her mother said little girls learned better if they learned at regular hours.

The screen was lit up, and it said: "Today's arithmetic lesson is on the addition of fractions. Please insert yesterday's homework in the proper slot."

Margie did so with a sigh. She was thinking about the old schools they had when her grandfather's grandfather was a little boy. All the kids from the whole neighborhood came, laughing and shouting in the school yard, going home together at the end of the day. They learned the same things, so they could help one another on the homework and talk about it.

And the teachers were people....

The mechanical teacher was flashing on the screen: "When we add the fractions $\frac{1}{2}$ and $\frac{1}{4}$—"

Margie was thinking about how the kids must have loved it in the old days. She was thinking about the fun they had.

$$\frac{1}{2} + \frac{1}{4}$$

Reflections

1. What did Tommy find, and why did it interest him so much?
2. Compare Margie's way of "going to school" with your own. Which way do you prefer? Tell why.
3. How did Margie "write" her homework?
4. How would you explain to Margie and Tommy what your school is like?
5. If you could create your own school, what would it be like?

The Quarrel

ELEANOR FARJEON

I quarreled with my brother,
I don't know what about,
One thing led to another
And somehow we fell out.
The start of it was slight,
The end of it was strong,
He said he was right,
I knew he was wrong!

We hated one another.
The afternoon turned black.
Then suddenly my brother
Thumped me on the back,
And said, "Oh, *come* along!
We can't go on all night—
I was in the wrong."
So he was in the right.

Miss Kirby's Room

JEAN HORTON BERG

Red Handlebars

It was the last inning. The score was fifteen to fourteen in favor of Miss Kirby's room. Mrs. Otto's room was up at bat. They had one out, and the bases were loaded. Hank Yurchenko, the hardest hitter in Mrs. Otto's room, came up to the plate.

Crack! Hank slammed Nick's first pitch on the ground to Scott Boles, the third baseman. Scott scooped up the ball and fired it to Jamie, the catcher, in time to force the man at home plate. That was the second out.

Swinging around in a complete circle, and without seeming to take aim, Jamie let the ball fly. Like an arrow, it flew straight to the target and caught Hank by a half step at first. The game was over.

Miss Kirby's room went wild. They had won!

Susan was waiting for Jamie at the edge of the playground. They were going to walk home together as usual. "You really were great," Nick was saying to Jamie as the team came to the gate. "And don't forget," he said to Scott, "you made as many funny jokes as anybody when I picked Jamie to be our catcher."

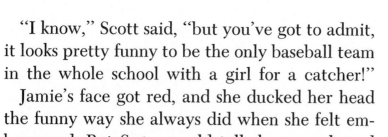

"I know," Scott said, "but you've got to admit, it looks pretty funny to be the only baseball team in the whole school with a girl for a catcher!"

Jamie's face got red, and she ducked her head the funny way she always did when she felt embarrassed. But Susan could tell she was pleased with what the boys were saying. In fact, Jamie was very popular with the boys in school. But except for Susan, she didn't have any really close friends among the girls.

As Susan stopped to tie her shoelace, she thought to herself, "I don't know why I keep Jamie for my practically best friend. Sometimes she doesn't even act like a girl. And it isn't just playing baseball. It's other things, like—well, like that rabbit's foot."

She looked up. The boys had run on ahead. Jamie was walking along slowly, waiting for her. Susan could see the back of Jamie's head. The red hair, parted unevenly, was pulled to either side and fastened in "handlebars," with a green rubber band on the right. Caught on the left handlebar by a little key chain was a white rabbit's foot. Jamie always wore it for luck. Susan could remember the time she had tried to get Jamie to take it off.

Jamie had answered her, "You wear a ribbon in your hair; I wear a rabbit's foot in mine. What's the difference?"

"There's a whole lot of difference, if you want to know so much!" Susan had yelled back. But the rabbit's foot had stayed.

She pulled the shoelace tight and got to her feet. "I don't know why I keep her for my practically best friend," she sighed and ran to catch up.

The next day, when the bell rang announcing the end of the lunch period, Susan had already started in from the playground.

"Come on, Pam; come on, Peggy," she called. "The sooner we get in, the sooner Miss Kirby will start to read *Treasure Island*." She ran lightly up the stairs to the room.

"Miss Kirby, are we going to—" Susan stopped short and drew back in confusion. Miss Kirby stood right inside the coatroom door, a frown on her usually gently smiling face. Beside her, fists scrubbing hard at his eyes, stood Nick.

Just then the last bell rang. When everyone was seated, Miss Kirby said, "Boys and girls, we have a problem to solve. Nick brought a dollar to school this morning, and now it's gone. Has anyone seen Nick's dollar?"

Everyone looked at everybody else.

"What is it, Tim? Have you seen Nick's money?" asked Miss Kirby.

"No ma'am," said Tim. "But maybe he only thought he brought it. Maybe he left it at home on his desk, like you forget your homework sometimes."

"No. I brought it with me. My mother gave it to me when I went out the door this morning. She wanted me to get some things for her at the store on my way home from school."

"Maybe it fell out of your pocket," said Scott.

"No, it didn't drop out of my pocket!" Nick was excited now. "It was right in my pocket till I got to school, and I put it in my cubbyhole as soon as I got in the room. I never touched it again, and I never saw it again."

"Maybe you stuck it so far back in your cubbyhole, you didn't see it when you looked," said Susan.

"I took every single thing out of that cubbyhole about a million times," Nick said. "It isn't there. It's gone. And what am I going to tell my mother?"

"Miss Kirby," said Jamie, "why don't we all look in our cubbyholes and see if Nick's money is in one of them? Maybe he made a mistake and put his money in the wrong one."

It seemed like a good idea. A lot of the boys and girls did find things they hadn't thought about in months. But no one found Nick's money.

Finally Susan said loudly, "If everyone doesn't hurry up and sit down, there won't be any time left for reading."

But even when everyone was seated, Miss Kirby only looked sadly around the room. "We won't have our reading today," she said. "We'll sit quietly in our seats and think. Whenever the person who took Nick's money decides to return it, we'll go back to reading *Treasure Island*."

For twenty minutes the class sat still. Feet shuffled, throats were cleared, a pencil or two dropped, and several sneezes were heard. But there wasn't any talking. Then, as though everything were normal, Miss Kirby said, "Take out your spelling books."

Everyone was glad to be doing something. Probably no spelling lesson had ever seemed so interesting.

At the end of school, Miss Kirby lent Nick a dollar. Now he could buy the things his mother wanted at the store. Everything seemed to be all right again.

Not Fair

The next morning Susan waited and waited for Jamie to walk to school with her. Finally at a quarter after eight, she gave up and ran down the street to meet Pam. By running almost the whole way, the two girls got to school on time. Jamie wasn't there. But then just as the last bell rang, Jamie rushed into the room and slid into her seat. It wasn't until recess that Susan had a chance to ask Jamie why she had been so late.

"I forgot my baseball glove," Jamie said, "and I had to go all the way back home to get it. We only have four more days to practice before our big game with Mr. Shock's room."

Pam joined them. "Why did you have to go home for your glove, Jamie? Why couldn't you borrow somebody else's when it's your turn to catch?"

"I'm the only one on the team that's left-handed," Jamie said. "I have to have my own glove. But it's getting so worn out, it isn't much good anymore. I wish I could get a new one."

After lunch Miss Kirby sat down quietly at the desk and began marking papers. Susan raised her hand, but Miss Kirby didn't see it. Then she cleared her throat, shuffled her feet, and waved her hand wildly. Miss Kirby looked up. "Yes, Susan, what is it?" she said.

"Miss Kirby, aren't you going to read?" Susan asked.

"No, Susan, I'm not," she said slowly. "I told you yesterday, there would be no extra reading until Nick's money was returned. There were lots of chances for whoever took it to put it on my desk or in Nick's cubbyhole without anyone seeing. You all understand, I'm sure."

"It's not fair to make everybody miss the story because one person is a thief," Pam whispered.

"That's not fair, Miss Kirby," Jamie said right out loud.

"Jamie's right," several others said loud enough for the whole room to hear.

Miss Kirby looked upset, but when she spoke, her voice was her regular calm, quiet voice. "I'll tell you what isn't fair," she said. "It isn't fair for one person to rob everybody. And that's what is happening. Our room is like a family. We should be able to trust one another. Now I am trusting whoever made the mistake of taking Nick's money to put it back. I'm going to go on without reading until the money is returned, because it's wrong to pretend that everything is all right when it isn't." Miss Kirby began marking papers again.

The rest of the day nothing was right in the room. You could practically see anger and suspicion walking up and down the aisles like an invisible imp touching this one and that one, making people treat each other differently.

"It's like nobody in our whole room is nice anymore," Susan thought. "It's bad enough having Miss Kirby be so mean and stop reading to us, but it's even worse to know that somebody in our own room is a thief!"

That night Susan made up her mind. "I'll try to stay by myself tomorrow," she thought before she went to sleep. "Then I won't have to hear anything about 'Maybe it was so-and-so' or 'Whoozis has got a guilty look if I ever saw one.' I'll leave home early, before Jamie comes and before Pam is out on the corner. I'll walk to school by myself and stay by myself."

That's what she did. Susan felt happier than she had for days as she ran up the steps and started to go in the first door to Miss Kirby's room.

"Well! It's nice to be the first one here," she thought.

But she wasn't the first one. There, just across the room from her, putting her hand in Nick's cubbyhole, was the last person in the world Susan would ever have expected to see. She covered her mouth to keep from crying out.

Without having any idea that she was being watched, Jamie dropped a dollar bill into the cubbyhole, slipped quietly out the other door, and ran noiselessly down the hall and out of the building.

In a few minutes the rest of the class began filing in quietly. When Nick came in, he started to put his books in his cubbyhole. "Hey!" he shouted. "Look, everybody! My dollar's back!" Waving the money high in the air, he began marching up and down the aisles singing, "It's back! It's back! My dollar's back!"

The rest of the boys and girls happily fell into step with him. Just before the bell rang, Pam and Jamie hurried into the noisy room. As soon as she saw what was going on, Pam grabbed Jamie and pulled her into line with the others.

Miss Kirby was as excited as anybody. She didn't say a word about the noise or the marching until the bell rang. After everyone had quieted down, Nick went up to the desk and handed Miss Kirby the money.

"Thank you for lending me the dollar until I got mine back," he said. Miss Kirby took it with a smile, and for the first time in days, everything in the room seemed to be right again.

But it wasn't all right for Susan. As the class stood for the pledge, she looked at Jamie standing straight and tall in front of her, her right hand over her heart, the rabbit's foot in her hair.

" . . . with liberty and justice for all." Jamie's voice rang out loud and clear as she finished pledging allegiance to the flag.

"How can she stand there like that?" Susan thought. "How can she even come to school?"

After lunch Jamie said, "Miss Kirby, couldn't you read two chapters of *Treasure Island* today? Then we could get caught up on what we've missed."

Miss Kirby looked at the clock and said, "I think we can do that today, Jamie. Thank you for the suggestion."

The Secret

Susan was spending Friday night at Pam's house. After everything that had happened that day, Susan wished she didn't have to go anywhere. She was afraid she might say something about seeing Jamie that morning. And she had made up her mind never to tell anyone that Jamie was a thief. After all, Jamie had returned the money. So that proved she wanted to do what was right, and there was no sense in thinking about it anymore. No one seemed to care who took the money, as long as it had been returned to its owner.

"I was mad at you this morning. I waited and waited for you on the corner," Pam said as they snuggled under the covers. "I was ready to go on by myself when Jamie came along. You know what, Susan? That was the first time I was ever alone with Jamie. I never really liked her. But now I do. She always seemed so different. But once you get to know her, she's nice. I like her next best to you, I guess."

Susan felt a nasty little stab of jealousy. To have Pam admire Jamie so much was almost more than Susan could bear.

"Hey!" Pam nudged Susan. "Don't go to sleep yet. I'm not finished. Jamie and I had a good talk about school and Miss Kirby and all the trouble over Nick's money. I bet Jamie's the only kid that wasn't good and mad at whoever took it.

You'd think she would be, wouldn't you, being so friendly with Nick? But she said, 'Well, it isn't fair to get mad at people when you don't know all about them. Maybe whoever took Nick's money thought he had a reason to take it.' "

"I guess she doesn't want to hate herself!" The words burst out before Susan could stop them.

"Why, what in the world are you talking about?" Pam sat straight up in bed.

"Nothing," Susan said.

"It is *not* nothing," Pam said. "It's something. You tell me right this minute what you're talking about."

Susan squirmed and tried not to say anything more. But before she knew it, she was telling Pam what she had seen that morning. And somehow it was comforting to be telling it—like taking off shoes that are too tight.

Pam kept clucking and saying, "My cow! Imagine Jamie!" and, "Why would she ever do such a thing?"

"I was wondering about that all day. Then I remembered the other day when she forgot her catcher's mitt. And she said it was almost worn out, and she wished she could get a new one."

"Yes!" Pam's voice cracked like a trap snapping. "Why didn't we think of that before?"

"Well, it doesn't make any difference now," Susan said. "She put the dollar back, and Nick gave it to Miss Kirby. Everything is just like it was before."

"Oh, sure," Pam said.

There was a long silence. Then Susan said sleepily, "Don't say anything to anybody else, will you, Pam? Because after all, Jamie's my practically best friend."

"I won't," Pam said. "Except maybe I ought to tell Chrissie. Sometimes she asks Jamie over after school. She ought to know about this. I'd better tell her."

"I guess you can tell Chrissie," Susan said. "But tell her not to tell anybody else."

Susan was glad she had told Pam about Jamie. It was even kind of fun at school on Monday for Susan to be able to give Pam a special smile and have Pam wink back at her.

Later in the afternoon, though, Susan began to feel funny. At lunch she had looked across the lunchroom and seen Jamie sitting alone in a corner. When Jamie looked up at her, Susan dropped her eyes quickly and pretended she was looking at Chrissie's new shoes. And at afternoon recess, Chrissie, whose cubbyhole was beside

Jamie's, took everything out of her cubbyhole except her school books. Susan heard her say to Pam, "My sister's going to keep my stuff for me. The kids in her room have desks. Hey, maybe I ought to say something to Myra. Her cubbyhole is right underneath Jamie's."

"Good idea," Pam said.

Susan realized that quite a few of the boys and girls had made it plain to Jamie that day that they didn't want her around. "I guess Pam told Chrissie, and Chrissie told those other kids," she thought as she walked home slowly. "I guess that's why they've started to be mean to her. I guess it's all my fault."

"Well, it's not!" she said out loud. "It isn't my fault if Jamie took the money. I didn't make her do it, and I'm not going to feel funny because I told Pam."

She did, though. No matter what Jamie had done, Susan didn't want to be the one who hurt her.

Falling Apart

On Wednesday the weather was perfect for a baseball game. And it was the day of the most important game of the season, the game between Miss Kirby's room and Mr. Shock's room. The class was too excited to work. Everyone wanted Nick to talk about the team's chances of winning.

"We have a pretty good chance," he said. "Mr. Shock's room has better batters, but we have a good outfield. And Jamie's the best catcher in the whole school. Nothing gets past her. I think we have a pretty good chance of winning, all right."

Nobody asked Jamie anything. Nobody paid any attention to her.

Susan tried to put out the guilty feeling that was growing bigger and bigger inside her. She twisted in her seat so she couldn't see Jamie out of the corner of her eye.

After lunch Susan realized with a start that Jamie wasn't in her seat. No red-hair handlebars fastened with rubber bands stuck out in front of her. No silly white rabbit's foot bobbed up and down.

"Where's Jamie, Miss Kirby?" Nick sounded worried.

"She had to take care of something downstairs," Miss Kirby answered carefully.

"Oh, boy! She's not sick, is she?" Nick sounded sick himself. "That's all we need! If Jamie can't play today, we're sunk!"

The buzzer on the wall telephone sounded. It was Mr. Blair, the principal.

"Oh, my," Miss Kirby said after a moment, "we can't have anything like that."

Everybody was looking at Miss Kirby. There wasn't a sound in the room. As Miss Kirby put the receiver back on the hook, she said, "Susan, it's time for afternoon recess. I have to go down to the office for a few minutes. If I'm not back when recess is over, you take charge of the class. Maybe you'd like to go ahead with reading *Treasure Island*. We're already up to the next to the last chapter."

During recess the boys were at the back of the playground, practicing. They were very noisy. Pee-Wee Brewster was acting as catcher since Jamie wasn't there, and the whole team seemed to be yelling at him.

"The team's falling apart," Nick said gloomily to Susan as they went back to the room. "If

Pee-Wee has to be the catcher, we're sunk. He'll be the greatest player for the other side you ever saw."

Miss Kirby wasn't back yet, so Susan sat at the big desk at the front of the room and began to read. A tap sounded on the door nearest the cubbyholes, and Chrissie's sister, Alice, poked her head in. Chrissie went up to the door, and the two girls stood whispering excitedly. Then Alice left.

"Guess what!" Chrissie called out in a loud voice. "Jamie got caught!"

The whole room was in an uproar. A few hadn't heard the ugly rumors. "Keep quiet!" Chrissie yelled. "If you keep quiet, I'll tell you what happened." When everyone quieted down, she began. "My sister had to take the absence slips from her room to the office," she said. "People were talking in Mr. Blair's office. His door was open a teensy bit, so she peeked in. *Jamie* was in there with Mr. Blair and Miss Kirby. Mr. Blair kept saying, 'Jamie, we want to help you. You must answer me.'

"And Miss Kirby kept saying, 'Jamie, dear, you've told us *when* you put Nick's money back. Why won't you tell us why you took it in the first place?' Finally Jamie said, 'It's late. May I go and get ready for the baseball game?' And Mr. Blair got red and shook his face like a turkey gobbler and said, '*No*, by thunder, you may *not* get ready for the baseball game. I asked you a simple question, and you won't answer it. Very well, young lady, you can stay right in this office until you do answer me. You'll stay here if it takes till the Fourth of July!' Then he said he was going to call Jamie's mother and see if *she* could do anything with Jamie."

For a minute nobody said anything. Then Nick said, "Well, Pee-Wee, that's it, I guess. You're the catcher. And I can tell you already what the score will be, zero for us and a million for them."

The score wasn't quite that bad. But Mr. Shock's room won, fifteen to five. Pee-Wee sat on the ground behind home plate and started to cry when the game was over.

"Oh, quit it, Pee-Wee," Nick said. "Nobody thinks you did it on purpose. You're just not Jamie."

"Of course he's not," Pam said. "Who'd ever want to be a thief?"

The Last Chapter

Jamie wasn't in school the next morning.

After lunch Miss Kirby settled herself comfortably in her chair with *Treasure Island*. She had just started to read when the telephone buzzer sounded.

When Miss Kirby came back from the telephone, she looked around the room. "I'm going to ask you all to do something that won't be easy," she said. "Mr. Blair called to tell me that Jamie is on her way up to the room. When she comes in, I'd like you to act as if she had left the room for a few minutes to go on an errand. Is that clear?"

The children nodded, and some said, "Yes, Miss Kirby."

In a moment the door opened quietly, and Jamie slipped into the room. Miss Kirby looked up from the book. "Oh, Jamie," she said, "it's a bit chilly. Would you mind getting me my sweater from the hanger in the coatroom before you sit down?

"Thank you, dear." Miss Kirby slipped her sweater on as Jamie walked to her seat. She went

on with the reading. As she read, Miss Kirby slipped one hand into her sweater pocket. She went on reading as she took her hand out of the pocket and laid something on her desk.

"Why, what's this?" she exclaimed.

The class watched as she unfolded a little paper-wrapped package. A dollar bill fluttered to the floor. Tim rushed to pick it up. Miss Kirby said, "Thank you, Tim," absentmindedly. She was busy reading the note that had been wrapped around the folded dollar.

In a minute she looked up. "Girls and boys," she said, "I've found something very interesting. Listen."

She read from the smudged paper:

"Here is Nick's dollar back. I don't want this old dollar, and I wish I'd never seen it. When I found out Jamie put the money back, I felt bad. She never took the money, cause I did. And we lost the game, too. I don't know if you can fix it up, but anyway I don't want the money. I'm not telling who I am. I don't want to be treated like Jamie."

A buzzing started in the room. Some of the girls and boys laughed, and some looked solemn. Susan didn't know what to do. She wanted Jamie to know she was glad everything was cleared up and that they could be friends as they always had been before. She leaned forward and poked Jamie. Jamie turned her head slowly.

"How about stopping at the drugstore with me on the way home?" Susan said, trying to return to the old friendly way.

Jamie looked right through her. Susan shivered, and all the warm, friendly words that had been ready to pop out froze on her tongue as Jamie turned back to face the front of the room.

Chrissie and Pam were whispering. Then Chrissie called out, "How do we know Jamie didn't take it anyway? How do we know that she didn't write the letter for a trick to get everybody on her side? Why would she give Nick a whole dollar if she didn't take it in the first place?"

Miss Kirby looked at Jamie. "Jamie," she said, "I think it's time you told everyone why you put the dollar in Nick's cubbyhole and where it came from."

Jamie ducked her head, and Susan could see the back of her neck getting red. "Well," she said in a hoarse voice, "it was awful. We couldn't have our reading, and the kids were all getting suspicious of each other and mean. I had all these nickels and dimes saved for a new catcher's mitt. So I asked my father to give me a paper dollar for it, and, well, I came in early one day and stuck it in Nick's cubbyhole. I thought that would fix everything. But it didn't." She shook her head sadly. "I'll never try a thing like that again."

"But, Miss Kirby," Chrissie broke the silence that followed Jamie's stumbling speech. "It's not fair that everybody got mad at Jamie on account of what this other—person—did. Don't you think we should know who it is? In case that—person—should try something bad again, I mean."

Susan couldn't stand it any longer. "Well, I don't!" she said. "I don't want to know who did it. If the rest of you feel the way I do, you don't even want to hear about anybody taking anything that doesn't belong to him for the next million years! I'm sick of the whole thing! I just want our room back the way it was!" And to her own surprise, she burst into tears.

"Me, too!" echoed from every side.

"Well, if that's the way everybody feels," Chrissie said, not very happily.

"That's the way we all feel," Nick said.

"Then I guess me, too," Chrissie said in a small voice.

Miss Kirby picked up *Treasure Island*. "Don't anybody dare look at the clock," she said. "I think we'll finish *Treasure Island* today, no matter how long it takes."

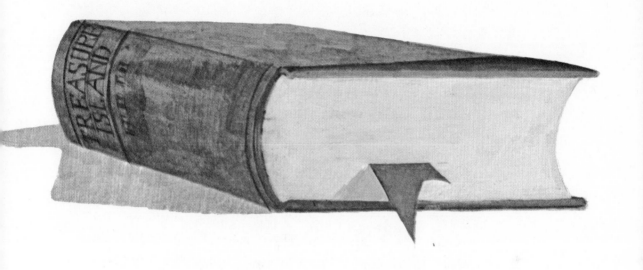

Reflections

1. Is this story mainly about a baseball game, about a theft, or about friendship? Give reasons for your answer.

2. Why did the children think Miss Kirby was unfair when she refused to read any more from *Treasure Island?* What did Miss Kirby think was unfair?

3. If you had been one of the children, would you have believed Jamie was a thief? What was the "evidence" against her?

4. From what you know about Jamie, do you think that she would forgive Susan for what she had done? Give reasons for your opinion.

5. Do you think this story could really have happened?

6. How do you feel about the ending of this story? Give reasons for your opinion.

7. Did you ever suspect that Jamie hadn't taken the money? If so, tell at what point in the story and why.

Pad and Pencil

DAVID McCORD

I drew a rabbit. John erased him
and not the dog I said had chased him.

I drew a bear on another page,
but John said, "Put him in a cage."

I drew some mice. John drew the cat
with nasty claws. The mice saw that.

I got them off the page real fast:
the things I draw don't *ever* last.

We drew a bird with one big wing:
he couldn't fly worth anything,

but sat there crumpled on a limb.
John's pencil did a job on *him*.

Three bats were next. I made them fly.
John smudged one out against the sky

above an owl he said could hoot.
He helped me with my wolf. The brute

had lots too long a tail, but we
concealed it all behind a tree.

By then I couldn't think of much
except to draw a rabbit hutch;

but since we had no rabbit now
I drew what must have been a cow,

with curvy horns stuck through the slats—
they both looked something like the bats.

And feeling sad about the bear
inside his cage, I saw just where

I'd draw the door to let him out.
And that's just all of it, about.

Until I Was Ten

DAVID McCORD

This is really a letter from me to you. All I ask
is that you read it slowly and *don't* skip the lines
of verse. I ask that you do this because my boy-
hood somehow edged me into poetry, and though
the poems I am quoting from were written long
after, they almost always talk about the boy who
was once somewhere near your age. For all his
faults, he was a boy who wanted desperately to
learn all he could about the world he lived in.
He would teach himself if necessary, and he
often did. You can do the same.

From the very beginning I was fascinated by the sight and sound and shape of everything that moved with rhythm—and everything that had a special motion or made a special noise. For rhythm, not rhyme, is the basis of poetry. I was living a kind of poetry and did not know it.

Of course, there is rhythm in your world today. But today we live, or seem to live, for speed alone, as I most happily did not. We live in a crowded world, as I did not. We youngsters had fewer things to be excited about, but we had time to enjoy and savor our excitements one by one.

I was born in New York City on East Tenth Street and lived near Washington Square until I was three. Then, after trying a small town on southern Long Island, we moved out into the country, into a farmhouse, and stayed there until I was almost ten.

I was two, however, and still in New York when I became very ill with malaria. The fever recurred now and then over the next six years and kept me pretty steadily out of school.

I had no brothers or sisters and saw very few people my own age. But freedom and solitude gave me two very precious things: the chance to read all sorts of books (beginning with *The Wizard of Oz*) and endless hours in which to learn something about life in the fields and in the woods which were close at hand. Mine was a green world, and I loved the color green.

So, in spite of spells of illness, it was a joyful time, a lucky time, and I am grateful beyond words for every minute of it. Our place looked big to me, but it was really small, with a barn, a tiny orchard, an outdoor well, a toolshed-playhouse, and a white picket fence all around it. To walk along that fence, with a stick dragging against it, made music. Seventeen years later I wrote "The Pickety Fence," now in a lot of different books. Perhaps you know it?

> The pickety fence
> The pickety fence
> Give it a lick it's
> The pickety fence
> Give it a lick it's
> A clickety fence
> Give it a lick it's
> A lickety fence
> Give it a lick
> Give it a lick
> Give it a lick
> With a rickety stick
> Pickety
> Pickety
> Pickety
> Pick

You have to say that *slowly* with the accent on the *pick* in *pickety*.

Summers seemed to last forever, like the sea wind passing over grasses in great waves with sunlight on them. There was tall yellow wheat in a neighboring field, and I would lose myself making tunnels through it. And there were walks in the woods on Sunday with my father.

"Walk,"
My Father used to say,
"Don't talk."

"Words,"
My Father used to say,
"Scare birds."

The roads in every direction were dirt—not paved—and we rarely saw more than two or three noisy, backfiring automobiles in a single day. Often the driver was busy changing a tire. If we didn't own a horse, we rented one, and my mother (who had ridden the plains around Denver as a little girl) drove me about the countryside in a high-wheeled Hempstead cart.

I remember those drives (as she did) mostly for the strong sea-smell of the marshlands and the sight of soaring gulls and the swifter flight of thin-winged terns as we neared the beaches and the sea. There were bicycle trips with my parents when I was old enough to ride. We had no boat, but we used to spend uncrowded hours at the seashore, often by the empty dunes. And on the hard sand, with my father—a man of great patience—we would fly a marvelous big box kite.

Above everything, in those Long Island days, there was that endless rhythm in the clouds. All my life I have loved the sky: it is my daily and nightly inspiration. I can remember lying on my back, the world forgotten, watching the serried progress of the summer cloud-fleets sailing out to sea. Why, I am always asking, don't more people ever watch the sky except at sunset for the colors? *Why?* No theater, no movie, no TV western ever equals the best of it for splendor and for drama.

The cool grey clouds at dawn devise the sea
in perfect stillness: just the beach and me.

Those thunderheads that pile above the sun,
so white before they blacken and I run,

are more than castles, mountains, what you will—
they're all my windows opening, opening still.

Several times each year I went up to New York with my mother. There were as yet no tunnels under the East River or the Hudson, so we took the ferry over from Long Island City. The ferryboats were brave and brassy, with real shiny brass. They were very fat and wide, like giant water bugs in action. They steamed out boldly from their slips (a kind of dock all made with wooden piles) and zigzagged through a thick cross-traffic of great ocean liners, tugs, all sorts of barges, freighters, small boats, flatboats with a lot of freight cars on them. And they went fast—no speedboats then—faster than anything afloat except the larger tugs. They often seemed to miss collision just by inches. On lucky days I saw the last of the old sailing ships standing into—which means "sailing into"—the harbor east of the Statue of Liberty, or tied up to the dock, with their huge bowsprits sticking straight out over the streets. You didn't just ride under or fly over all this movement and confusion: you were part of it.

I listened always for the sound of harbor whistles, but being aboard that agile ferry somewhat lessened their effect. I think we heard them best on other days down by the old aquarium at Battery Park. So many whistles talking to and answering each other! Sixteen years later I wrote about it in "The Conning Tower" in the *New York World*. The poem began like this:

On a windy day, for a lark, a lark,
They took me down to Battery Park;
On a windy day when the harbor boats
Whistled their long and lovely notes. . . .

I wish that Aaron Copland, the composer, would write a symphony about those whistles. He must have heard them as I did.

Today you hear the sirens, catch a flash or two of red, and know that somewhere there's a fire. But walking down a New York street when I was a boy, we might well hear the sudden clang of bells, the thundering hoofs of great white horses at the gallop, till they and the old fire engine hurtled by. There was time enough to see the big fat polished upright boiler streaming sparks out through the chimney at the top.

Or then—while I am talking of stupendous rhythms—to stand one chilly morning in the country at the edge of that long, bumpy, new-mown field not thirty feet from one of the first Wright biplanes taking off, the first real plane I

ever saw! Was it going down that farmer's field on bicycle wheels and up into the sky? "Look at it," I thought, "a double kite made out of struts and ribs and wire and canvas, and one noisy stuttering engine and propeller." But up it rose, all wobbly, steadied itself, and *flew.*

And did we cheer! We were seeing a new sight and hearing a new rhythm. We were *in* on the beginning of a new age.

Just beyond our house there was a chicken farm with thousands of white leghorn pullets, moving in white flocks quite like the drifting clouds across the landscape. When I was eight, I began to raise chickens myself, hatching the eggs in an incubator.

> I've broken lots of eggs, I guess.
> The ones in pockets make a mess,
> The ones on floors don't clean up well,
> The older ones may leave a smell.
> Eggs in a bag when dropped won't splash;
> The thrown egg will—a yellow smash.

All this time I was falling deeper and deeper in love with words. My mother, of strong will, courage, laughter, and imagination, was original in speech. She could always find the surprising word to express the surprising idea. She knew that happiness has to be earned or won: it is *never* given for free. She was a rare and lovely human being; and whenever she laughed or sang or smiled or read to me aloud, there was music for a long time.

My grandmother (my mother's mother) had an even finer speaking and singing voice. She played the piano until she was nearly ninety. She read most of the Bible through to me—parts of it twice—before I was ten. And if you don't know the sound of the fall of syllables in the King James Version of the Psalms, you will never understand the true range and power of the English language. Far better than this letter would be a recording of my grandmother reading *you* the Bible. I don't know why, but her untroubled voice comes back to me at night sometimes when I am looking at the stars.

But don't let me forget Uncle Robert, my mother's brother. He was a Westinghouse electrical engineer and had spent two years in Japan in the 1890's, installing generators to light the city of Tokyo. He was full of Japan, full to the brim of the love of books and reading, full of the quaint, queer songs he taught me, full of poems he had got by heart, full of imagination, charm, and gaiety, but fullest of all of bantering good humor. He taught me the value of ideas, for he was an inventor. He made me feel that I was not alone in loving the sound of words and the rhythm of words put together in the right order.

So there I was—raising chickens, fooling around with electricity, learning the Morse code, and building apparatus on the way to becoming an early licensed wireless telegraph operator; working at carpentry with my father on weekends, feeding a twelve-inch alligator, finding turtles and cocoons, climbing trees, catching crabs, getting stung by bees, and digging in a garden of my own. What school ever equaled *that?* And what school would ever have taught me a love of nonsense and nonsense words?

> One mouse adds up to many mice,
> One louse adds up to lots of lice,
> One chickenhouse to chickenhice.

At five I learned "The Owl and the Pussy-Cat" by heart, and sometimes I sang it. Do you know it? Do you know that Edward Lear wrote it? If you don't, then get *The Complete Nonsense Book* (Dodd, Mead, 1956) from the library today.

Last of all, a word about the Pocono Mountains in Pennsylvania, where we spent a month each summer for six or seven years. It was there I learned to find red newts in the woods. After rain at five or six in the morning is the best time, for then they walk abroad, though not for long. Spotting these tiny dots of brilliant color in among the leaves sharpened my eyes. If you have never held a newt in your hand and watched his delicate, dry (not slimy) way of walking, you have missed something.

> The little newt
> Is not a brute,
> A fish or fowl,
> A kind of owl:
> He doesn't prowl
> Or run or dig
> Or grow too big.
> He doesn't fly
> Or laugh or cry—
> He doesn't try.

In spite of my instinctive love of nature and the woods, until I was eight I had never read many nature stories. But in the Poconos I read nine or ten books by the New Brunswick writer, Charles G. D. Roberts. He wrote *Red Fox*—one of the two greatest animal stories in the world. If I have told you nothing else, let me urge you to search for it. Ask your librarian. *Red Fox* was the *one* book that somehow *made* me want to become a writer. Of course, I was far from being ready. I had simply entered the world of books.

But I was nearly ready for three more schoolless years on a ranch in the south of Oregon just two miles from the wild Rogue River. A life on the real frontier! And what an exciting life it was to be! Well, you are right this very minute on the frontier of the greatest and most flexible language in the world. Learn to use it well. Learn to listen to the sound of your words as you put them together and speak them. Read everything you can that is good and *well written*. Learn—but learn above all to teach yourself. *Be proud of your ability to be exact.* Learn to love words, especially those words that *sound* the way they mean:

Like wind upon the mouth
Sad, summer, rain, and south.
Amen. Put not asunder
Man's *first* word: wonder . . . wonder . . .

Reflections

1. Why would an older person want to tell young people about himself?
2. David McCord says that he was greatly attracted to things that moved with rhythm. Look back through the "letter" and name some of these things. What are some things that move with rhythm that you especially like?
3. David McCord loves words. He is always searching for the right words to describe what he has seen or felt. What vivid ways of saying things and of painting pictures with words can be found in this selection?
4. David McCord remembers favorite sounds from his childhood. What are some of *your* favorite sounds? What makes each of them one of your favorites?
5. David McCord is a poet. Why is the love of rhythm and of words especially important to a poet?
6. Why is the ability to wonder important to a poet?

SPOKEN AND WRITTEN LANGUAGE

Suppose you were walking by a cool lake on a hot day and wanted to go swimming. But you saw a sign that had these words on it:

Suppose someone came along and added some punctuation marks to the sign. He put a question mark after the word *private;* he added an exclamation point after the word *no;* he put a period after *allowed.* Could you go swimming then?

Try changing the meaning of the sign below with punctuation marks.

Now discuss the following pairs of sentences, telling how the words are alike but how punctuation, capitals, and the space that separates words make a difference in meaning.

1. What's up the road ahead?
   What's up the road, a head?
2. John Henry is here.
   John, Henry is here.
3. We visited the White House in Washington.
   We visited the white house in Washington.
4. It's snowing! No school today!
   It's snowing? No school today?

You cannot see punctuation, capitals, and space between words in spoken English. But they appear in written English. Try reading this selection aloud.

twinkleberryandsixotherlittlesquirrelseach
carriedafatminnowbutnutkinwhohadnonicemanners
broughtnopresentatallheraninfrontsinging
themaninthewildernesssaidtomehowmany
strawberriesgrowintheseaiansweredhimasi
thoughtgoodasmanyredherringsasgrowinthewood
butoldmrbrowntooknointerestinriddlesnot
evenwhentheanswerwasprovidedforhim

Copy the selection on a sheet of paper. Use space between each word and capital letters when needed. Use whatever punctuation you think helps make the meaning clear.

Spoken and Written English

All of us who use English really use it in two forms—spoken and written. Of all living things, only man has developed spoken and written language. Spoken language means the sounds we make. We learn it by listening to and imitating the spoken language of our families and friends. But no two people in the world speak exactly alike. Even you cannot say the same word twice exactly the same way.

Written words do not speak. Written English uses the twenty-six letters of the alphabet, the numerals 0 to 9, punctuation marks, and space between words. Most of us learn it in school. Our ears are our biggest help in learning spoken English. Our eyes, fingers, pencil, and paper are our biggest help when we learn to write.

Reading is like a code. When we first learn to read, we match the sounds of spoken language with the letters of the alphabet: letters arranged into words printed on a page. When we read aloud, we bring sounds to letters. Most of us learn to read in a very few years, but it took man thousands of years to develop oral and written language.

Matching Sounds and Letters

The exercises you have already done showed you many of the differences between spoken and written language. As you study reading, you will learn more and more about how the sounds of spoken language and the letters of written language work together.

In some languages one letter stands for one sound. In English there are more sounds than letters, so we often combine several letters to stand for a sound. Since most of us know all the sounds of spoken English, it is not very difficult to match these sounds with the letters chosen to represent them.

Twelve Ways to Spell a Sound

Listen as your teacher reads the following words. Notice especially the underscored letters.

b<u>e</u>	C<u>ae</u>sar	rec<u>ei</u>ve
sw<u>ee</u>t	p<u>eo</u>ple	bel<u>ie</u>ve
<u>ea</u>ch	am<u>oe</u>ba	mach<u>i</u>ne
k<u>ey</u>	qu<u>ay</u>	<u>Y</u>vonne

What sound is alike in all of these words? How many different ways is this sound spelled? With what letter or letters is it spelled? What letter in our alphabet has the name of this sound? Do letters make sounds?

Suppose you were making a new alphabet and you decided that you would design a new letter which would stand for the twelve spellings seen above. Use your new letter and respell each of the twelve words above.

The sooner you learn to match the sounds of spoken language with the letters of written language, the sooner you will master reading. You already know the sounds of English. As you continue to read, you will learn more and more about matching spoken sounds to written letters.

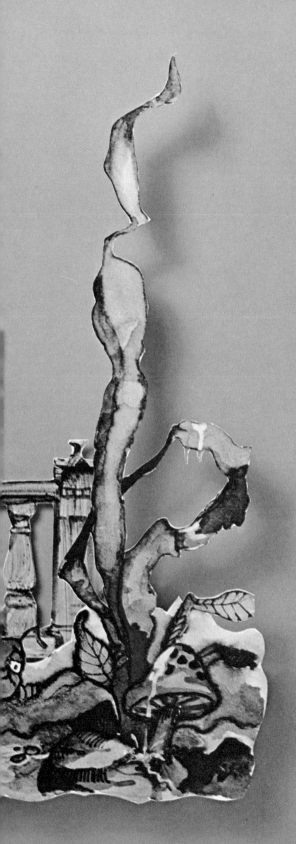

Unit 2
THE GIFT
OF LANGUAGE

English

As gardens grow with flowers
English grows with words,
Words that have secret powers,
Words that give joy like birds.

Some of the words you say,
Both in and out of school,
Are brighter than the day,
And deeper than a pool.

Some words there are that dance,
Some words there are that sigh,
The fool's words come by chance,
The poet's to heaven fly.

When you are grown, your tongue
Should give the joys of birds;
Get while you are young
The gift of English words.

Eleanor Farjeon

The Loudest Noise in the World

BENJAMIN ELKIN

Once upon a time the noisiest place in the world was a city called Hub-Bub. The people of Hub-Bub never talked; they yelled. They were very proud that their ducks were the quackiest, their doors the slammiest, and their policemen's whistles the shrillest in the whole world.

111

Their favorite song was the following:

"Slam the door,
Bang the floor.
Days we roar,
Nights we snore.
Hub-Bub!"

Of all the noisy people in Hub-Bub, the noisiest was a young prince named Hulla-Baloo. He could make more noise than the grown-ups. Hulla-Baloo loved to yell, bang pots and pans together, and blow a whistle, all at the same time.

His favorite game was to climb up a ladder, piling up trash cans and tin pails as high as he could, and then knock over the whole pile with a loud crash. He used to make the piles higher and higher, and they made louder and louder crashes. But still he wasn't satisfied. Prince Hulla-Baloo wanted to hear the loudest noise in the world.

A few weeks before the prince's birthday, his father, the King of Hub-Bub, asked him what he wanted for a birthday present. "I want to hear the loudest noise in the world," answered Prince Hulla-Baloo.

"Fine," said the king. "I'll order the royal drummers to get out the special super-loud drums for the whole day."

"But I've heard them before," complained the prince. "That wouldn't be the loudest noise in the world."

"All right," promised the king. "I'll also order all policemen to blow their special super-loud whistles."

"I've already heard those, too," said Hulla-Baloo. "They wouldn't be loud enough."

"Tell you what," said the king. "At the same time I'll close the schools and have the children stay home all day and slam the super-slammy doors. How's that?"

"That would help," agreed the prince, "but it still wouldn't be the loudest noise in the world."

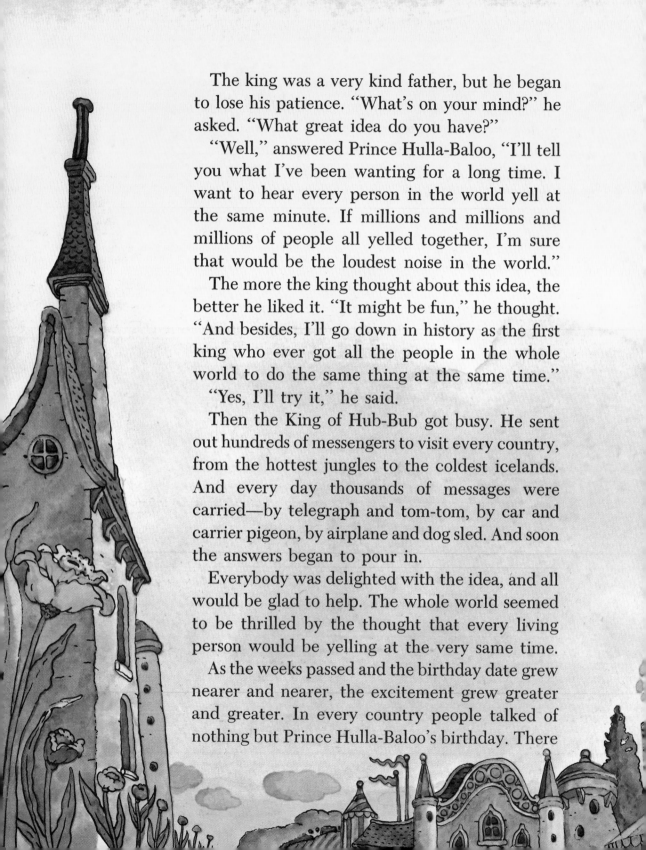

The king was a very kind father, but he began to lose his patience. "What's on your mind?" he asked. "What great idea do you have?"

"Well," answered Prince Hulla-Baloo, "I'll tell you what I've been wanting for a long time. I want to hear every person in the world yell at the same minute. If millions and millions and millions of people all yelled together, I'm sure that would be the loudest noise in the world."

The more the king thought about this idea, the better he liked it. "It might be fun," he thought. "And besides, I'll go down in history as the first king who ever got all the people in the whole world to do the same thing at the same time."

"Yes, I'll try it," he said.

Then the King of Hub-Bub got busy. He sent out hundreds of messengers to visit every country, from the hottest jungles to the coldest icelands. And every day thousands of messages were carried—by telegraph and tom-tom, by car and carrier pigeon, by airplane and dog sled. And soon the answers began to pour in.

Everybody was delighted with the idea, and all would be glad to help. The whole world seemed to be thrilled by the thought that every living person would be yelling at the very same time.

As the weeks passed and the birthday date grew nearer and nearer, the excitement grew greater and greater. In every country people talked of nothing but Prince Hulla-Baloo's birthday. There wasn't a village in the world that didn't have a poster in its own language giving the exact minute of local time at which to yell, "Happy Birthday!"

One afternoon, in a city far away, a lady was talking to her husband about Prince Hulla-Baloo's birthday. "What bothers me," she said, "is how I'm going to hear everyone else yelling when I'm making so much noise myself. All I'll hear is my own voice."

"You're right," answered her husband. "When the time comes, let's open our mouths with the rest of the crowd, but we won't make a sound. Then, while the others are shouting their heads off, we'll be quiet and really hear the noise." That seemed to be a wonderful idea.

Without meaning any harm, the lady told her neighbors about her plan.

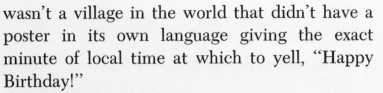

Without meaning any harm, her husband told his friends at the office where he worked. Still without meaning any harm, the friends told their friends, and those friends told other friends.

Before long, people all over the world, even in the city of Hub-Bub, were privately telling one another to open their mouths at the right time but not to yell, so they would be able to hear all the noise made by everyone else.

No one was trying to spoil the prince's birthday celebration. It was just that each person thought, "My voice won't be missed among so many millions. While all the others are yelling and screaming, it won't hurt if I stay quiet so I can really listen."

And so the important moment came closer and closer. In all corners of the earth, crowds of people began gathering in their public meeting

places. All over the world, eyes stared at large clocks ticking away the seconds. It seemed that a shock of excitement, like electricity, swept around the entire globe. In Hub-Bub, of course, the excitement was especially great.

Thousands of people jammed the palace grounds, cheering and shouting, while high on the balcony the young prince waited happily for what would be the loudest noise in the world.

Fifteen seconds to go . . . ten seconds . . . five seconds . . . NOW!

Two billion people strained their ears to catch the loudest noise in the world—and two billion people heard nothing but absolute silence. Every person had kept quiet so he could hear the others yell. Every person had expected the others to do the work, while he sat back and enjoyed it.

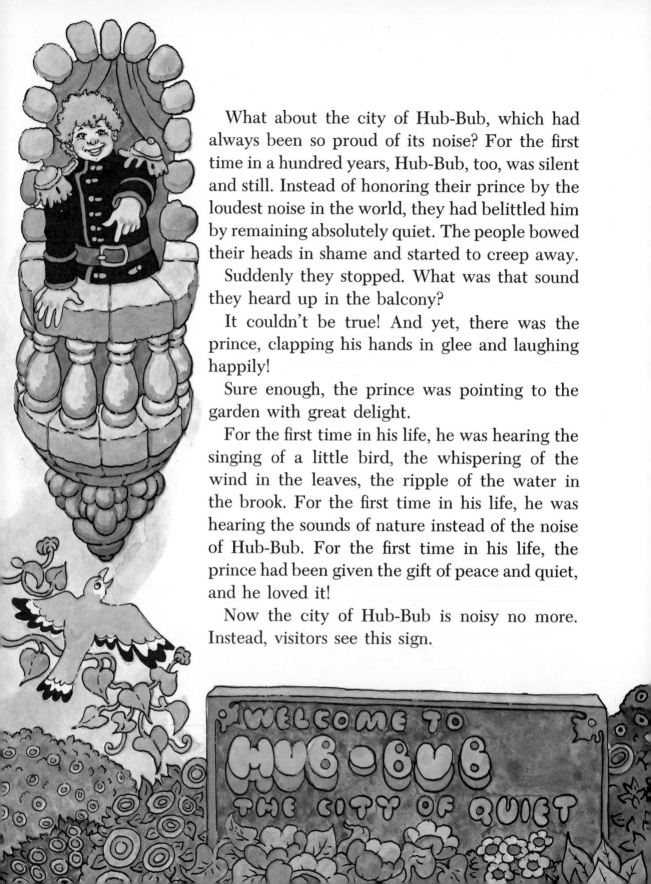

What about the city of Hub-Bub, which had always been so proud of its noise? For the first time in a hundred years, Hub-Bub, too, was silent and still. Instead of honoring their prince by the loudest noise in the world, they had belittled him by remaining absolutely quiet. The people bowed their heads in shame and started to creep away.

Suddenly they stopped. What was that sound they heard up in the balcony?

It couldn't be true! And yet, there was the prince, clapping his hands in glee and laughing happily!

Sure enough, the prince was pointing to the garden with great delight.

For the first time in his life, he was hearing the singing of a little bird, the whispering of the wind in the leaves, the ripple of the water in the brook. For the first time in his life, he was hearing the sounds of nature instead of the noise of Hub-Bub. For the first time in his life, the prince had been given the gift of peace and quiet, and he loved it!

Now the city of Hub-Bub is noisy no more. Instead, visitors see this sign.

WELCOME TO
HUB-BUB
THE CITY OF QUIET

The people of Hub-Bub speak gently. They are proud that their ducks are the quietest, their doors the lightest, and their policemen's whistles the softest in the whole world.

Reflections

1. Read the first and last paragraphs of the story. When would you have preferred to live in Hub-Bub?

2. Did the king succeed in getting all the people in the world to do the same thing at the same time? Explain your answer.

3. In what way were the man and woman who wanted to keep silent sensible? In what way were they foolish?

4. This story could easily have had a different ending. Look back to where the people bow their heads in shame. Starting there, make up a different happy ending. What sad ending can you think of?

5. Which parts of the story do you think are especially funny? What funny words can you find?

6. People often make noises that are not words but that have special meanings. What might each of the following noises mean?

   a. a sigh
   b. a giggle
   c. a moan
   d. a yawn
   e. a hiss
   f. a cough
   g. a clapping of hands
   h. a snap of the fingers
   i. a stamp of the foot

The Boy Who Wouldn't Talk

LOIS KALB BOUCHARD

One day Carlos stopped talking. It was not exactly a sudden decision. When his family had moved from Puerto Rico to New York City, all at once he couldn't read his school books or understand what people said—he couldn't even ask directions. Then Carlos had begun to think about this matter of talking. And he had decided he was just fed up with words—with Spanish names for things and English names for things. He, Carlos Vega, did not need to talk; he could point, nod, make faces, or draw pictures instead.

No one was happy with the situation, least of all Carlos. He didn't like worrying his parents. He was sad that his younger brother, Angel, felt hurt and lonely, and he was sorry he couldn't join his school friends' games. But Carlos still didn't want to talk—until a new friend, Ricky, forced him to think about how words might, after all, be more than just names for things.

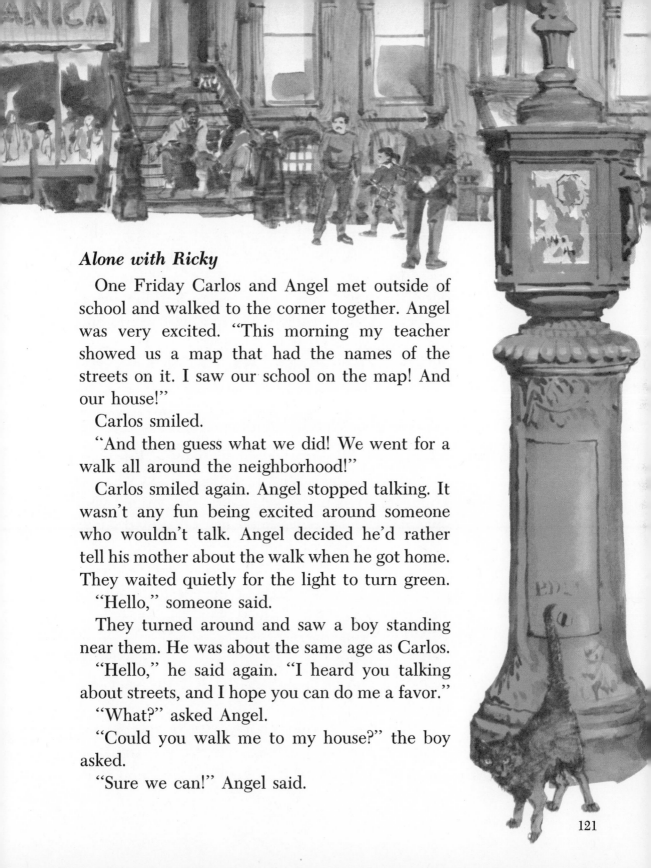

Alone with Ricky

One Friday Carlos and Angel met outside of school and walked to the corner together. Angel was very excited. "This morning my teacher showed us a map that had the names of the streets on it. I saw our school on the map! And our house!"

Carlos smiled.

"And then guess what we did! We went for a walk all around the neighborhood!"

Carlos smiled again. Angel stopped talking. It wasn't any fun being excited around someone who wouldn't talk. Angel decided he'd rather tell his mother about the walk when he got home. They waited quietly for the light to turn green.

"Hello," someone said.

They turned around and saw a boy standing near them. He was about the same age as Carlos.

"Hello," he said again. "I heard you talking about streets, and I hope you can do me a favor."

"What?" asked Angel.

"Could you walk me to my house?" the boy asked.

"Sure we can!" Angel said.

121

Carlos nodded his head to the boy and smiled. But he wondered why the boy wanted someone to walk him home. Carlos had been going home by himself for a long time.

"Do you go to this school?" Angel asked.

"I go to a school six blocks from here," the boy said. "My mother meets me at my school and takes me home. And if she's late, I'm supposed to wait for her. But today I didn't want to wait. A boy walked me to this corner, but then he had to meet his sister."

"What's your name?" Angel asked.

"Ricky Hernández."

"I'm Angel Vega. And this is my brother Carlos."

Ricky smiled and put out his hand. "I'm glad to meet you," he said. Angel shook Ricky's hand. Then Carlos shook Ricky's hand. "Why don't you say anything?" Ricky asked Carlos. "Why doesn't your brother say anything?"

"He doesn't like to talk," said Angel. "He can talk when he wants to, but he doesn't want to any more." Suddenly Angel shouted "Oh!"

"What's the matter?" Ricky asked.

"I forgot the hamster! It's my turn to take it home for the weekend. And I left the cage on my desk!"

"Will it be all right there?" Ricky asked.

Carlos shook his head. He didn't think a hamster should stay in school all weekend. His class had a hamster, too, and Anna had taken it home with her.

"No," Angel answered. "It won't be all right in school. It's just a baby, and it has to get food every day. I have to go back in the school and get it."

"We can wait for you," said Ricky.

"No, you better not wait," Angel said, "because my teacher went home, and I'll have to look for Mr. Davis so he can open the door of my classroom. He has all the keys because he's the cus—, cust—"

"Custodian," Ricky said.

"That's right. But Carlos will take you home." Then Angel looked sad. "I wish I had the hamster now so I could go home with you . . . Well. 'By, Carlos. I'll tell Mommy you're taking Ricky home." Angel ran back into the school, and Carlos was left alone with Ricky.

"Say, Carlos, you don't know where I live yet, do you?" Ricky asked.

Carlos shook his head.

"I wish you'd talk. Will you *listen* if I tell you how to get to my house?"

Carlos nodded his head.

"Listen, Carlos. If you're not going to talk to me at all, I'm going to wait for Angel to come out."

Carlos opened his eyes wide in surprise. "My other friends don't get so angry," he thought.

"Why won't he tell me where he lives? Why wait for Angel?"

"Say—what if Angel comes out another door?" Ricky asked. "And doesn't come this way? Maybe I'll go home with you and wait for Angel there. Okay? Where do you live?"

Carlos pointed around the corner.

"Do you live far from here?" Ricky asked.

Just This Once

Carlos didn't know what to do. All his other friends understood him when he pointed somewhere. Then Carlos thought of something. He

took a piece of chalk from his pocket, bent down,
and drew a map of the streets. He drew one
building to show where his school was and
another building to show where his house was.
Then he stood up and smiled at Ricky.

"I know you don't like to talk much," Ricky
said. "Your brother told me you don't like to talk
much. But I wish just this once you'd talk to
me."

Carlos threw his chalk down on the sidewalk.
It broke in three pieces. He was so angry, he
thought of walking away.

"I can't see what you wrote on the sidewalk,
you know," Ricky said. "I know you wrote something because I heard the chalk rub against the
sidewalk. But I can't see it. I can't see you or
anything else. So will you please just take me to
your house to wait for Angel?"

Carlos stood very still. This was the first boy
he had ever met who could not see. He was very
curious to know why. But he knew he'd have to
ask Ricky to find out why. For a minute Carlos
didn't know what he wanted to do. Then he
said, "Why can't you see?" It felt strange to
talk again.

"My eyes don't work," Ricky said. "Boy, I'm
glad you talked to me!"

"I draw pictures a lot," Carlos told him. "Like
I drew on the sidewalk. I wish you could see it."

"You could tell me about it," Ricky answered.

"But if you make something out of clay, you don't have to tell me about it. I can tell by myself."

"How?"

"By touching it." Ricky thought a second. "But I'd still want you to tell me about a clay thing. It's easier that way. And I like talking."

Carlos thought for a minute. He didn't want to start talking to Ricky and then change his mind again later. But Ricky couldn't see him nod his head or draw pictures. "Okay," Carlos said. "I'm going to talk to you. Not to everybody. Just to you. Where do you live?"

"We go down two blocks and right two blocks, and it's the fifth house."

"I live three blocks the other way. That's what I drew on the sidewalk." Carlos took Ricky's hand. He waited for the traffic light to change and made sure there were no cars coming. Then he took Ricky across the street.

"If you *can* talk," Ricky said, "why don't you talk to everybody?"

"I don't know. There are too many words. And I don't like every word there is."

"What do you mean," asked Ricky, "you don't like every word?"

"Well," said Carlos, "some words I like in Spanish better than English."

"Like what?" asked Ricky, very interested. "I like Spanish, too. I can't speak it, though, because

126

my father and my mother talk in English at home. They only talk Spanish when they visit my aunt and uncle or when they don't want me to know what they're saying."

"I like *libro* better than *book*," said Carlos, "and *muchacho* better than *boy*. And I think I like *casa* better than *house*."

"They sound nice in Spanish," said Ricky. "You teach those words to me some day, and I'll say them in Spanish, too."

They came to the next corner. The light was green, so Carlos told Ricky to step down off the curb, and they crossed the street. Carlos walked very slowly with Ricky, holding his hand all the time.

"Wait a second." Ricky stopped walking, put his hand into his pocket, and took out some money. "My father gave me two dimes this morning. So now we can buy something."

"*Bueno*—good," Carlos said. "I see an ice cream man. Let's go and get some ice cream." They walked over and waited while the man handed an ice cream cone to a girl. "Hey, Ricky," Carlos whispered. "Could you tell the man we want some? I want chocolate."

"Okay," Ricky said. "I'll tell him if you want me to."

Carlos took the ice cream cones from the man and gave one of them to Ricky. Then they went on their way again to Ricky's house.

Spelling with Blocks

When the boys got to Ricky's apartment house, Ricky's mother was walking out of the door. "Ricky! What are you doing here? You know you're supposed to wait for me at school even if I'm late!"

"Yes, I know," said Ricky. "And I thought you'd be angry. But just this once I didn't want to wait for you."

Ricky's mother looked sad. "I know what you mean," she said quietly. "It's hard on a boy as old as you to have to be taken home from school. But please," she said louder, "wait for me next time."

"Okay," Ricky said. "This is Carlos. This is my mother."

"Hi, Carlos. Thank you for walking Ricky home. Did you meet him at his school?"

Carlos shook his head.

"One boy walked me part way. And then I met Carlos and his brother, and I asked them to walk me the rest of the way. But his brother had to go back to school."

"Come on up for a while, Carlos," said Mrs. Hernández. "Does your mother know you'll be late from school?"

Carlos nodded. He looked at her smile and then at her eyes. He tried to figure out if she could see him. Carlos hoped she could understand him if he didn't talk.

"I wish you'd talk to my mother," Ricky said. "But you don't have to. She can see you if you move your head yes or no. Carlos doesn't like to talk," Ricky explained to his mother. "He decided to talk to me, but that's all." They went upstairs to Ricky's apartment.

In Ricky's room Carlos saw a big book open on the desk. The book had no letters on the page. It had lots of bumps instead. "What's this book?" Carlos asked Ricky. "With bumps on it."

"That's how I read," Ricky said. "The bumps are letters. I read by touching the bumps with my fingers."

Carlos touched the bumps on the page. "*Es bueno*—that's good," he said. "I like touching letters. I wish I could touch the letters I read."

"Of course you can," Ricky said. "I learned your letters, too, by touching them." He went over to a closet, opened it, and felt all the toys on the bottom. "Here they are." He pulled out a bag of blocks and emptied the blocks onto the floor.

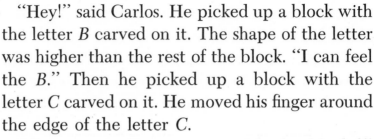

"Hey!" said Carlos. He picked up a block with the letter *B* carved on it. The shape of the letter was higher than the rest of the block. "I can feel the *B*." Then he picked up a block with the letter *C* carved on it. He moved his finger around the edge of the letter *C*.

"Can you spell my name with the blocks?" Ricky asked.

"No. That's *difícil*—that's hard."

"I'll show you how," Ricky said, smiling. "It would be fun to show you how."

Carlos thought to himself, "But I don't like spelling. I don't even like names." He almost said, "Don't show me."

"I said I'll show you how," Ricky told him. He stopped smiling. "Don't you want me to?"

Carlos looked at Ricky's serious face. Then he moved his finger around the edge of the letter *C* again. "Okay. Show me," he said.

Ricky felt all the blocks and picked out the letters that spelled his name. "See? *R–i–c–k–y*. That's how you spell *Ricky*." He was smiling again. "Can you spell your name?"

"Yes," said Carlos. He picked out the letters. "Here's my name." He put Ricky's hand on the blocks that spelled *Carlos*.

"I'll learn it," said Ricky, and he felt each letter slowly. "*C–a–r–l–o–s*."

"I can spell the Spanish word for *yes*," said Carlos. He picked out the letters *S* and *I* and put Ricky's hand on the blocks. "That word is *sí*," he told Ricky.

They played a game with the blocks. Carlos spelled words, and Ricky tried to read them. And Ricky spelled words, and Carlos tried to read them. Carlos did not know as many words as Ricky knew, but he didn't care. He liked spelling with blocks.

After a while Ricky's mother brought in two glasses of milk and a plate of cookies. "Why don't you lend your blocks to Carlos for a while?" she asked Ricky. "Then he can play with them at home."

"Okay," Ricky said.

"*Bueno!*" said Carlos. He smiled at Ricky's mother. "And I can show them to my brother." Then he stopped smiling. He was thinking that he had just talked to Ricky's mother. "I guess I'll talk to your mother, too," he said to Ricky.

"Good," Ricky said.

"Thank you," said Ricky's mother. "Let me know if you want more milk." And Ricky's mother smiled as she left the room.

"I have a great idea, Carlos. Sometimes on Saturdays my father takes me to a park that has lots of flowers. And he lets me take a friend along."

"Flowers?" asked Carlos.

"You know," said Ricky. "They smell good."

"Oh, I know," said Carlos. "*Flores*—flowers."

He said the word *flowers* to himself so he would remember it.

"We have to take a train there," said Ricky. "How would you like to go with us?"

"*Bueno.* I want to."

"We can't touch the flowers much," Ricky said. "But there's a special part for blind people where they let you touch the plants all you want. And they have plants there that feel great."

"Can I touch the plants, too?" Carlos asked.

"Sure. My father can sit on a bench and read his newspaper. And you can show me where to walk. Okay?"

"Okay," said Carlos. "I could tell you when we get to a tree. Or the water. Does this park have water?"

"Oh yes."

"Great," said Carlos. "I like water."

"So do I," said Ricky. "And we can make believe we're firemen putting out a forest fire."

"Make believe?" asked Carlos. "What does that mean?"

"We play that *we're* the firemen," Ricky said. "Or anything else we want to be."

"Oh. I know how to play make-believe. I used to play it with my brother." Carlos remembered how much fun that game was. "Let's do that now," he said to Ricky.

"Sure!" Ricky went over to his desk. "This is the fire engine." He pretended to pull something from the fire engine.

"I see!" said Carlos. "You're pulling the—"

"The hose," said Ricky. "Turn on the water!" he shouted.

Carlos ran to the desk and turned his hand in the air. "Okay! I put the water on! Now I'll show you where the fire is."

"When we make believe," Ricky said softly, "I know where the fire is." He went over to the bed. "The fire's in this tree, okay?"

"Sure," said Carlos very low. He suddenly felt bad that Ricky couldn't see. "Sure. The fire's in this tree."

They carried the hose over to the fire and made noises like water. They thought the noises were so funny that they started laughing. And then Carlos didn't feel so bad that Ricky couldn't see. "He has a lot of fun," Carlos thought. "He can play make-believe and have a good time."

Soon Ricky said, "Whew! The fire's out."

"Whew!" said Carlos. "Let's put the hose back on the truck."

Things to Tell

Then they made believe they were chopping down trees in the forest. Carlos was having such fun that he didn't hear Ricky's mother come into the room.

"Carlos," she said, "it's five thirty. Don't you think you should go home for supper now so your parents won't worry? But I hope you come again soon."

"Oh. I guess I have to go now," Carlos told Ricky. He took a long time putting on his sweater.

Ricky put the blocks in the bag and gave the bag to Carlos. "Can you come with us to that park on Saturday?" Ricky asked.

"Sure," said Carlos. "Well, I guess I'll have to ask my father and mother first. But I think they'll say yes."

"You mean you're going to talk to them?" asked Ricky.

Carlos shrugged his shoulders. "I don't know yet."

"I hope you ask them," Ricky said.

When Carlos got to his house, he climbed the stairs very slowly. He didn't know if he wanted to talk to everybody or if he didn't. He knocked softly on the door.

Angel opened the door. "Hi, Carlos!"

Carlos didn't smile. He walked into the room and stood near the door. Everyone was at the table eating supper, and they all said hello. The whole family was watching him.

Carlos was afraid to start talking again. It would be such a big change. And he was afraid his family might laugh at him. He ran into his room and closed the door and started to cry. He didn't hear Angel come into the room.

"What's in the bag?" Angel asked.

Carlos looked down at the bag. He had forgotten he still had the bag of blocks in his hand. He kept his eyes down on the bag and took a deep breath. "Blocks," Carlos whispered.

"What?" Angel asked.

Carlos looked at his brother and saw that Angel wasn't laughing. "Blocks," Carlos said louder. "Blocks with letters on them. Why are your fingers crossed?"

"I was wishing you would talk tonight," Angel said. He still wasn't laughing. "Let's go and eat."

Carlos looked at the door, but he didn't move.

"Come on," Angel said. "Bring the blocks with you and show me." Carlos took another deep breath. Then he went with Angel to the table.

Carlos slowly took two blocks out of the bag and put them on the table. Everyone was quiet. "These are blocks with letters on them," Carlos said. He looked at his family. No one laughed.

"Where did you get them?" one of his sisters asked.

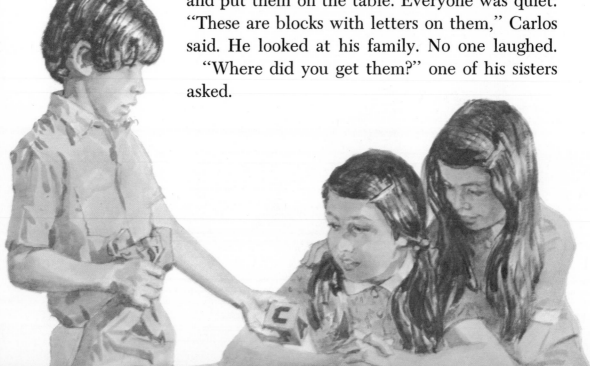

"Ricky let me have them for a while," Carlos said. He sat down in his chair. He felt funny talking to everyone again. But he felt good, too. He smiled at his family. "I have a whole lot of things to tell you about Ricky. I can't just draw pictures to tell you. It would take far too many pictures."

"That's good," everyone said. They were all smiling.

"First there's the blocks. And then Ricky's book. And me walking Ricky home. And the park. Can I go with him to the park?"

"Wow!" said Mr. Vega. "One thing at a time!"

Reflections

1. Why did Angel leave Carlos alone with Ricky? How is this fact important to the outcome of the story?
2. How does Ricky usually read? How was he able to learn the shape of the letters Carlos uses to read and write?
3. Suppose you had to describe a tree to someone who did not know the word for it. What would you tell him?
4. Pretend that you are spending an afternoon alone with Ricky. Make up a game that you could both play equally well.
5. Why was Carlos afraid to start talking again to his family? What do you think made him start talking?

What Is Your Name?

CLARENCE WACHNER

What is your name? Why do you have it? Where did it come from? Of course, you can answer the first question, but can you answer the other two? Perhaps your parents will be able to help you. Dictionaries, encyclopedias, and books about names will also be useful.

People have probably had names almost since language began. The very first words may have been the names or sounds people used to identify themselves. It is likely that long ago each person had only one name. Much later, people began to have more than one name.

Today everyone usually has a given and a family name. A family name is called a surname. A person may have one or more middle names, or a middle initial, in addition to his given name and surname.

Given Names and Nicknames

At one time a given name described a person in some way. *Bernard* means "bold as a bear," and *Bonita* means "pretty." An Indian boy with the name *Morning Cloud* might later earn the name *Deer Slayer* because of his hunting skill. Today people have names that may not describe them at all, but their nicknames might. *Lefty* and *Smiley* are such nicknames.

Other nicknames are short ways to say a name. *Bill, Will,* and *Willie* are nicknames for *William. Pat* and *Patty* (or *Pattie*) are short for *Patrick* or *Patricia. Rob* or *Bob* may be used instead of *Robert.* Some nicknames have endings that mean "little." *Annie* means "little Ann." Other nicknames come from the way young children mispronounce names. *Lilibet* comes from *Elizabeth.* Sometimes a name that started as a nickname will be the given name of another person.

Your own given name probably has a special story behind it. Do you know what language it comes from? Does your parents' choice of a name for you show that they hoped you would be strong, smart, good, joyful, pretty, or handsome? Did they name you for a jewel, a flower, a place, or something that happened when you were born? Did they like the sound or spelling of your

name? Does your name come from the Bible, a story, a play, or a poem? Were you named after a parent, a relative, or a movie star? Was your name made from another name? Was your name made from two or more names put together? Or was it just made up?

SOME GIVEN NAMES

If your name is not in this short list, you can probably find it in a reference book in your library.

Name	Source	Meaning
John	Hebrew	God is gracious
Dorothy	Greek	the gift of God
Victor	Latin	conqueror
Harold	Anglo-Saxon	to rule the army
Norman	Scandinavian	a Northman
Lewis	German	famous warrior
Celeste	French	celestial, heavenly

Surnames

Family names became important because there were mix-ups among people with the same given name. In England long ago, last names were often the words for jobs people did. If a person named John was a weaver, he was probably called John the Weaver, and then just John Weaver. Other names describing work are *Singer, Carpenter, Taylor* (tailor), and *Smith.*

Surnames were given for other reasons, too. If someone lived in a house on a hill, his last name might have been *Hill*. *Wells, Banks, Fields, Brooks,* and *Woods* are some other names describing places where people lived. *Hall, Church,* and *Temple* are surnames that probably came from buildings where people worked or ones near their homes. You can probably guess why people had names such as *North, Eastman, West,* and *Southey.*

Kinships were also used to make surnames. If a man named William had a son called Harold, the son may have been known as Harold, son of William. Later, the son's name became *Harold Williamson. Richardson, Johnson,* and *Anderson* are other names made like *Williamson.* Sometimes such surnames have been shortened to *Williams, Richards,* and *Johns.*

Winters, Summers, Long, Short, and *Little* hold clues to other ways in which family names began. And there are many other sources, too. Here are some of them.

Fruits	Body Parts	Animals
Cherry	Foot	Lyon (lion)
Peach	Hand	Fox
Pear	Head	Lamb
Apple	Hair	Wolf

Some family names may sound strange to you because they are not formed from English words. *Verdi* is an Italian name, *Ruiz* is a Spanish name, *Wong* is a Chinese name, and *Dubois* is a French name. Because many names in foreign languages are difficult to pronounce in English, some families modified the original foreign spellings to make their names sound more American.

Some people's names have changed completely. During the late 1700's, for example, many Negroes were brought from Africa as slaves. Often, their African names were replaced by the family names of the people for whom they worked.

So you see, there are stories behind people's names. Perhaps in the future there will be some new names that come from words for new inventions. Explorations of space and new ways of life may also provide words for names.

Reflections

1. Why did it become necessary for people to have surnames?

2. What four nicknames can you think of that are short forms of given names? What four nicknames can you think of that describe the people or tell something about them?

3. What surnames can you think of that are related to different sorts of jobs? to places? to animals?

4. In Scotland and Ireland, *Mac* and *Mc* mean "son of" and are placed before the surname. The sons of a man named Donald would become known as the MacDonalds. Make family names for the children of men called Gregor, Hale, and Lean.

5. Here are some German words with their English meanings:

Stein—stone	*Eisen*—iron
Baum—tree	*Rosen*—roses
Thal—valley	*Silber*—silver
Blumen—flowers	*Berg*—mountain

We can combine these words to make German surnames. For example, the surname *Silberberg* means "mountain of silver." Use the German words above to make German surnames having these meanings:

a. stone of iron
b. tree of roses
c. valley of flowers

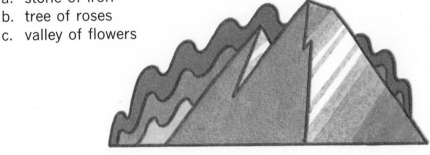

Names for Twins

ALASTAIR REID

Each pair of twins,
rabbits or dogs,
children or frogs,
has to have names
that are almost the same
(to show that they're twins)
but are different too;
so here's what you do.
Find double words,
like Higgledy-Piggledy
(good names for pigs)
or Shilly and Shally
or Dilly and Dally
or Knick and Knack.
Namby and Pamby
are better for poodles;
Whing-Ding for swallows;
Misty and Moisty
and Wishy and Washy
especially for fish.
Call twin kittens
Inky and Pinky
or Helter and Skelter,
or Pell and Mell.
(It's easy to tell
they are twins if their names
have a humdrum sound.)

Crinkum and Crankum
are perfect for squirrels,
like Hanky and Panky
or Fiddle and Faddle;
but Mumbo and Jumbo
are mainly for elephants.
(Airy and Fairy
would never suit *them*.)
Willy and Nilly
will fit almost any twins.
Hubble and Bubble
or Hodge and Podge
or Roly and Poly
are mainly for fat twins.
Chitter and Chatter
or Jingle and Jangle
or Pitter and Patter,
of course, are for noisy twins.
Further than that,
there's Harum and Scarum,
or Hocus and Pocus,
or Heebie and Jeebie,
but these are peculiar,
and have to be used,
like Mixty and Maxty,
for very *odd* pairs....
You see what begins
when you have to name twins.

Talk

HAROLD COURLANDER and GEORGE HERZOG

Once, not far from the city of Accra on the Gulf of Guinea, a country man went out to his garden to dig up some yams to take to market. While he was digging, one of the yams said to him:

"Well, at last you're here. You never weeded me, but now you come around with your digging stick. Go away and leave me alone!"

The farmer turned around and looked at his cow in amazement. The cow was chewing her cud and looking at him.

"Did you say something?" he asked.

The cow kept on chewing and said nothing, but the man's dog spoke up.

"It wasn't the cow who spoke to you," the dog said. "It was the yam. The yam says leave him alone."

146

The man became angry, because his dog had never talked before, and he didn't like his tone besides. So he took his knife and cut a branch from a palm tree to whip his dog. Just then the palm tree said:

"Put that branch down!"

The man was getting very upset about the way things were going, and he started to throw the palm branch away, but the palm branch said:

"Man, put me down softly!"

He put the branch down gently on a stone, and the stone said:

"Hey, take that thing off me!"

This was enough, and the frightened farmer started to run for his village. On the way he met a fisherman going the other way with a fish trap on his head.

"What's the hurry?" the fisherman asked.

"My yam said, 'Leave me alone!' Then the dog said, 'Listen to what the yam says!' When I went to whip the dog with a palm branch, the tree said, 'Put that branch down!' Then the palm branch said, 'Do it softly!' Then the stone said, 'Take that thing off me!'"

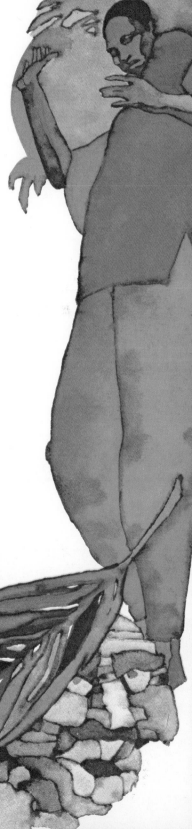

"Is that all?" the man with the fish trap asked. "Is that so frightening?"

"Well," the man's fish trap said, "did he take it off the stone?"

"Wah!" the fisherman shouted. He threw the fish trap on the ground and began to run with the farmer, and on the trail they met a weaver with a bundle of cloth on his head.

"Where are you going in such a rush?" he asked them.

"My yam said, 'Leave me alone!' " the farmer said. "The dog said, 'Listen to what the yam says!' The tree said, 'Put that branch down!' The branch said 'Do it softly!' And the stone said, 'Take that thing off me!' "

"And then," the fisherman continued, "the fish trap said, 'Did he take it off?' "

"That's nothing to get excited about," the weaver said, "no reason at all."

"Oh yes it is," his bundle of cloth said. "If it happened to you, you'd run too!"

"Wah!" the weaver shouted. He threw his bundle on the trail and started running with the other men.

They came panting to the ford in the river and found a man bathing.

"Are you chasing a gazelle?" he asked them.

The first man said breathlessly:

"My yam talked at me, and it said, 'Leave me alone!' And my dog said, 'Listen to your yam!'

And when I cut myself a branch, the tree said, 'Put that branch down!' And the branch said, 'Do it softly!' And the stone said, 'Take that thing off me!'"

The fisherman panted:

"And my trap said, 'Did he?'"

The weaver wheezed:

"And my bundle of cloth said, 'You'd run too!'"

"Is that why you're running?" the man in the river asked.

"Well, wouldn't you run if you were in their position?" the river said.

The man jumped out of the water and began to run with the others. They ran down the main street of the village to the house of the chief. The chief's servants brought his stool out, and he came and sat on it to listen to their complaints.

"I went out to my garden to dig yams," the farmer said, waving his arms. "Then everything began to talk! My yam said, 'Leave me alone!' My dog said, 'Pay attention to your yam!' The tree said, 'Put that branch down!' The branch said, 'Do it softly!' and the stone said, 'Take it off me!'"

"And my fish trap said, 'Well, did he take it off?'" the fisherman said.

"And my cloth said, 'You'd run too!'" the weaver said.

"And the river said the same," the bather said hoarsely, his eyes bulging.

The chief listened to them patiently, but he couldn't refrain from scowling.

"Now this is really a wild story," he said at last. "You'd better all go back to your work before I punish you for disturbing the peace."

So the men went away, and the chief shook his head and mumbled to himself, "Nonsense like that upsets the community."

"Fantastic, isn't it?" his stool said. "Imagine, a talking yam!"

Reflections

1. What unusual things happened to the farmer, the fisherman, the weaver, and the bather?
2. If you had been the chief, what would you have said when the four men told you their story? Would you have done anything?
3. What sort of man was the chief? Be ready to show the class how he probably walked and sat and spoke.
4. The setting of this story is near Accra, a city in Africa. Although the story is written in English, the farmer and all the other men speak the language of their tribe. What language do you think the yam, the dog, the palm tree, and the other things speak? Give the reasons for your answer.
5. What is meant when we talk of a tree "whispering in the wind"? Do you think trees really can talk or whisper? Explain.

Ululation

EVE MERRIAM

With a bray, with a yap,
with a grunt, snort, neigh,
with a growl, bark, yelp,
with a buzz, hiss, howl,
with a chirrup, mew, moo,
with a snarl, baa, wail,
with a blatter, hoot, bay,
with a screech, drone, yowl,
with a cackle, gaggle, guggle,
with a chuck, cluck, clack,
with a hum, gobble, quack,
with a roar, blare, bellow,
with a yip, croak, crow,
with a whinny, caw, low,
with a bleat, with a cheep,
    with a squawk, with a squeak:

animals
      —and sometimes humans—
            speak!

The Story of Lengthwise

ERNESTINE COBERN BEYER

From **A** *to* **B**

Lengthwise was a bookworm who made his home in a dictionary. He began life among the A's and started nibbling right away. A-words were very tasty. They were flavored with printer's ink, and the paper had a crispy, crunchy crackle like cornflakes. As he swallowed each A-word, Lengthwise digested its meaning. It wasn't long before he had tunneled his way from *an* to *at*, having grown smarter and stronger with every bite.

Then one day Lengthwise reached the end of the A's, and he decided that he was now strong enough and smart enough to leave his bookshelf and go out into the world. So he left his dictionary home and crawled along the bookshelf until he came to an open window. Then over the sill and down the outside wall he went. It was a long, difficult trip, but he made it.

When he reached the outside, Lengthwise looked around. The day was cold and drizzly, but since he had never been outdoors before, he felt satisfied and cheerful. He ambled along the damp,

153

green grass until his path was blocked by a plant whose name he knew at once, for it began with the letter A, an amaryllis.

Lengthwise climbed the amaryllis and sat down in its topmost blossom, which swayed like a tiny rocking chair in the breeze. From this dizzy height, he looked down at the garden. His eyes, which were round and darkly rimmed as if he wore black spectacles, grew wider with all that he saw. What did he see? He saw a sparrow on a bough, a butterfly hovering over a tulip, and an ant bringing a crumb to her family.

He didn't know what a sparrow or a butterfly was. But when he saw the ant, he recognized her, for he had come across her name among the A's. The ant, who was a friendly little creature, put down her crumb and stared at Lengthwise. "Hi!" she said. "You're new around here, aren't you?"

"An accurate assumption!" replied Lengthwise, using A-words, which were all he had so far digested.

"Horrible weather we're having!" the ant continued.

"Aye, aye," Lengthwise replied. "Absolutely awful!"

"How funny you talk!" the ant exclaimed.

Lengthwise gazed at her wistfully. He wanted very much to be her friend. He wanted, in fact, to ask her to go walking with him and share the many marvels in the garden. But how could he do this when all he knew were A-words? Once more Lengthwise did his little best.

"Advance, amiable ant!" he began. "Amazing adventures await!"

"Goodness gracious!" said the ant. "What a show-off!" Then she picked up a crumb and scurried away.

"Adieu!" said Lengthwise sadly.

Feeling puzzled and hurt, Lengthwise crawled up the wall and over the sill. He returned to his dictionary, thinking that perhaps A's were not quite enough to have under his belt and that he would most certainly have to have a few B's before he could visit the garden again. Many weeks passed as he tunneled his way through the pages. B-words were delightful. Lengthwise enjoyed them so much that he nibbled steadily from *baa* to *buzz*. By the time he had digested *Byzantian*, he felt strong enough and smart enough to go again into the wide, wide world. So once more he sought the open window and crawled down the outside wall.

Back in the garden, the little bookworm found to his amazement that everything looked different. This was because the sun was shining. Grass and moss were astir with busy bugs, all talking excitedly together. How he wished he knew what they were saying! At last he spied a bug whom he recognized at once. It was a beetle. He had come across the word *beetle* not long ago. "Beautiful big black beetle," he burst out in a flurry of lately digested *B*-words, "behold a backward bookworm!"

"Huh?" gasped the beetle. "Why all the big words, pal?"

Lengthwise took a deep breath and tried again. "Beautiful big black beetle, befriend a befuddled bookworm baffled by bewildering bug-babble!"

Like the ant, the beetle thought Lengthwise was a show-off. Disgusted, he dived into a rose and pulled its petals over him.

Poor Lengthwise wondered what he should do now. He had just about decided to return to the dictionary when a boy entered the garden. Under his arm he carried a geography book. He opened the book and sat down under a tree to study his lesson. Lengthwise crawled close. "Boy!" he said. "Brave bright boy bearing beautiful big book, befriend a bewildered bookworm." The boy did not hear him; he continued reading. Lengthwise noticed he did not swallow the words on the page. He seemed to nibble them with his eyes. "Bye-bye, boy," said Lengthwise.

Back to the Book

Since neither beetle nor boy paid any attention to him, Lengthwise returned to his bookshelf and started chewing again. Many days passed as he went from the *C*-section to the *M*'s. He liked *M*-words immensely. "Mmmmm!" he murmured happily. He nibbled *M*-words until he could hold no more. Then he went again for another adventure in the garden. But what was wrong? Where *was* the garden? He thought it had disappeared, but it was nighttime, and the garden was lost in shadows. Suddenly something round and silvery peeped from behind a cloud.

"Moon!" Lengthwise whispered. "Marvelous mellow moon!" Awed, he continued to stare up at the sky. He had never seen the stars before. He didn't even know they *were* stars, for he had not yet come to the S-section in the dictionary. Then a tiny light twinkled in the bushes. Lengthwise thought at first that one of the lights in the

sky must have fallen to earth. But it was not a falling star. It was only a firefly. "Miraculous midget meteor!" exclaimed Lengthwise.

The firefly's light blinked nervously. "Big words frighten me," he said.

"Mortification makes me miserable," apologized Lengthwise.

The light in the bushes went out. It was obvious that the firefly did not want to be his friend.

Poor Lengthwise didn't know how he had failed. He sat himself down on a stone and thought about it. It must be that he had not eaten *enough* words. Yes, that was it. He must go back to the dictionary and eat more. In fact, he would not stop eating words until he had eaten the very last one. And so he returned to his dictionary and ate his way right through to the Z's.

It was then that the trouble began. Z-words did not agree with Lengthwise. They had sharp corners which scratched as they went down. He turned white when he swallowed *zigzag;* it was almost more than he could bear. Hoping to take the taste from his mouth, he hastily gobbled *zucchini,* and that was his final mistake. His eyes grew cloudy, his skin became damp, and his body began to tremble. He lost his grip on the page and tumbled out of the dictionary and onto the shelf.

"Now I will surely die," he thought. But he didn't die. He slowly regained his strength and crawled weakly to the garden to get some air, and there he lay curled up in pain.

Not far off, an elf sat on a moss-covered stone doing a crossword puzzle. Hearing the bookworm's groans, he glanced up. "What's the matter?" he asked. "Are you sick?"

"Zounds!" exclaimed Lengthwise. "I've lost my zest. My zip has come unzipped." But even with unzipped zip, Lengthwise was not able to use all the words he had digested.

"How funny you talk," said the elf. "You sound as though you've swallowed a dictionary."

"I have," said Lengthwise. "That's the trouble with me."

"Hmmmm!" said the elf. "If you've swallowed a dictionary, perhaps you can help me with my crossword puzzle."

"I know lots of cross words," Lengthwise replied. "*Don't* is a cross word, and *won't* is a cross word, too—especially if you say it in a cross tone of voice."

"That's not what I mean," said the elf. "I've been working on this puzzle all day, and I can't go any further. I can't find the word that fits into this space. See?"

Lengthwise studied the puzzle. "The word is *knowledge*," he said, and he spelled it out for the elf.

The elf was very grateful. "You've helped me a lot," he said. "Now, how may I help *you*? You were unhappy being a bookworm. How would you like to be a lion?"

"No, thanks," said Lengthwise. "I'd be afraid of myself."

"What about an elephant?" suggested the elf. "Or a zebra, maybe?"

"No." Lengthwise shook his head sadly.

"Wait a minute," said the elf. "I have an idea. You helped me with a word I needed; maybe you can do the same for someone else. We wouldn't have to change you into anything. Would you like that?"

"Oh, yes, more than anything," replied Lengthwise. "What is your idea?"

"I know a man who is an author. Sometimes when he is writing a story, he has a very hard time thinking of just the right word he needs in a certain place. You could live with him and help him."

Lengthwise was very happy. "Let's do it right away," he said.

And that is exactly what happened. Lengthwise, the bookworm, went to live with Mr. Wright, the author, who also loved words. He was a bespectacled man, the bookworm type. They became friends immediately, and that very day they set to work on a story. From that time on, Mr. Wright dedicated every book he wrote: "To my friend L." And nobody but Mr. Wright knew that the *L* was for Lengthwise.

Reflections

1. Lengthwise had a serious problem in this story. What was it?

2. Instead of using just *B*-words the second time he went out, how could Lengthwise have increased his vocabulary?

3. Why couldn't the ant understand Lengthwise?

4. Do you think *Lengthwise* is a good name for a bookworm?

5. A pun is a joke based on the fact that some words sound the same but have different meanings. Find the pun that Lengthwise made when he met the elf. Did Lengthwise know it was a pun? What pun was made with the author's name?

6. Alliteration is the repetition of the same beginning sound or letter in two or more words in a row. Find an example of alliteration in the fourth sentence of this story. Then find other examples in things Lengthwise said. Now make up several examples of your own.

Dialects in America

Here's a picture of something that you've seen many times. How would you finish this sentence about it: "The bottle is half full of _____"?

Did everyone in your class use the same word to complete the sentence? Did anyone use a different word? If anyone did, then probably that person comes from some other part of the country. In other parts of our country, people talk about the picture in different ways.

Here are some things that people in different parts of the country would say about the picture.

Did you use one of these words? Did you say *soda* or *tonic* or *pop?* Or did you use some other word?

Here's something important to know about English. In our country most people learn to speak English when they're growing up. But not everyone speaks English the same way. The different ways that people speak English are called **dialects.**

There are many different dialects in our country. If you ever travel to other parts of the United States, then you will almost certainly hear different dialects. But you can also sometimes hear different dialects by listening carefully to people on TV. You might hear words that sound different from the way you say them. You might hear words that are different from the ones you use to name things. You might even hear words put together in sentences in a way that's different.

Differences in Pronunciation

If you look in a good dictionary, you'll see that some words can be pronounced in more than one way. One word that's like this is *aunt*. In some parts of the country, people say the word so it sounds like *an* with a *t* at the end. In other parts of the country, people say the word so it sounds something like *on* with a *t* at the end. Which way do you say it?

Another word that people say differently is *route*. Some people say it so it rhymes with *out*. Other people say it so it rhymes with *boot*. A good dictionary will show both ways.

Then there are words which sound about the same when some people say them, but don't sound the same when other people say them. Many people say *pin* and *pen* so they sound about the same. When other people say them, the two words sound different. Some people say the words *Mary*, *marry*, and *merry* so they sound alike. Other people say each word differently.

If two people pronounce a number of words in different ways, then these two people speak different dialects.

Differences in Vocabulary

Here are some other things for which people use different words. What name do you use for the insect in picture A? How would you complete this sentence about picture B: "The groceries are in a _____"? What do you call the object in picture C? Different dialects have different words for these things.

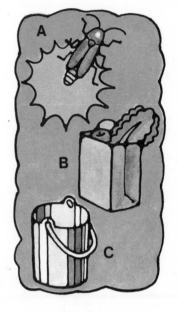

Dialect Regions

Here's a map in which different parts of the country are marked in different colors. These are just some of the **dialect regions** of our country. The people in one region don't speak exactly the same way as people who live in another region.

Even this map doesn't show all of the dialect regions in our country. In parts of the country, people who speak one dialect can go thirty miles one way and find another dialect. Or they can go thirty miles another way and find a third dialect.

Standard Dialects

Everyone who speaks English speaks a dialect of English. In the United States our English dialects are more alike than they are different. And so people who speak one dialect of American English can almost always understand people who speak a different one.

This isn't true in a country like England, which also has many different dialects. In England some people don't understand the dialects that other people speak. And this can be a problem.

Some people in England learn more than one dialect. Some people learn the dialect spoken in the regions where they live, and they also learn a special dialect that they can use to talk to people who live in other parts of the country.

This special dialect is sometimes called a **standard dialect.** English people speak this standard dialect the same way all over their country.

But we don't have one standard dialect. Instead, we have different standard dialects in different parts of our country. If you speak one of these standard dialects, then most other people can understand you, no matter where you live.

Reflections

1. What are some of the ways that dialects differ in our country?
2. If you listened to someone who spoke a dialect of American English that's different from yours, do you think you'd be able to understand him?
3. Why do some people who live in England need to learn more than one dialect?
4. Here are some more pictures for you to talk about with your friends.

Do you call the animal in picture A a *skunk* or a *polecat?* Do you call it something else? Would you say that the clock in picture B says quarter *to* four or *of* four or *till* four? What do you call the object in picture C? Do you say *faucet* or *tap* or *spigot?* Or do you use some other word?

My Dog

TOM ROBINSON

My dog listens when I talk.
He goes with me for a walk.
When I sleep, he's sleepy too.
He does everything I do.
He has eyes that always show
He knows everything I know.
I never do a thing but he
Thinks it is all right for me.
When I speak, he always minds.
He shares with me the things he finds.
When other people say I'm bad,
He hangs his head and looks so sad..
He cuddles up and laps my hand
And tells me he can understand.

No Schools for the Deaf Ones
ETTA DeGERING

Something Different

Thomas Hopkins Gallaudet sat in the July sun on the porch steps of his family's home on Prospect Street. He was thinking about what he might do after his graduation from school.

His thoughts were interrupted by his younger brothers and sisters and their playmates. They all came trooping around the corner of the house, laughing and panting from some running game. He watched them form a circle on the grass to rest up with a guessing game. He noticed one girl who sat apart from the group, with her face turned toward it. There was something different about this girl. It wasn't her pink ruffled dress nor her blond curls nor her pretty face—but wait, it *was* her face. Her face was the face of a four-year-old child, but her size showed she must be twice that age.

Thomas called Theodore, his nine-year-old brother, from the circle. "Who is the little girl sitting over there by herself?"

Teddy looked in the girl's direction. "Her? Why, don't you know? She's Alice Cogswell. Doc Cogswell's girl—lives next door."

"Why doesn't she play with the group?" asked Thomas.

Teddy shrugged. "She can't. She's deaf and dumb."

Deaf and dumb. So that was it. "Bring her to me. Maybe I can think of a game she can play. She looks lonesome."

Teddy ran over to Alice, made a sweeping motion to come, left her with Thomas, and hurried back to the circle. Thomas smiled and patted the step beside him. Alice sat on the very edge like a pink butterfly—if there are pink butterflies—ready to take flight. Thomas wanted to give her a way to speak to other children. He picked up his hat, gave it to Alice, stooped down, and wrote *hat* in the sand of the path.

Alice looked at him blankly. The marks in the sand meant nothing to her. Again and again Thomas handed her the hat and wrote *hat* in the sand. He pointed to the writing and then to other things and shook his head. He pointed to the hat and nodded vigorously.

Alice's forehead puckered. She was trying to understand. She looked from the hat to the writing. What did those marks in the sand have to do with the thing she held in her hand?

Thomas breathed a prayer.

Finally a glimmer of light shone in Alice's eyes. Her forehead smoothed. She smiled and nodded. For the first time in her life, Alice understood that things had names, names that could be written in the sand. She showed that she wanted to write. Thomas helped her until she could write *hat* from memory.

He turned the writing into a game. When Alice wrote *hat,* he offered her his handkerchief, a twig, a stone. She laughed and shook her head until he held out the hat.

Suddenly Alice pointed to herself and then to the sand. She wanted to write the word that meant herself. When Thomas wrote *Alice,* she again pointed to herself and looked at him, asking. He nodded. Satisfied, she began practicing her name.

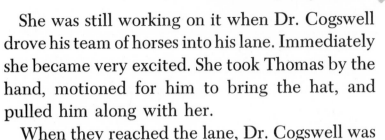

She was still working on it when Dr. Cogswell drove his team of horses into his lane. Immediately she became very excited. She took Thomas by the hand, motioned for him to bring the hat, and pulled him along with her.

When they reached the lane, Dr. Cogswell was coming toward the house. Alice ran to him. Thomas saw by their actions how close this father and daughter were. Alice tugged at her father to come. Thinking Alice wanted him to meet her friend, he smiled and shook hands with Thomas.

But Thomas knew what Alice wanted. He handed her his hat. She passed it to her father and dropped to her knees. In the roadway she wrote *hat* in the dust.

Thomas would never forget the look in Dr. Cogswell's eyes—astonishment, joy, and love—all mixed up with tears that wouldn't stay back. He tried to hug his little daughter, but she would have none of it. She hadn't finished. She pointed to herself and began to write. She wrote *Ali* but could not go on and held up her hand to Thomas for help. Together they completed her name. Now she was ready for the hug and the "well-done" pat.

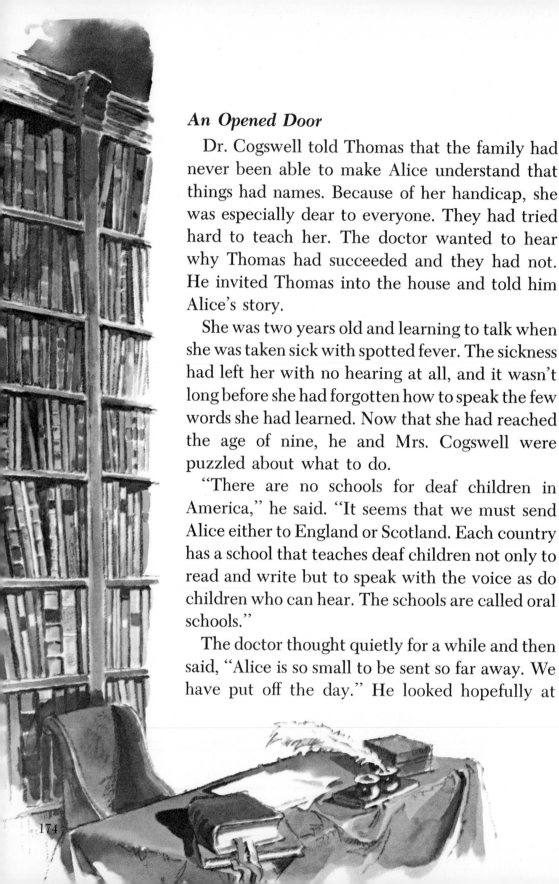

An Opened Door

Dr. Cogswell told Thomas that the family had never been able to make Alice understand that things had names. Because of her handicap, she was especially dear to everyone. They had tried hard to teach her. The doctor wanted to hear why Thomas had succeeded and they had not. He invited Thomas into the house and told him Alice's story.

She was two years old and learning to talk when she was taken sick with spotted fever. The sickness had left her with no hearing at all, and it wasn't long before she had forgotten how to speak the few words she had learned. Now that she had reached the age of nine, he and Mrs. Cogswell were puzzled about what to do.

"There are no schools for deaf children in America," he said. "It seems that we must send Alice either to England or Scotland. Each country has a school that teaches deaf children not only to read and write but to speak with the voice as do children who can hear. The schools are called oral schools."

The doctor thought quietly for a while and then said, "Alice is so small to be sent so far away. We have put off the day." He looked hopefully at

Thomas. "Since you have opened the door to written language for her, would it be possible for you to teach her more, and show us how? Then we could wait until she is older to send her away to school."

"I will be glad to do what I can, but I have no training," Thomas answered.

Dr. Cogswell went to his library and took down a book called *Theory of Signs*. He turned the pages of the book and said, "Most of this book lists signs and words for deaf-mutes to use. There is a sign for each word. The back of the book has the manual alphabet. You will see that the letters of the alphabet are made by different positions of the fingers on only one hand. The book is like a dictionary, except that it lists signs instead of definitions." Dr. Cogswell stopped speaking and passed the book to Thomas.

Thomas thought it was very interesting that the deaf could talk with their hands and also spell words with their fingers. "Have you tried to teach Alice finger spelling?" he asked.

"With no more success than our efforts at teaching her writing," answered the doctor. "She imitates our motions as a sort of game, but they mean nothing to her. Would you care to take the book home and see if you can use it?"

Thomas told him he would be glad to and then asked, "Are there many deaf-mutes in Connecticut?"

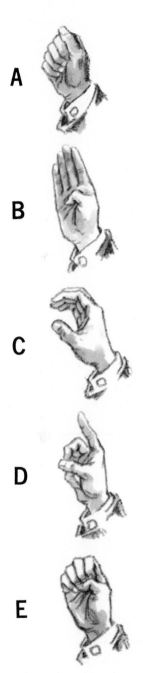

A

B

C

D

E

"Eighty-four in the ministers' census of 1812," said the doctor. "I figure that means there are at least four hundred in New England and more than a thousand in America."

Thomas left for home after setting a time for Alice to come for a lesson the next day. He stopped at his house only long enough to leave the book. He walked on and on, thinking over what he had just heard: eighty-four deaf in Connecticut, four hundred in New England, a thousand in America! No schools for them! No education for them!

He thought of Alice's happiness on learning just two words. What would it be if she could read a book! If only there were a school for her in America . . . for all those other deaf ones, too.

Thomas walked until late. Before returning home, he had outlined a plan of work for himself. When he finished college, he would search out the deaf. He would try to help them help themselves.

Before Alice came for class the next day, Thomas made out a list of words to teach her, and then he tore it up. He would let Alice lead the way. As she needed a word, he would teach her to write and finger-spell it. *Hat* she had already learned to write. Today she would spell it on her fingers.

Thomas was astonished at how rapidly Alice learned. Sometimes she learned more than twenty words at a lesson, and the next day she remembered them. Thomas's brothers and sisters also

wanted to learn the new way of talking. Alice was delighted to be in a class. They talked to each other by spelling words on their fingers and by signs.

Signs were fun. They were like drawing pictures in the air. Sometimes they were shortcuts to spelling words like *elephant.* To sign *elephant,* one just swooped his hand down as if along an elephant's trunk. The sign for *boy* was hand reaching up as if grasping the bill of a cap. The sign for *girl* was hand closed, with the thumb tracing an imaginary bonnet string from the cheek to under the chin. By learning signs, Alice built many kinds of words into her vocabulary.

Thomas kept the children laughing as he acted out the meaning of *sad, angry, fast, slow, tumble,* and *fly.* He gave the children stories to read. Alice was very excited when she could read a whole story.

Thomas's interest in helping the deaf continued. With the support of citizens in Hartford, Connecticut, he founded the first school for the deaf.

Today, there are several schools for the deaf in our country. One of them is Gallaudet College in Washington, D.C. There are also groups that raise money and do research in deafness. Signs, the manual alphabet, speech, and lipreading are ways for the deaf to communicate today. Deaf children and adults owe a great deal to Thomas Gallaudet, who brought language into their lives.

Reflections

1. Why did Thomas Gallaudet decide to help Alice Cogswell?
2. How did Thomas teach Alice the word *hat?*
3. When Thomas saw Alice with her father, what did he learn from their actions?
4. When Thomas began teaching Alice, how were new words chosen? Why was this a good method?
5. In what ways, do you think, did the early settlers communicate with the Indians? How many of these ways resemble methods used today to communicate with the deaf?
6. What signs do ordinary people often use to
   a. hitch a ride?
   b. say good-by?
   c. tell someone not to speak?
   d. say that something doesn't matter?
   e. say that something is secretly funny?

Little Girl,
Be Careful What You Say

CARL SANDBURG

Little girl, be careful what you say
when you make talk with words, words—
for words are made of syllables
and syllables, child, are made of air—
and air is so thin—air is the breath of God—
air is finer than fire or mist,
finer than water or moonlight,
finer than spider-webs in the moon,
finer than water-flowers in the morning:
    and words are strong, too,
      stronger than rocks or steel
stronger than potatoes, corn, fish, cattle,
and soft, too, soft as little pigeon-eggs,
soft as the music of hummingbird wings.

    So, little girl, when you speak greetings,
when you tell jokes, make wishes or prayers,
      be careful, be careless, be careful,
      be what you wish to be.

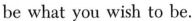

KNOWING WORDS

Our English language has many words. Most of us will never master all these words. But we can master a large number of them by knowing some ways that words came into our language and how these words are put together.

English, like you, has parents and grandparents. The English we use today is in many ways like Anglo-Saxon, or Old English. Old English was written and spoken in England hundreds of years ago.

Our English language has borrowed many words from Greek, a language over three thousand years old. We have also borrowed many words from Latin. Latin was used in parts of Europe for over two thousand years, and much of it is based on Greek.

Because today's English has borrowed from these three older languages to make its words, we have many ways of saying things. Let's see how this works by studying the word *foot*.

A Word from Old English

From the time you were very young, you have used the word *foot*. This word is descended from the Old English word *fot*. The plural of *foot* is *feet*. *Foot* may be added at the beginning of six of the following words to make compound words. Which words do you think they are?

ball	apple	step
stool	lights	pen
book	wear	print

How does knowing the meaning of *foot* help you define the six compound words you have made?

A Word from Latin

As Old English grew and changed, it borrowed words from many languages including Latin. In Latin the word for *foot* is *pedes* (pronounced ped' āz). Knowing that *pedes* means "foot," see if you can define these words.

pedal	expedition	pedestal
pedestrian	biped	peddler

These clues may help you:

- Where do you place your feet when you ride a bicycle?
- A lib*rarian* is a person who works with books. What does a person use when he walks?
- *Ex–* is a Latin word part that means "from"; *–ion* is a Latin word part showing action. What is an expedition?
- How does a ped*dler* use his feet in his work?
- *Bi–* is a Latin word part that means "two."
- The Latin word part *–al* often means "belonging to."

How does knowing that *pedes* means "foot" help you with your definition of the words above?

A Word from Greek

The Greek word for *foot* is *pous*. In English *pous* is often *–pod–* or *–pus–*. We find the Greek word for *foot* in the following words:

tripod	octopus
monopode	podiatrist

Discuss a definition for each of these words. These clues may help you:

- How many wheels does a tricycle have?
- If a quadruped has four feet, how many feet does a monopode have?
- If eight people make an octet for singing, how many "feet," or tentacles, does an octopus have?
- If your feet hurt, you may visit a special kind of doctor.

Check your definitions with those in a dictionary.

Adding Parts to Word Roots

Foot, *–ped–*, and *–pod–* or *–pus–* are called word roots. Word roots may sometimes be words. As you know, *foot* is a word.

Many roots always appear with another word part attached to them. For example, *tripod* has *tri–* before *–pod–*. *Podium* has *–ium* after *–pod–*. Parts of words that come before roots are called prefixes, because *pre–* itself means "before" or "in front of." The word part after a root is called a suffix, since in Latin *suffix* means "to fasten to."

There are several hundred prefixes and suffixes used in English. Many are mostly used in books about science and medicine. But others like *re–*, *un–*, *ex–*, *in–*, *tri–*, *bi–*, *mono–*, *–ium*, *–y*, and *–ion* are used in many other words. These little pieces of Greek, Latin, and Old English are always clues to word meanings because each of them has a meaning of its own. You will learn many of these meanings as you study reading.

See How It Works

One word root we have borrowed from Latin is *–port–*. Its meaning in Latin is "to carry." Study the following:

re–
"back or again"

–er
"one who does"

trans–
"across or beyond"

–ation
makes nouns

im–
"in or into"

–s
shows plural for nouns
or singular present action

ex–
"out of"

–ed
shows past action

de–
"from or down or away"

–ing
shows present action

See how many words you can make by combining word parts in the left column with *–port–*. After you have done this, see if *–er, –ation, –s, –ing* or *–ed* may be added to some of your words. Then tell how the meaning of *–port–*, "to carry," may be found in each word you made. Check the meanings of your words in a dictionary.

One of the secrets of good reading is to know word parts and what they mean. You already know thousands of words. By learning a few new word parts each week, you can increase your reading power. You cannot break the reading code without knowing the meaning of words.

Unit 3
THE WONDER
OF LIFE

In Time of Silver Rain

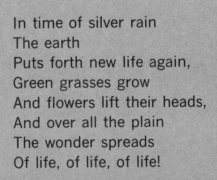

In time of silver rain
The earth
Puts forth new life again,
Green grasses grow
And flowers lift their heads,
And over all the plain
The wonder spreads
Of life, of life, of life!

In time of silver rain
The butterflies lift silken wings
To catch a rainbow cry,
And trees put forth
New leaves to sing
In joy beneath the sky
As down the roadway passing boys
And girls go singing, too,
In time of silver rain
When spring
And life are new.

Langston Hughes

James Henry Trotter and the Fantastic Peach

ROALD DAHL

James Henry Trotter lived in a house on the top of a hill in England. One day he met a little old man who gave him a strange mixture in a paper bag. The mixture was magic and contained tiny green things that moved. The old man told James that he would have wonderful adventures if he put the mixture in water and drank it. Then the man disappeared.

Very excited, James rushed home to get water. But, just as he was passing the old peach tree in the garden on the top of the hill, he slipped and fell. The paper bag burst, and the tiny green things in the magic mixture sank into the soil. When James got up, he was startled to see a huge peach growing on a branch of the peach tree. The peach grew and grew until its weight bent the branch down and the peach lay on the ground.

That evening James stood in the garden and stared at the huge peach.

The Giant Peach

"Something else," he told himself, "something stranger than ever this time, is about to happen to me again soon." He was sure of it. He could feel it coming.

He looked around him, wondering what on earth it was going to be. The garden lay soft and

silver in the moonlight. The grass was wet with dew, and a million dewdrops were sparkling and twinkling like diamonds around his feet. And now suddenly the whole place, the whole garden seemed to be *alive* with magic.

Almost without knowing what he was doing, as though drawn by some powerful magnet, James Henry Trotter started walking slowly toward the giant peach. He climbed over the fence that surrounded it and stood directly beneath it, staring up at its great bulging sides. He put out a hand and touched it gently with the tip of his finger. It felt soft and warm and slightly furry, like the skin of a baby mouse. He moved a step closer and rubbed his cheek lightly against the soft skin. And then suddenly, while he was doing this, he happened to notice that right beside him and below him, close to the ground, there was a hole in the side of the peach.

It was quite a large hole, the sort of thing an animal about the size of a fox might have made.

James knelt down in front of it and poked his head and shoulders inside.

He crawled in.

He kept on crawling.

"This isn't just a hole," he thought excitedly. "It's a tunnel!"

The tunnel was damp and murky, and all around him there was the curious bittersweet smell of fresh peach. The floor was soggy under

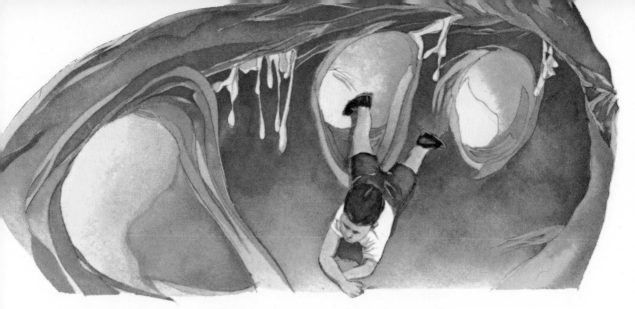

his knees, the walls were wet and sticky, and peach juice was dripping from the ceiling. James opened his mouth and caught some of it on his tongue. It tasted delicious.

He was crawling uphill now, as though the tunnel were leading straight toward the very center of the gigantic fruit. Every few seconds he paused and took a bite out of the wall. The peach flesh was sweet and juicy and marvelously refreshing.

He crawled on for several more yards, and then suddenly—*bang*—the top of his head bumped into something extremely hard blocking his way. He glanced up. In front of him there was a solid wall that seemed at first as though it were made of wood. He touched it with his fingers. It certainly felt like wood, except that it was very jagged and full of deep grooves.

"Good heavens!" he said. "I know what this is! I've come to the stone in the middle of the peach!"

Then he noticed that there was a small door cut into the face of the peach stone. He gave a push. It swung open. He crawled through it, and before he had time to glance up and see where he was, he heard a voice saying, "*Look* who's here!"

Another said, "We've been *waiting* for you!"

James stopped and stared at the speakers, his face white with horror.

He started to stand up, but his knees were shaking so much, he had to sit down again on the floor. He glanced behind him, thinking he could bolt back into the tunnel the way he had come, but the doorway had disappeared. There was now only a solid brown wall behind him.

James's large frightened eyes traveled slowly around the room.

The creatures, some sitting on chairs, others reclining on a sofa, were all watching him quite intently.

Creatures?

Or were they insects?

An insect is usually something rather small, is it not? A grasshopper, for example, is an insect.

So what would you call it if you saw a grasshopper as large as a dog? as large as a *large* dog? You could hardly call *that* an insect, could you?

There was an Old-Green-Grasshopper as large as a large dog, sitting on a chair directly across the room from James now.

And next to the Old-Green-Grasshopper, there was an enormous Spider.

And next to the Spider, there was a giant Ladybug with nine black spots on her scarlet shell.

Each of these three was squatting upon a magnificent chair.

On a sofa nearby, reclining comfortably in curled-up positions, there were a Centipede and an Earthworm.

On the floor over in the far corner, there was something thick and white that looked as though it might be a Silkworm. But it was sleeping soundly, and nobody was paying any attention to it.

Every one of these "creatures" was at least as big as James himself, and in the strange greenish light that shone down on them from somewhere in the ceiling, they were absolutely terrifying to behold.

"I'm hungry!" the Spider announced suddenly, staring hard at James.

"*I'm* famished!" the Old-Green-Grasshopper said.

"So am *I!*" the Ladybug cried.

The Centipede sat up a little straighter on the sofa. "*Everyone's* famished!" he said. "We need food!"

Four pairs of round, black, glassy eyes were all fixed upon James.

The Centipede made a wriggling movement with his body as though he were about to glide off the sofa—but he didn't.

There was a long pause—and a long silence.

The Spider (who happened to be a female spider) opened her mouth and ran a long black tongue delicately over her lips. "Aren't *you* hungry?" she asked suddenly, leaning forward and addressing herself to James.

Poor James was backed up against the far wall, shivering with fright and much too terrified to answer.

Very, Very Peculiar

"What's the matter with you?" the Old-Green-Grasshopper asked. "You look positively ill!"

"He looks as though he's going to faint any second," the Centipede said.

"Oh, my goodness, the poor thing!" the Lady-bug cried. "I do believe he thinks it's *him* that we are wanting to eat!"

There was laughter from all sides.

"Oh dear, oh dear!" they said. "What an awful thought!"

"You mustn't be frightened," the Ladybug said kindly. "We wouldn't *dream* of hurting you. You are one of *us* now, didn't you know that? You are one of the crew. We're all in the same boat."

"We've been waiting for you all day long," the Old-Green-Grasshopper said. "We thought you were never going to turn up. I'm ever so glad you made it."

"So cheer up, my boy, cheer up!" the Centipede said. "And meanwhile I wish you'd come over here and give me a hand with these boots. It takes me *hours* to get them all off by myself."

James decided that this was most certainly not a time to be disagreeable, so he crossed the room to where the Centipede was sitting and knelt down beside him.

"Thank you so much," the Centipede said. "You are very kind."

"You have a lot of boots," James murmured.

"I have a lot of legs," the Centipede answered proudly. "And a lot of feet. One hundred, to be exact."

"*There* he goes again!" the Earthworm cried, speaking for the first time. "He simply cannot stop telling lies about his legs! He doesn't have anything *like* a hundred of them! He's only got forty-two! The trouble is that most people don't bother to count them. They just take his word. And anyway, there is nothing *marvelous*, you know, Centipede, about having a lot of legs."

"Poor fellow," the Centipede said, whispering in James's ear. "He's blind. He can't see how splendid I look."

"In my opinion," the Earthworm said, "the *really* marvelous thing is to have no legs at all and to be able to walk just the same."

"You call that *walking!*" cried the Centipede. "You're a *slitherer,* that's all you are! You just *slither* along!"

"I glide," said the Earthworm primly.

"You are a slimy beast," answered the Centipede firmly.

"I am *not* a slimy beast," the Earthworm said. "I am a useful and much-loved creature. Ask any gardener you like. And as for you . . . "

"I am a pest!" the Centipede announced, grinning broadly and looking round the room for approval.

"He is *so* proud of that," the Ladybug said, smiling at James. "Though for the life of me, I cannot understand why."

"I am the only pest in this room!" cried the Centipede, still grinning away. "Unless you count Old-Green-Grasshopper over there. But he is long past it now. He is too old to be a pest any more."

The Old-Green-Grasshopper turned his huge black eyes upon the Centipede and gave him a withering look. "Young fellow," he said, speaking in a deep, slow, scornful voice, "I have never been a pest in my life. I am a musician."

"Hear, hear!" said the Ladybug.

"James," the Centipede said. "Your name *is* James, isn't it?"

"Yes."

"Well, James, have you ever in your life seen such a marvelous, colossal Centipede as me?"

"I certainly haven't," James answered. "How on earth did you get to be like that?"

"*Very* peculiar," the Centipede said. "*Very, very* peculiar indeed. Let me tell you what happened. I was messing about the garden under the old peach tree, and suddenly a funny little green thing came wriggling past my nose. Quite a bright green it was, and extraordinarily beautiful, and it looked like some kind of a tiny stone or crystal . . ."

"Oh, but I know what that was!" cried James.

"It happened to me, too!" said the Ladybug.

"I swallowed three!" the Centipede cried. "But who's telling this story anyway? Don't interrupt!"

"It's too late to tell stories now," the Old-Green-Grasshopper announced. "It's time to go to sleep. We've got a tough day ahead of us tomorrow. So would you be kind enough, Miss Spider, to make the beds?" . . .

Down . . . Down . . . Down . . . Down . . .

"We're off!" someone was shouting. "We're off at last!"

James woke up with a jump and looked about him. The creatures were all out of their hammocks and moving excitedly around the room. Suddenly the floor gave a great heave, as though an earthquake were taking place.

"Here we go!" the Old-Green-Grasshopper shouted, hopping up and down with excitement. "Hold on tight!"

"What's happening?" cried James, leaping out of his hammock. "What's going on?"

"In case you didn't know it," the Ladybug said, "we are about to depart forever from the top of this ghastly hill that we've all been on for so long." . . .

And now the peach had broken out of the garden and was over the edge of the hill, rolling and bouncing down the steep slope at a terrific pace. Faster and faster and faster it went, and the crowds of people who were climbing up the hill suddenly caught sight of this terrible monster plunging down upon them, and they screamed and scattered to right and left as it hurtled by.

At the bottom of the hill, it charged across the road, knocking over a telegraph pole and flattening two parked automobiles as it went by.

Then it rushed madly across about twenty fields, breaking down all the fences and hedges in its path. It went right through the middle of a herd of fine Jersey cows and then through a flock of sheep and then through a paddock full of horses and then through a yard full of pigs, and soon the whole countryside was a seething mass of panic-stricken animals stampeding in all directions.

The peach was still going at a tremendous speed, with no sign of slowing down, and about a mile farther on it came to a village.

Down the main street of the village it rolled, with people leaping frantically out of its path right and left. At the end of the street, it went crashing right through the wall of an enormous building and out the other side, leaving two gaping round holes in the brickwork.

This building happened to be a famous factory where they made chocolate, and almost at once a great river of warm, melted chocolate came pouring out of the holes in the factory wall. A minute later this brown sticky mess was flowing through every street in the village, oozing under the doors of houses and into people's shops and gardens. Children were wading in it up to their knees, and some were even trying to swim in it, and all of them were sucking it into their mouths in great greedy gulps and shrieking with joy.

But the peach rushed on across the country-side—on and on and on, leaving a trail of destruction in its wake. . . .

Then it began to fall . . .

Down . . .

Down . . .

Down . . .

Down . . .

Down . . .

SMACK! It hit the water with a colossal splash and sank like a stone.

But a few seconds later, up it came again, and this time, up it stayed, floating serenely upon the surface of the water. . . .

"Pardon me," murmured the Ladybug, turning a trifle pale, "but am I wrong in thinking that we seem to be bobbing up and down?"

"*Bobbing* up and down!" they cried. "What on earth do you mean?"

"You're still giddy from the journey," the Old-Green-Grasshopper told her. "You'll get over it in a minute. Is everybody ready to go upstairs now and take a look around?"

"Yes, yes!" they chorused. "Come on! Let's go!"

"I *refuse* to show myself out of doors in my bare feet," the Centipede said. "I simply *must* get my boots on again first."

"For heaven's sake, let's not go through all that nonsense again," the Earthworm said.

"Let's *all* lend the Centipede a hand and get it over with," the Ladybug said. "Come on."

So they did, all except Miss Spider, who set about weaving a long rope ladder that would reach from the floor up to a hole in the ceiling. The Old-Green-Grasshopper had wisely said that they must not risk going out of the side entrance when they didn't know where they were, but must first of all go up onto the top of the peach and have a look around.

So half an hour later, when the rope ladder had been finished and hung and the forty-second boot had been laced neatly onto the Centipede's forty-second foot, they were all ready to go out. Amid mounting excitement and shouts of "Here we go, boys! The Promised Land! I can't wait to see it!" the whole company climbed up the ladder one by one and disappeared into a dark, soggy tunnel in the ceiling that went steeply, almost vertically, upward.

A Rather Awkward Situation

A minute later they were out in the open, standing on the very top of the peach near the stem, blinking their eyes in the strong sunlight and peering nervously around.

"What happened?"

"Where are we?"

"But this is *impossible!*"

"Unbelievable!"

"Terrible!"

"I *told* you we were bobbing up and down," the Ladybug said.

"We're in the middle of the sea!" cried James.

And indeed they were. A strong current and a high wind had carried the peach so quickly away from the shore that already the land was out of sight. All around them lay the vast black ocean, deep and hungry. Little waves were lapping against the sides of the peach.

"But how did it happen?" they cried. "Where are the fields? Where are the woods? Where is England?" Nobody, not even James, could understand how in the world a thing like this could have come about.

"Ladies and gentlemen," the Old-Green-Grasshopper said, trying very hard to keep the fear and disappointment out of his voice, "I am afraid that we find ourselves in a rather awkward situation."

"Awkward!" cried the Earthworm. "My dear Old Grasshopper, we are finished! Every one of us is about to perish! I may be blind, you know, but that much I can see quite clearly!"

"Off with my boots!" shouted the Centipede. "I cannot swim with my boots on!"

"I can't swim at all!" cried the Ladybug.

"Nor I!" said Miss Spider. "None of us girls can swim a single stroke."

"But you won't *have* to swim," said James calmly. "We are floating beautifully. And sooner or later a ship is bound to come along and pick us up."

They all stared at him in amazement.

"Are you quite sure that we are not sinking?" the Ladybug asked.

"Of course, I'm sure," answered James. "Go and look for yourselves."

They all ran over to the side of the peach and peered down at the water below.

"The boy is quite right," said the Old-Green-Grasshopper. "We are floating beautifully. Now we must all sit down and keep perfectly calm. Everything will be all right in the end."

"What absolute nonsense!" cried the Earthworm. "Nothing is ever all right in the end, and well you know it!"

"Poor Earthworm," the Ladybug said, whispering in James's ear. "He loves to make everything into a disaster. He hates to be happy. He is only happy when he is gloomy. Now isn't that odd? But then, I suppose just *being* an Earthworm is enough to make a person pretty gloomy, don't you agree?"

Strange and Scrumptious Dishes

"If this peach is not going to sink," the Earthworm was saying, "and if we are not going to be drowned, then every one of us is going to *starve* to death instead. Do you realize that we haven't had a thing to eat since yesterday morning?"

"By golly, he's right!" cried the Centipede. "For once Earthworm is right!"

"Of course, I'm right," the Earthworm said. "And we're not likely to find anything around here either. We shall get thinner and thinner and thirstier and thirstier, and we shall all die a slow and grisly death from starvation. I am dying already. I am slowly shriveling up for want of food. Personally, I would rather drown."

"But good heavens, you must be *blind!*" said James.

"You know very well I'm blind," snapped the Earthworm. "There's no need to rub it in."

"I didn't mean that," said James quickly. "I'm sorry. But can't you *see* that—"

"See?" shouted the poor Earthworm. "How can I see if I am blind?"

James took a deep, slow breath, "Can't you *realize,*" he said patiently, "that we have enough food here to last us for weeks and weeks?"

"Where?" they said. "Where?"

"Why, the peach, of course! Our whole ship is made of food!"

"Jumping Jehoshaphat!" they cried. "We never thought of that!"

"My dear James," started the Old-Green-Grasshopper, laying a front leg affectionately on James's shoulder, "I don't know *what* we'd do without you. You are so clever. Ladies and gentlemen—we are saved again!"

"We are most certainly not!" said the Earthworm. "You must be crazy! You can't eat the ship! It's the only thing that is keeping us up!"

"We shall starve if we don't!" the Centipede said.

"And we shall drown if we do!" the Earthworm said.

"Oh dear, oh dear," said the Old-Green-Grasshopper. "Now we seem to be worse off than before!"

"Couldn't we just eat a *little* bit of it?" asked Miss Spider. "I am so dreadfully hungry."

"You can eat all you want," James answered. "It would take us weeks and weeks to make any sort of dent in this enormous peach. Surely you can see that?"

"Good heavens, he's right again!" cried the Old-Green-Grasshopper, clapping his hands. "It would take weeks and weeks! Of course, it would! But let's not go making a lot of holes all over the deck. I think we'd better simply scoop it out of that tunnel over there—the one that we've just come up by."

"An excellent idea," said the Ladybug.

"What are you looking so worried about, Earthworm?" the Centipede asked. "What's the problem?"

"The problem is . . ." the Earthworm said, "the problem is . . . well, the problem is that there is no problem!"

Everyone burst out laughing. "Cheer up, Earthworm!" they said. "Come and eat!" And they all went over to the tunnel entrance and began scooping out great chunks of juicy, golden-colored peach flesh.

"Oh, marvelous!" said the Centipede, stuffing it into his mouth.

"*Dee*-licious!" said the Old-Green-Grasshopper.

"Oh, my!" said the Ladybug primly. "What a heavenly taste!" She looked up at James, and she smiled, and James smiled back at her. They sat down on the deck together, both of them chewing away happily. "You know, James," said the Ladybug, "up until this moment, I have never in my life tasted anything except those tiny little green flies that live on rosebushes. They have a perfectly delightful flavor. But this peach is even better."

"Isn't it glorious!" Miss Spider said, coming over to join them. "Personally, I had always thought that a big, juicy, caught-in-the-web blue-bottle was the finest dinner in the world—until I tasted *this.*"

"*What* a flavor!" the Centipede cried. "It's terrific! There's nothing like it! There never has been! And I should know because I personally have tasted all the finest foods in the world!" Whereupon, the Centipede, with his mouth full of peach and with juice running down all over his chin, suddenly burst into song.

"I've eaten many strange and scrumptious dishes
    in my time,
Like jellied gnats and dandiprats and earwigs
    cooked in slime,
And mice with rice—they're really nice
When roasted in their prime.
(But don't forget to sprinkle them with just a
    pinch of grime.)

"I've eaten fresh mudburgers by the greatest
    cooks there are,
And scrambled dregs and stinkbugs' eggs and
    hornets stewed in tar,
And pails of snails and lizards' tails,
And beetles by the jar.
(A beetle is improved by just a splash of
    vinegar.)

"I often eat boiled slobbages. They're grand
    when served beside
Minced doodlebugs and curried slugs. And have
    you ever tried
Mosquitoes' toes and wampfish roes
Most delicately fried?
(The only trouble is they disagree with my
    inside.)

"I'm mad for crispy wasp stings on a piece of
    buttered toast.
And pickled spines of porcupines. And then a
    gorgeous roast
Of dragon's flesh, well hung, not fresh—
It costs a buck at most.
(And comes to you in barrels if you order it
    by post.)

"I crave the tasty tentacles of octopi for tea
I like hot dogs, I *love* hot frogs, and surely
    you'll agree
A plate of soil with engine oil's
A super recipe.
(I hardly need to mention that it's practically
    free.)

"For dinner on my birthday, shall I tell you
    what I chose:
Hot noodles made from poodles on a slice of
    garden hose—
And rather smelly jelly
Made of armadillo's toes.
(The jelly is delicious, but you have to hold
    your nose.)

"Now comes," the Centipede declared, "the
    burden of my speech:
These foods are rare beyond compare—some
    are right out of reach;
But there's no doubt I'd go without
A million plates of each
For one small mite,
One tiny bite,
Of this *FANTASTIC PEACH!*"

Everybody was feeling happy now. The sun was shining brightly out of a soft blue sky, and the day was calm. The giant peach, with the sunlight glinting on its side, was like a massive golden ball sailing upon a silver sea.

Reflections

1. The old man told James to *drink* the mixture. What do you think might have happened to James if he had?

2. Why did the garden seem magical to James? Reread the lines that describe how it looked.

3. Inside the peach stone James met a number of "creatures." Compare what the story says about these creatures with facts you know about them or, if necessary, with what an encyclopedia says about them.

4. What kind of personality did the Centipede have? How do you know? What kind of personality did the Ladybug have? the Earthworm?

5. This selection is only a small part of a much longer story. How do you think that James and the others were rescued from their plight? Make up your own ending for this wonderful adventure with the fantastic peach.

JEAN HENRI FABRE: ENTOMOLOGIST
LYMAN C. HUNT

BUMBLEBEE

TARANTULA

Jean Henri Fabre was a college teacher who spent much of his life observing insects and spiders in the gardens and fields near his home in France. He wrote fascinating essays describing what he saw. For example, he told about the food, shelter, mating, egg laying, and song of grasshoppers. He also described how spiders make webs. Some of Fabre's books of essays translated from French into English are *The Life of the Grasshopper, Animal Life in Field and Garden,* and *Insect Adventures.*

In *Insect Adventures* the essay called "The Boy Who Loved Insects" is Fabre's autobiography. In that essay Fabre said:

> We have all of us, men and animals, some special gift. One child takes to music; another is always modeling things out of clay; another is quick at figures. It is the same way with insects. One kind of bee can cut leaves; another builds clay houses. Spiders know how to make webs. . . . In human beings we call the special gift genius. In an insect we call it instinct. Instinct is the animal's genius.

Scientists everywhere have honored Fabre for his work, and people everywhere have enjoyed reading his essays.

FIELD CRICKET

210

DRAWINGS BY FABRE

RED-LEGGED GRASSHOPPER

The Puzzled Centipede
ANONYMOUS

A centipede was happy quite,
Until a frog in fun
Said, "Pray, which leg comes after which?"
This raised her mind to such a pitch,
She lay distracted in the ditch
Considering how to run.

Firefly

A Song
ELIZABETH MADOX ROBERTS

A little light is going by,
Is going up to see the sky,
A little light with wings.

I never could have thought of it,
To have a little bug all lit
And made to go on wings.

Grasshoppers

THE WORLD BOOK ENCYCLOPEDIA

What Is a Grasshopper?

The grasshopper is an insect that can leap about twenty times as far as the length of its own body. If a man had the same ability, he could jump about forty yards.

Grasshoppers live in most parts of the world, except in the cold regions near the North and the South poles. They spend their lives in fields and meadows, where there are plenty of leaves to eat. Some kinds of grasshoppers eat only certain kinds of plants. Others eat any plants they can find. They may destroy whole crops of alfalfa, clover, cotton, and corn and other grains. In the western United States, grasshoppers damage more than $30 million worth of crops every year. Farmers spray their crops with chemicals that kill the insects.

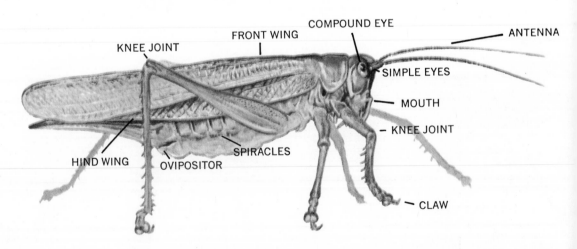

When grasshoppers are handled, they "spit" a brown liquid. Some scientists believe this liquid may help protect grasshoppers from attacks by ants and other insects. Grasshoppers try to escape from their enemies by jumping up and flying away or by hiding among leaves or in the grass.

The greatest enemies of grasshoppers include certain kinds of flies that lay their eggs in or near grasshopper eggs. After the fly eggs hatch, the newborn flies eat the grasshopper eggs. Some kinds of flies lay their eggs on a grasshopper's body even while the grasshopper is flying. The newborn flies then eat the grasshopper. Other enemies of grasshoppers include beetles, birds, mice, snakes, and spiders.

There are two main groups of grasshoppers: (1) *long-horned grasshoppers* and (2) *short-horned grasshoppers*. The animals are divided according to the length of their *antennae* (feelers), which are also called horns. Short-horned grasshoppers usually are called locusts.

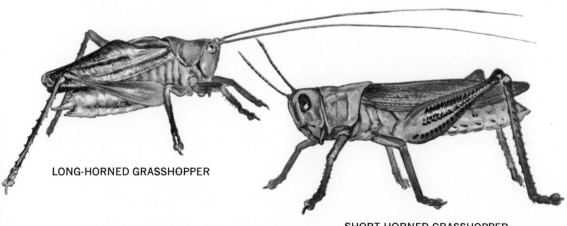

LONG-HORNED GRASSHOPPER

SHORT-HORNED GRASSHOPPER

The Grasshopper's Body

The body of a grasshopper has three main sections: (1) the head, (2) the thorax, and (3) the abdomen. The body is covered by a stiff shell, much like that of a crab.

Two antennae grow forward and curve upward from the head. The grasshopper uses them to examine food before it eats. Two lips and two powerful jaws with sharp teeth form the main parts of the animal's mouth. Thin, fingerlike parts called *palpi* grow on both sides of the mouth and on the lower lip. These parts contain the insect's "taste buds."

A grasshopper has five eyes. A large *compound* eye, consisting of thousands of single lenses, is on each side of its head. With these eyes, the insect can see well to the front, to the side, and to the back. A grasshopper also has three small single eyes—one above the base of each antenna and one below and midway between the two antennae. No one knows what these small eyes do.

A grasshopper's wings and legs are attached to its thorax. Most kinds of grasshoppers have two pairs of wings. Some species have short, useless wings, and others have no wings at all.

A grasshopper's front wings are narrow and tough. They cover and protect the large, thin hind wings. When the insect rests, its hind wings fold up like fans under its front wings. When a grasshopper flies, the downstroke of the wings

gives the insect "lift" and moves it forward. The upstroke helps keep the grasshopper moving until the wings are ready for the next downstroke.

A grasshopper has six legs and uses all of them when it walks. The front legs hold food when the animal eats. The hind legs are much longer and stronger than the others and have powerful thigh muscles. These muscles supply the force that pushes the insect forward in a leap or shoots it into the air to fly.

The abdomen of a grasshopper expands and contracts to pump air in and out of ten pairs of breathing holes. These holes, called *spiracles,* are along the sides of the abdomen and thorax. Tubes branch out from the spiracles and carry air to all parts of the body.

The female has strong, sharp parts called *ovipositors* at the rear of the abdomen. She uses them to dig holes in the ground or to slit leaves or plant stems to make hiding places for her eggs.

The Grasshopper's Young

Female grasshoppers lay as few as 2 or as many as 120 eggs at a time. The eggs, held together by a sticky substance made by the female's body, are packed into the holes dug by her ovipositor. The female sprays more of the sticky material over the eggs, and it hardens quickly into a waterproof covering. The mass of eggs is called a *pod*. The number of pods a female lays varies widely among individual grasshoppers and among the different species.

Most kinds of grasshoppers begin to lay their eggs in late summer and continue into autumn. The eggs hatch the following spring. Unlike the young of most other kinds of insects, newborn grasshoppers look like the adults except that they have no wings. During the first forty to sixty days after birth, the young grasshopper *molts* (sheds its shell and grows a new one) five or six times. The wings grow to full size during the last molt, when the insects reach adulthood.

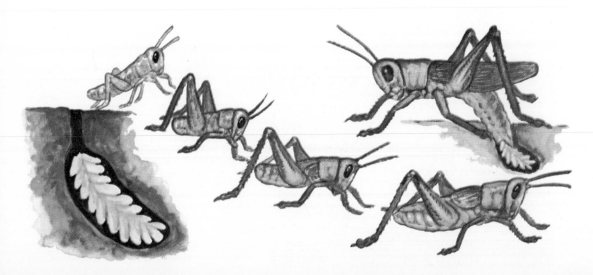

Long-Horned Grasshoppers

Long-horned grasshoppers have threadlike antennae that may grow longer than the insect's body. Grasshoppers in this group include katydids and Mormon crickets.

Many long-horned grasshoppers are green, but some are black, brown, or gray. Although most kinds live on the ground, katydids usually live in trees. Male long-horned grasshoppers "sing" to attract their mates. They rub the bases of their front wings together, and special areas of the wings vibrate and make a loud sound. Different species have their own special "songs." Long-horned grasshoppers hear by means of organs below the knee joint on their front legs.

Short-Horned Grasshoppers

Short-horned grasshoppers, known as locusts, have shorter, thicker antennae than the long-horned kinds. They include lubber grasshoppers and migratory locusts. Locusts may be brown, gray, red, or yellow, and some kinds have brightly colored hind wings.

Locusts sometimes suddenly increase in number, form large swarms, and migrate—but no one knows exactly why. Wherever the swarms go, they damage crops and other plants by eating the leaves. Like long-horned grasshoppers, locust males "sing" to their mates. Most species make sounds by rubbing their hind legs against their front wings. These grasshoppers have hearing organs on their abdomens just above the base of the hind legs.

Reflections

1. What physical features does a grasshopper have that are primarily for defense? How does a grasshopper escape from most of its enemies?
2. How can you tell to which major group a grasshopper belongs? What are some members of each group called?
3. How many parts does a grasshopper's body have? What are they?
4. What is unusual about a grasshopper's eyes?
5. What happens to a grasshopper's outer covering as it grows? Compare what happens to a grasshopper's outer covering with what you think happens to your skin.
6. Would you consider a grasshopper a pest or a help to mankind? Give reasons for your answer.
7. Suppose you had a grasshopper's jumping ability and could leap over your house with ease. How would you most want to use this ability?

The Grasshopper

CONRAD AIKEN

Grasshopper
grasshopper
all day long
we hear your scraping
summer song
  like
    rusty
      fiddles
        in
      the
    grass
as through
  the meadow
     path
      we pass
such funny legs
such funny feet
and how we wonder
what you eat
maybe a single blink of dew
sipped from a clover leaf would do
then high in air
  once more you spring
    to fall in grass again
      and sing.

The Time of Deep Darkness

VIVIAN L. THOMPSON

In the Time of Deep Darkness, before the memory of man, the great gods Kane, Ku, Lono, and Kanaloa came out of the night. . . .

Kane, god of creation, picked up a vast calabash floating in the sea and tossed it high into the air. Its top flew off and became the curved bowl, sky. Two great pieces of the calabash broke away; one became the sun, the other the moon. The seeds scattered and became stars. The remainder of the calabash became the earth and fell back into the sea.

Kane said, "I shall make a chief to rule the earth. Let us provide for his needs."

Kanaloa, god of the vast, endless sea, said, "I shall fill the waters with living things—sea creatures for the chief's use." This he did.

Born was the coral, born was the coral,
Born was the starfish,
Born was the conch shell;
Born was the fish,
Born was the porpoise,
Born was the shark in the sea there swimming.

Kane said, "I shall fill the earth with living things: flyers and crawlers, slow movers and swift

movers, land creatures for the chief's use." This
he did.

Born was the caterpillar, the parent;
Out came the child, a moth, and flew.
Born was the egg, the parent;
Out came its child, the bird, and flew.
Land birds were born,
Sea birds were born,
Birds that fly in a flock,
Shutting out the sun.

The sea crept up to the land,
Crept backward, crept forward,
Producing the family of crawlers:
The rough-backed turtles,
The sleek-skinned geckos,
Mud dwellers and track leavers.

Ku, god of forests, said, "I shall cause trees to
grow—trees to give wood for the chief's use."
This he did.

Thick grew the forests: koa and candlenut;
Thick grew the forests: hau, wiliwili.
Koa for paddles,
Hau for lashings,
Soft wiliwili for outrigger floats;
Woods for the chief's canoe, swift as an arrow.
Candlenut torches, to light the chief's way.

Lono, god of growing things, said, "I shall cause food plants to grow—food for the chief." This he did.

Green blades came sprouting:
Coconut, breadfruit, sweet potato, sugarcane,
Taro, banana, arrowroot, yam.

When all was ready, Kane said to Ku, Lono, and Kanaloa, "Now it is time. Go, find what is needed to make a chief."

To the north and west, to the south and east went the gods. On the sunrise side of a hill near the sea, they found rich, red earth. This they took to Kane, who made the figure of a man and breathed life into it. The man walked about and spoke, and the gods were pleased.

Kane said, "We shall call him Red Earth Man."

Red Earth Man was happy. Soon he saw that wherever he went, something went with him. It walked when he walked and rested when he rested. He was pleased to have company, and he called this thing Ke Aka, or shadow. He talked to it, he laughed at it, and sometimes he even sang to it. But Ke Aka never answered.

After a time the songs of Red Earth Man stopped. His laughter died away, and he no longer spoke. The gods saw that Red Earth Man was lonely.

"He needs a living companion," said Kane.

While Red Earth Man slept, Kane breathed life into Ke Aka. When Red Earth Man woke, he stretched and looked about. "It's a fine day," he said aloud.

"A fine day indeed," a voice at his side agreed.

Red Earth Man was startled. "Ke Aka, you speak!"

Ke Aka nodded, smiling. Then Red Earth Man laughed, and his laughter was good to hear. He sang, and Ke Aka sang with him. Their song was so beautiful that the birds flew down to listen.

Red Earth Man said, "You were my shadow, but now you are alive! I shall call you Living Shadow."

Then Red Earth Man and Living Shadow knelt and touched their heads to earth to give thanks to the great gods for the wonderful gifts of life and companionship.

In time, men multiplied.
In time, men came from afar.
Born were the fair-haired,
Born the dark-haired.
Born were the broad-chested,
Born the big eaters.
Born were the song chanters,
Born the family men.
Born were war leaders,
Born the high chiefs of long life.
Ever increasing in number, men spread abroad.
Man was here now; it was DAY.

Reflections

1. Almost every nation or group of people has its own myth, or story, about how the earth was first created and how man was first made. Why do people tell these creation myths? Tell any others you know.

2. In this myth, what did the gods provide to fill man's needs? Judging from these things, what kind of place is Hawaii? What is its climate like?

3. When the gods saw that Red Earth Man was lonely, they changed his shadow into a woman, a living person. Do you suppose that Red Earth Man had a shadow after that? Make up a story of your own, telling how Red Earth Man and Ke Aka persuaded the gods to give each of them a shadow. If you wish, tell part of your story in poetry so that it can be chanted.

4. How would you feel if you were the only person on earth? Do you think that everyone needs a companion? Explain why or why not.

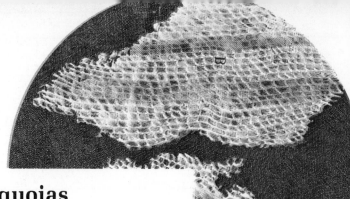

From Cells to Sequoias

BERNARD WEISS

Man has wondered about life for thousands of years. He has wanted to know how living things came to be, what they are made of, why they differ from each other, and how life can be preserved. Each of the four people pictured here has contributed to the study of the wonder of life.

ROBERT HOOKE (1635–1703)

Robert Hooke, a British scientist, was the first to observe and identify cells. Cells are the basic units of all life. Looking at a thin slice of cork through a simple microscope, Hooke noticed tiny, empty, rectangular holes. He called these holes *cells*. Today's scientists have much more powerful microscopes to help them study cells many times smaller than the cork cells Hooke saw.

ERNEST E. JUST (1883–1941)

Ernest Just, a professor of physiology at Howard University Medical School, was one of the first scientists to investigate the mystery of how a single-celled egg develops into a living thing containing many cells. He investigated the structure of cells many years before there were modern microscopes. He also experimented with making parts of cells change. Scientists today are still trying to find out why cells do change and produce new cells.

JOHN MUIR (1838–1914)

John Muir was interested in preserving the life of the giant redwoods and sequoias of California. Through his efforts, a bill was passed by the Congress of the United States establishing Yosemite and Sequoia National Parks. Muir Woods National Monument, a redwood forest near San Francisco, was named in honor of his contributions to forest conservation. Muir once said, "When we try to pick out anything by itself, we find it hitched to everything else in the universe."

JESSIE I. PRICE (1930–   )

When Jessie I. Price, a bacteriologist, found out that many ducks on Long Island, New York, were dying, she wanted to find out what was causing the deaths and be able to prevent them. She studied the one-celled bacteria that were causing the deadly disease and worked to develop a vaccine against it. Since most ducks sold in the United States come from Long Island, Miss Price's work is important to the whole duck-farming industry.

Ong, of Canada

VERA HENRY

When the wild geese settled on the marsh on their way north, Holly knew that it would be for the last time. A new highway had been built, and the marsh was being drained to make a summer resort. Suddenly a shot rang out, and the whole flock flew away except the mate of the dead bird. She built a nest in the long grass and laid her eggs.

Holly's friend, Johnny Salt, was an Ojibwa Indian who lived on the nearby reservation. One day he accidentally destroyed the goose's nest and broke all the eggs but one. Holly took the egg home. Her grandfather, a retired captain who carved wooden figures for a living, suggested letting Jessica, a hen that had been trying to hatch a doorknob, sit on the egg.

When the gosling hatched, the first thing he saw was Tavish, Holly's collie, and immediately he adopted the dog as his mother. Holly decided to name the bird Ong after the sound that geese make.

Mrs. Plumley, the fat, red-headed housekeeper who cleaned and cooked for Holly and the captain, thought that draining the marsh would be good for the community and Holly, too. She felt that Holly's friends should be girls Holly's age, not a dog and a wild goose.

228

The Enemies

Ong and Mrs. Plumley were not friends. In the first place, she blamed him because Holly had caught a cold the time she fell in the pond.

The truth was Mrs. Plumley didn't really approve of wild geese. They flew around at night, making a racket like a jammed automobile horn and waking people out of a sound sleep.

It was going altogether too far when one of those nasty, snake-necked creatures tracked up the ground around her kitchen and then had the nerve—the absolute nerve—to knock at the door.

Ong on his part didn't think too much of Mrs. Plumley. She had odd red feathers that stood straight up around her head. When he knocked at the door with his beak, it was Holly or the captain he wanted.

If Mrs. Plumley happened to answer, she waved her apron and cried, "Shoo! Shoo!" in a voice like a loud mosquito.

As Ong grew larger, so did the feud. Whenever she saw him around the door, Mrs. Plumley took her broom and chased him away.

"Shoo! You nasty creature!" she cried, waving the straw broom. "Shoo!"

"Honk-honk," protested Ong and waddled away with as much dignity as possible.

Then one warm June day, Ong had had quite enough.

On this occasion all he had done was take bites from the green tomatoes growing in the garden. Mrs. Plumley took her broom and chased him almost out to his own pen under the russet apple tree.

Suddenly Ong halted. His black neck twisted in an indignant manner. His wings, which now were quite large and strong, began to beat. He rushed at his enemy, beak open, hissing angrily.

Mrs. Plumley was so surprised, she didn't know what to do. She waved the broom in vain. Then she turned and ran, with Ong pursuing her, hissing like a leaky tire. Just before she escaped into the kitchen and slammed the screen door, he nipped her plump leg.

It wasn't a very big nip, but Mrs. Plumley was as upset as if she had been bitten by a lion.

Holly and the captain tried to soothe her. For all her faults, Mrs. Plumley was a kind woman who made excellent chocolate cakes.

"I am sure he was only trying to play," Holly said. "Sometimes he chases Tavish like that."

The captain, who didn't seem quite so sure of Ong's good intentions, went back to his studio, where he carved a little wooden figure of a fat lady being pursued by a wild goose.

Instead of taking the figure down to Mrs. McNab's store or putting it on the studio shelf, the captain rather regretfully hid it in a drawer.

Next to flapjacks, there was nothing that the captain enjoyed as much as Mrs. Plumley's chocolate cake.

If Mrs. Plumley was a poor loser, Ong wasn't a very generous winner either.

From that time on, he terrorized poor Mrs. Plumley. Holly and the captain had to stand guard when she arrived in her little car in the morning or left at night.

Every so often during the day, Ong's long black neck would appear below the kitchen window, waving like the hose on a vacuum cleaner.

Mrs. Plumley found it quite unnerving. She said he looked as if he were laughing at her.

One day, looking out the window, Mrs. Plumley discovered Ong pecking at the valves on her car tires.

"It isn't anything personal, Mrs. Plumley," Holly explained. "Ong is just curious. You know how the handle of a bucket or that piece of rope hanging from the fence fascinates him."

"I'll fascinate him," Mrs. Plumley said grimly. "He's spoiled, that's what he is. What that creature needs is a good lesson."

The next time Ong tried to chase her, Mrs. Plumley was prepared. She had a can of black pepper in her apron, and she threw it at him.

As it happened, the breeze was blowing in the wrong direction, so as much pepper got on Mrs. Plumley as got on Ong.

Mrs. Plumley sneezed and sneezed and sneezed. Ong made strange strangled noises—"Hon-on-on-on-k! O-o-ng!"

After that day Mrs. Plumley and Ong simply ignored each other.

They never did get to be friends.

First Flight

Ong was no longer content to waddle awkwardly after Tavish. He had discovered that he could fly.

It came as quite a surprise to him.

One afternoon Tavish, who missed the peace and quiet of his bachelor days, tried to sneak away for a ramble in the woods.

"W-on-k. W-on-k—Wait for me!" squalled Ong, running and trying to catch up, but Tavish was too far away.

"Wonk! Wonk!" cried Ong, beating his wings in indignation. He was up on a little hill, and then suddenly he was in the air.

He was so surprised, he came in for a crash landing. How had he done it? He wasn't quite certain. He knew that the robins and sparrows who sometimes shared his bathtub-swimming pool could soar through the air. But Tavish couldn't fly, and neither could Holly nor the

captain nor Johnny Salt. On the other hand, Mrs.
Plumley came close to it sometimes when he
chased her.

Ong tried again, moving his wings rapidly back
and forth.

This was splendid. It was even better than
swimming. Up-up-up! The best Jessica ever managed was the perch in the hen coop, but he was
far higher than that. He wished he had known
before that he didn't need to waddle on the
ground.

He was so delighted, he forgot all about following Tavish. With a little practice he was able to go from his pen to the pond in the meadow without once touching the earth.

Holly laughed as she watched his acrobatics. Then she frowned. Now that he had discovered he could fly, Ong might wander too far.

"Do you think we should clip Ong's wings, Grandfather?" Holly asked later. "Suppose he flies away?"

"Do you want to turn him into a barnyard creature like Jessica?" the captain demanded.

"No," Holly admitted, "only the wild geese will soon fly south. Suppose he decides he wants to leave us?"

Her grandfather brushed the bangs back from her forehead. "Ong is almost full-grown. When you are older, you may want to leave here, too."

Holly shook her head. "This is my home. I am going to live here forever and ever."

She leaned sleepily against her grandfather. They were sitting as they often did out on the porch where they could watch the stars. The new highway was about half a mile away, and through the trees she caught glimpses of headlights that seemed to be a reflection of the dart of fireflies in the woods. She listened to the crickets chirrup, the croak of frogs in the pond, and the sad, lonely cry of the whippoorwill.

"Whip-poor-will! Whip-poor-will."

Her grandfather glanced at the luminous dial of his watch. "Time for Echo to go over," he said. "I sure wish I was still young enough to be an astronaut."

Holly watched the satellite pass overhead.

"Grandfather," she said, "now that they are sending spaceships to the moon, do you suppose they'll ever take along two of all the animals, like Noah did on the ark?"

Her grandfather slapped at his arm. "As far as I'm concerned, they're welcome to the mosquitoes, although Mrs. Plumley is right. There are less of them now the marsh has been drained."

Holly jumped up. "Oh, I forgot to put Ong in his pen! I'd better do it now."

As soon as it began to grow dark, Jessica and the other hens climbed up on a perch, tucked a head under a wing, and fell asleep. The phoebes, the swallows, the mourning doves, the thrush went to bed with the sun. But not Ong. Jessica had done her best to teach him proper habits, but Ong's webbed feet weren't meant for perching. And even after it began to grow dark, he liked to wander in the cool clover blossoms around his pen.

Ong wasn't in his pen. He didn't seem to be any place in the yard.

Holly took a flashlight and, with Tavish beside her, ran out to the pond, thinking Ong might have gone there for a late swim.

She called his name, "Ong, Ong, O-n-g!" She threw back her head and gave an Indian war cry, but Ong didn't answer as he usually did. She began to be frightened.

Far off in the woods, she heard the yap of the fox. An owl hooted from a nearby tree. It wasn't safe for a silly young gander to wander alone at night.

"Find Ong, Tavish," she ordered. "Go find Ong."

Mrs. Plumley was fond of remarking that Tavish understood every single word that was said. Now he went over to Ong's pen and sniffed. He ran around in a circle with his long nose to the ground. Then he looked up in the air and barked.

Ong must have been trying out his wings.

"Find him, boy," Holly repeated. "Go look for him."

Tavish barked and disappeared into the night.

The grandfather's crutch tapped on the path. "Go to bed, Little One," he said gently. "Ong has probably found himself a nice quiet corner and gone to sleep. Tavish will find him."

Holly did as she was told and went to bed. Once she thought she heard Tavish bark. She closed her eyes and said a prayer, but it was a long time before she fell asleep.

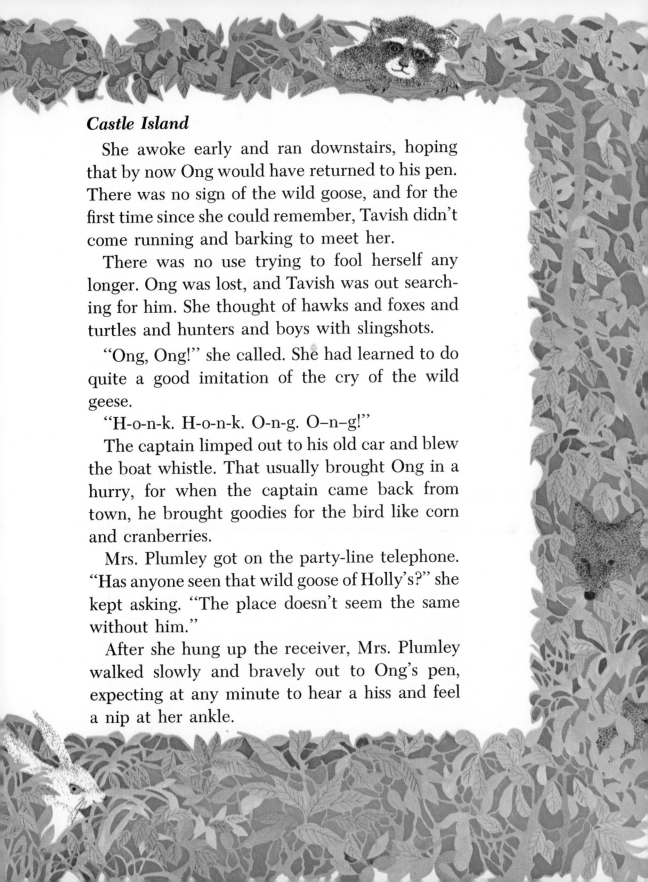

Castle Island

She awoke early and ran downstairs, hoping that by now Ong would have returned to his pen. There was no sign of the wild goose, and for the first time since she could remember, Tavish didn't come running and barking to meet her.

There was no use trying to fool herself any longer. Ong was lost, and Tavish was out searching for him. She thought of hawks and foxes and turtles and hunters and boys with slingshots.

"Ong, Ong!" she called. She had learned to do quite a good imitation of the cry of the wild geese.

"H-o-n-k. H-o-n-k. O-n-g. O–n–g!"

The captain limped out to his old car and blew the boat whistle. That usually brought Ong in a hurry, for when the captain came back from town, he brought goodies for the bird like corn and cranberries.

Mrs. Plumley got on the party-line telephone. "Has anyone seen that wild goose of Holly's?" she kept asking. "The place doesn't seem the same without him."

After she hung up the receiver, Mrs. Plumley walked slowly and bravely out to Ong's pen, expecting at any minute to hear a hiss and feel a nip at her ankle.

When that didn't work, she went sadly back to the house.

Only Jessica, peacefully laying an egg in the hen house, seemed unconcerned. She had, it seemed, more important things to do.

All that long day Holly and the captain searched for Ong and Tavish. They drove along back roads, blowing the boat whistle. Holly ran down the Indian trail and the beach, calling and calling.

Mrs. Plumley scolded, but gently, because Holly and the captain barely touched the good dinner she had fixed for them. Then she walked slowly out to her little car and drove off to her own home in town.

When it began to grow dark, Jessica flew up on her perch, tucked her head under her ruffled feathers, and went to sleep.

Johnny Salt, looking very grave, stopped by at the farmhouse. He was on his way to a council meeting. He said there was no sign of either Tavish or Ong around the bay or in the Indian reservation. His people promised to keep watch.

For a long time after she went to bed, Holly lay awake, listening to the night sounds. She could hear the wind in the pines and the tree toads and the far-off sound of the lake. She heard the captain moving around downstairs, making another pot of coffee. Sometimes he worked all night. She could hear the deep thump-rumble of frogs in the swamp. No matter how hard she tried, she could not hear Tavish or Ong.

In the morning they were still missing.

Johnny Salt came over in his red sports car. "I'm taking the day off to look for Ong and Tavish," he said. "The boss is giving me his boat. I'm going over to Castle Island. It's the only place we haven't looked."

"I don't see what good that would do, Johnny," the captain said. "An old dog like Tavish could never swim that far, even if he thought Ong might be there."

"Please!" begged Holly, trying not to cry. "Let me go with Johnny."

"All right, Little One," the captain said gently, "but wear slacks and something to cover your arms. That place is full of poison ivy."

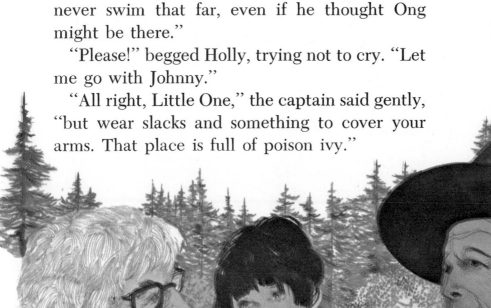

On any other day Holly would have enjoyed the boat trip. Mrs. Plumley had insisted on packing a picnic lunch with peanut butter and carrot sandwiches for Holly and thick beef and a dill pickle for Johnny.

Back on the beach the bulldozers and workmen dwindled in size until they looked like toys. Sea gulls screamed overhead, dipping and skimming along the waves. Holly trailed her fingers in water, green as the early leaves of spring.

Huge, jagged rocks jutted out from the water around Castle Island. The waves here were much higher and rougher than they had been in the bay.

While Johnny circled the island, Holly looked through the powerful field glasses at the rocky beach, but there was no sign of Tavish or Ong. She called and called, but her voice was snatched away by the wind.

The sun, reflected on the water, was extremely hot. She was grateful for the big straw hat Mrs. Plumley had made her wear.

"I'm afraid we might as well start back," Johnny said at last. "I'm apt to wreck the boat if I try to take it in any closer."

He reached for the motor cord.

"Listen!" cried Holly. "Listen."

Did she just imagine that she heard a faint bark? It was hard to be certain with the shrill crying of the gulls and the crash of waves.

She cupped her hands to her mouth. "Tavish!"
she called. "Ong—Tavish!"

"Your ears must be better than mine," Johnny
said gently.

"I know he is somewhere back there in the
woods!" Holly cried. "I know I heard him!"

Johnny started to shake his head, and then he
stopped.

"I hear something, too," he admitted. "It's not
a fox. Maybe, as my ancestors would say, it is
some kind of evil spirit. Make sure your life belt
is fastened, Holly. The boss will kill me if I even
scratch his boat, but I'm going to try to land."

He took the oars, and as skillfully as if the big
boat had been a birchbark canoe, he guided it
towards the beach. When they reached shallow
water, he anchored and carried Holly piggyback
onto the beach.

A bedraggled, furry body hurled itself through
the bushes, almost knocking Holly down. Yelping
with joy, Tavish leaped on Johnny, then ran back
to Holly. He licked at Holly's face as she knelt
and wound her arms about him.

"I thought I had lost both you and Ong," Holly
sobbed.

At the sound of his friend's name, Tavish broke free and limped a few feet away, then stopped, waiting for them to follow.

It was a rough, difficult path through brambles and rocks, but at last he brought them to Ong.

The wild gander was lying motionless in a little hollow of leaves beneath the upturned roots of a fallen tree. His lovely breast was stained with dried blood. Tavish whimpered gently and touched his friend with his golden nose.

"Is Ong dead, Johnny?" Holly whispered.

At the sound of his name, the gander stirred slightly, then quivered, and was still again.

"He must have been shot several days ago," Johnny said. "If Tavish hadn't been keeping guard, a weasel or fox would have had him long before this. We'll have to get him home as fast as possible."

"You'll know what to do, won't you, Johnny?" Holly asked.

"The Midewiwin of my tribe—the Medicine Men—would have cleaned his wound with the fluid from boiled cattail stems and made a poultice of herbs and roots from the woods. I'll have to do the best I can with antibiotics."

Flapjacks and Medicine Men

On the boat trip back, Holly cradled Ong in her arms while Tavish crouched at her feet, his burr-matted head against her, his eyes never leaving her face.

"Good Tavish," Holly said. "You couldn't bring Ong home, so you stayed to protect him. But how did you find him on Castle Island?"

While the captain and Johnny Salt dressed Ong's wound, Mrs. Plumley tried to feed Tavish, but though he was half starved, time after time he left his food to return to Ong.

He lifted his golden nose in the air and barked and whined, trying to tell his friends what had happened.

"I wish I could understand you, boy," the captain said. "Even if by some miracle you realized Ong was hurt and on the island, I don't see how you managed to swim so far. No wonder you look all worn out."

Johnny pried Ong's yellow beak open, and the captain poured down a little medicine.

The bird seemed to shudder. He made a feeble sound—"Ark-ark."

Holly ruffled his neck feathers. "You're safe home now, Ong," she told him. "You must never leave again."

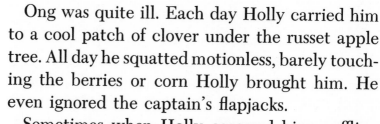

Ong was quite ill. Each day Holly carried him to a cool patch of clover under the russet apple tree. All day he squatted motionless, barely touching the berries or corn Holly brought him. He even ignored the captain's flapjacks.

Sometimes when Holly caressed him, ruffling his neck feathers gently to let in air rather than stroke them as one would a dog, he lifted his head and gave a faint, sad sound of thanks.

Tavish spent most of the time lying on the ground beside his friend, whining encouragement and keeping guard as he must have done on the island.

When the antibiotics didn't seem to work, Johnny Salt brought a worn, leather, beaded bag from the reservation. He took a grayish powder out of it and sprinkled it on Ong's wound.

He grinned at the captain. "The Midewiwin of my tribe were wise men. In time the scientists of the world may catch up with them."

Whether it was the antibiotics or the Medicine Man's little leather pouch, that day Ong staggered to his feet and took a few weak steps. When Johnny carried him down to the pond in the meadow, he drifted around, occasionally spraying the water over his dull feathers.

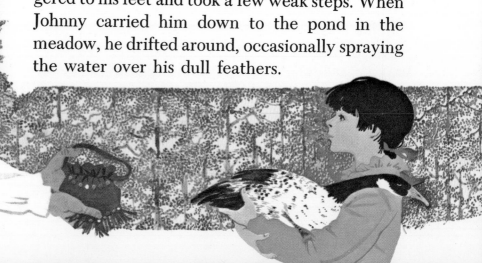

He began to eat again. Mrs. Plumley made him cornmeal mush. Holly and Johnny Salt brought him little treats of cranberries and gumdrops. Every morning he ate one of the captain's flapjacks and demanded more.

"If we'd given him the flapjacks in the first place instead of all that medicine, he'd be better by now," the captain grumbled. "That's what he needed to get him back on his feet."

One afternoon when Mrs. Plumley was walking towards her car, ready to go home, she heard a hissing sound behind her, and then she felt a little nip on her ankle.

She was so pleased, she almost cried.

Ong was well again.

Reflections

1. Suppose that you had to depend entirely on this story for information about Canadian geese. What have you learned here about their appearance (size, color, shape), their manner of walking and flying, and their personality and behavior?

2. How do you feel when you see a sick animal?

3. How did Johnny Salt feel about the Midewiwin of his tribe? Give details from the story to support your answer.

4. The author of this story often uses *similes*. To give you a vivid idea about something, the author says it was like something else. For example, she says that Mrs. Plumley didn't like geese because at night they made a racket "like a jammed automobile horn." Find three other similes in the first section of the story.

Haiku

Now wild geese return . . .
     What draws them crying crying
All the long dark night?

         —Roka

      Out of the sky, geese
    come honking in the spring's cold
     early-morning light.

           —Soin

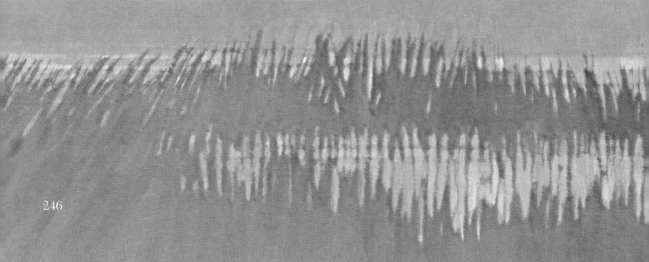

Wild geese have eaten
        All of my barley . . . Alas,
They are flying on!

          —Yasui

        Night over the pond
     of the temple garden . . . geese
       adrift and asleep. . .

              —Shiki

247

JOHN JAMES AUDUBON: ORNITHOLOGIST
LYMAN C. HUNT

GREAT HORNED OWL

AUDUBON, PAINTED BY HIS SONS JOHN AND VICTOR

WILD TURKEY

John James Audubon (1785–1851) was one of the first to study the habits of American birds. He painted over four hundred life-sized pictures of birds in their natural surroundings. The National Audubon Society, devoted to the conservation of soil, water, plants, and wildlife, was named in his honor. Even today, bird watchers use his pictures to help them identify wild birds.

MALLARD DUCK

The Animal Parade

DONALD CULROSS PEATTIE

Fellowship with animals is easy to feel when you race your barking dog down the street or when you stroke a sleepy kitten till it purrs. A warm friendliness runs between you and the creature with a heart beating like your own under its soft hide. You can see, too, that you depend on animals for many daily needs. When you eat meat or slip into a woolen sweater or put on your leather shoes, you have an animal to thank every time.

But life is given far more freely than just to man and the beasts he feels closest to. It has been reckoned that there are about 700,000 known species of animals now living on this spinning globe which is our common home. Only a few of them are the kind that a person usually means when he says "animal." He is apt to mean a warm-blooded, furry or hairy creature, the kind that brings forth its young alive (instead of laying eggs) and feeds them at first on mother's milk. That's a mammal, of course, one of the "higher" animals, as they are sometimes called.

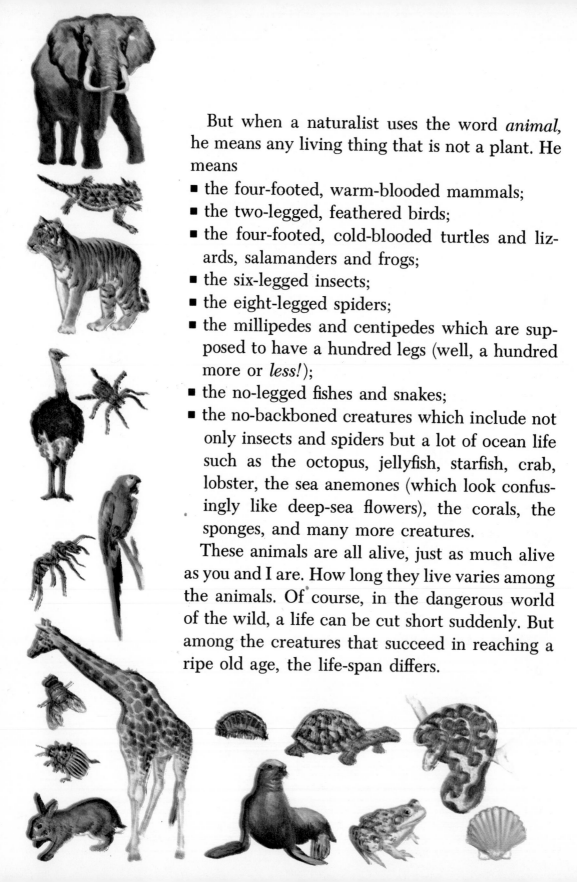

But when a naturalist uses the word *animal*, he means any living thing that is not a plant. He means

- the four-footed, warm-blooded mammals;
- the two-legged, feathered birds;
- the four-footed, cold-blooded turtles and lizards, salamanders and frogs;
- the six-legged insects;
- the eight-legged spiders;
- the millipedes and centipedes which are supposed to have a hundred legs (well, a hundred more or *less!*);
- the no-legged fishes and snakes;
- the no-backboned creatures which include not only insects and spiders but a lot of ocean life such as the octopus, jellyfish, starfish, crab, lobster, the sea anemones (which look confusingly like deep-sea flowers), the corals, the sponges, and many more creatures.

These animals are all alive, just as much alive as you and I are. How long they live varies among the animals. Of course, in the dangerous world of the wild, a life can be cut short suddenly. But among the creatures that succeed in reaching a ripe old age, the life-span differs.

How old, then, is "old"? A lively grandmother or a brisk gentleman of seventy will say, "You're just as old as you feel," which has some cheerful truth in it. But a cat near twenty doesn't feel much like mouse-hunting any more. The field mouse itself finds life too much for it before it can finish its second winter. But the anemone, a creature very simply constructed, lives a long time. A well-known English biologist kept one in his laboratory for sixty-six years—a long life, but not a very merry one! A sea anemone spends most of its time attached to a rock. When it does creep on its one "foot" or pedal disk, it goes so slowly, you cannot see it move.

A mayfly, though it lives as a fly but a day or so, has a life of light and air and dancing. A clam can live fifteen to twenty years, but who wants to be a clam? A salamander may live half a century, but it doesn't see much of the world. An eagle can live as long as that, but, soaring over mountain and forest, it reaches heights of adventure and experience impossible to the cold-blooded salamanders. So, length is no measure for life. It is what you get out of life and what you put into it that matters.

Yet to all live creatures, life is so precious that they will struggle or fight to the end to preserve it. And the winners at the great game of endurance are admired. That is why people are apt to exaggerate the ages of old animals. It is hard to know for sure, too, about creatures in the wild. The records kept of animals in captivity are more exact. Even so, it is easy to boast about a pet's age. It may have been in the family so long that no one is very sure any more just how old it is.

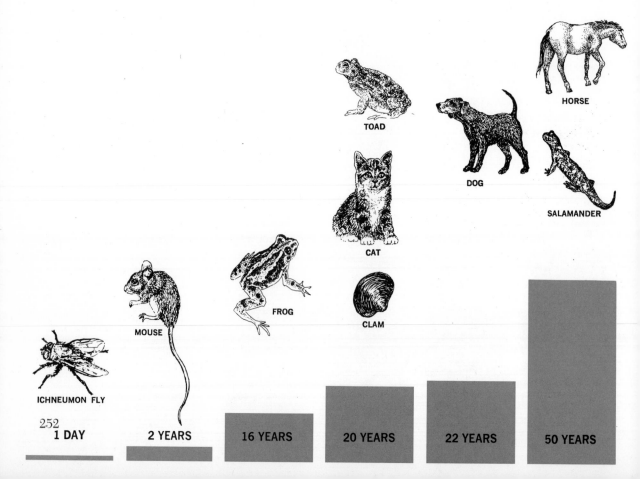

TOAD

HORSE

DOG

SALAMANDER

CAT

FROG

CLAM

MOUSE

ICHNEUMON FLY

1 DAY

2 YEARS

16 YEARS

20 YEARS

22 YEARS

50 YEARS

Parrots are often said to live to be a hundred, but there is no real proof of that. They probably have lives half as long. The elephant, too, is commonly thought to grow as old as he is big, but no one has ever learned of an elephant known to have been older than sixty-nine.

But that *is* old, very old, for an animal. The record age for a horse is fifty years, for an owl sixty-eight, for a dog twenty-two, for a toad twenty, for a lobster fifty, for a pelican fifty-one,

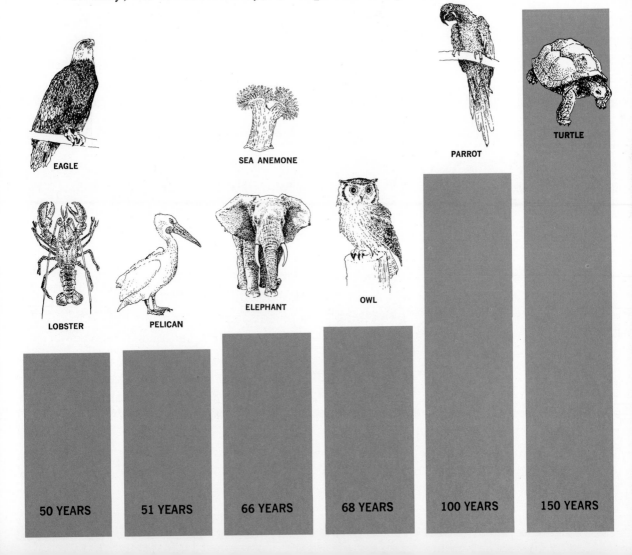

EAGLE

SEA ANEMONE

PARROT

TURTLE

LOBSTER

PELICAN

ELEPHANT

OWL

| 50 YEARS | 51 YEARS | 66 YEARS | 68 YEARS | 100 YEARS | 150 YEARS |

for a bullfrog sixteen. The creature that beats all the records is the giant land tortoise. Most people believe that these slow old hard-shells can live a hundred years, perhaps a hundred and fifty—a long time to go crawling about the earth, your blood running chill and sluggish, with no braver way to meet danger than to draw into your shell!

It is better, a man will feel, to stand upright on two feet and face the world for as long as it may be granted him to enjoy it. And this is longer than any other mammal is allowed. Even the wrinkled elephant is second to man in life-span. With every year's discoveries in medicine and science, too, the human life-span is prolonged. Well may we give thanks, walking the crowded world, for our own generous share of the grand adventure!

Reflections

1. What does the word *mammal* mean? Name as many mammals as you can.
2. According to this selection, how many species of animals inhabit our earth? Name six or seven large groups of animals very different from each other.
3. The writer of this piece says that length is no measure for life. Why do you think he feels this way?
4. Suppose that a great many different animals (a fish, an eagle, a lizard, a flea, a tiger, etc.) held a meeting to decide which one had the most pleasant life. What might each say he liked about his life?

I Shall Not Live in Vain

EMILY DICKINSON

If I can stop one heart from breaking,
I shall not live in vain;
If I can ease one life the aching,
Or cool one pain,
Or help one fainting robin
Unto his nest again,
I shall not live in vain.

GROUPING WORDS IN SENTENCES

In every English sentence we read, one word comes first, and others follow from left to right across the page. Try the sentence below by reading down each column of words. You will find that the words make a sentence.

Each	laughter	who
day	to	love
brings	all	fun

Now read these sentences aloud.

1. A funny brown puppy   is playing   down the street.
2. That blue coat   by the door   is mine.
3. My green and blue notebook   will soon be found.
4. The big red apple   on the oak desk
   is ready   for eating.

Words in the sentences above have been so spaced in each line that the words which fit together are grouped together. This is not the usual way to print words. But it is an easy way to read them. We learn to group the words that go together with our eyes and in our thinking. Such grouping of words is something that we bring to the written line. Seldom, except sometimes in poetry, does a line of print bring special arrangements of words to us.

Certain words themselves act as stop-and-go traffic signs in sentences. They signal ways for us to group other words within a sentence. A little practice will show you how the signal words work. If you can solve the puzzles that follow, you will learn some good ways to group words as you read.

Puzzle One

All the sentences below have some blanks. Try working some of these words into the blanks: *a, an, the, this, that, these, those, his, no, all, her, our, my, their, one, two,* or *three.* Sometimes only one of the words will fit; sometimes two words may fit together in one blank space.

1. —— boys have —— secret meeting place.
2. Allen keeps —— games and models in —— place.
3. —— apple tree grows by —— cabin.
4. John went there, but he forgot —— ball and —— bat.
5. —— boys are —— ones I mean.
6. —— own house is near —— secret place.

Notice that each blank comes close to a noun.

Now use each of the italicized words listed in the first paragraph above in a sentence. These signal words are grouped with nouns and other words that follow them when we read. For example:

1. The boys   have   a secret meeting place.
2. Those boys   are   the ones I mean.
3. No apple tree   grows   by their cabin.

One way, then, to group words is to keep words like *a, an,* and *the* with the words that follow them.

Puzzle Two

Words of another kind are missing in the paragraph that follows. Copy the paragraph and supply the word or group of words that you think fits best in the blanks.

The frisky squirrel lives —— our backyard. One day I chased him. He ran —— the tree. He jumped —— limb —— limb. Then he ran —— the tree. He scooted —— the yard, —— two bushes, and jumped —— the fence. He ran —— the rocks. I could not catch him. So I went —— the house, —— the stairs, and sat down —— my window to rest.

Words like *up, from, to, by, over, under, with, at, after, upon, across, off, on, between, from, into, down, before,* and *beneath* are called prepositions. Try fitting some of these into the blanks above. Prepositions are most often used to show direction or place. In reading, we group prepositions with the words that follow them in the sentence.

Puzzle Three

Words like *who, that, when, if, since, so, after, although, where, whose, which, whom, because,* and *as* also act as signals. We group them with the words that follow them. It works like this:

1. John,   who is my cousin,   visits us often.
2. The model car   that came in the mail   is mine.
3. Mary,   when you finish,   come over to my house.
4. I will go   if you come with me   to his house.

Rewrite the four sentences above, grouping other words with *who, that, when,* and *if.*

Learn to group words like *who, that, when, if, since, what, so, as, after,* and *although* with the words that follow them. They help you keep sentence parts together.

Puzzle Four
Sometimes, in our reply to certain questions, we say or write sentences with just two words.

John is.	He could.	They might.
They are.	She may.	He does.
I have.	She can.	I do.

More often, however, verbs like *is, are, have, could, may, can, might, does,* and *do* and others like *would, must,* and *should* are signals that other verbs are coming.

John *is eating.*	He *does enjoy* our company.
He *may have eaten.*	He *might have been seen.*
Allen *has been swimming.*	He *could have gone.*

What other words listed above can you use in the six sample sentences instead of *is, may, has, does, might,* and *could?*

Watch for words like *is, are, have,* and the others in the list. You can often expect them to signal that other verbs are coming. Learn to group these words together as you read.

The good reader must make word groups in his thinking. Using correct word groupings, you will have a better understanding of what you are reading. You will also read with the rhythm of natural speech.

A DIFFERENT
DRUMMER

The Friendly Cricket

Costa Rican Folk Song

1. Once I met a crick - et   wan - der - ing a - far,___
2. Then I saw this fel - low   far a - way in France,
3. Then in mer - ry Eng - land,   en - ter - ing an inn,___

There he was, this crick - et,   strum - ming a gui - tar;___
There he played a fid - dle,   call - ing off a dance;
There was crick - et pluck - ing   on a man - do - lin;___

When I saw him there   in the pas - sage - way,
When we part - ed soon   near his ho - tel door,
Pleas - ant as could be   when he saw my face,

We shook hands to - geth - er,   then we said good day.
We shook hands po - lite - ly,   as we had be - fore.
Crick - et bowed and curt - seyed   in that dis - tant place.

4. On a day last summer, when to Spain I'd come,
   There was Mister Cricket banging on a drum;
   When he spied me there, sipping at my tea,
   He approached my table, bowed, and greeted me.

5. Cricket is a trav'ler, as you surely know,
   So I always find him ev'rywhere I go;
   As he comes toward me, strolling down the street,
   We shake hands together, any time we meet.

The Magic Bagpipe

GERRY and GEORGE ARMSTRONG

Every year on the Isle of Skye, a great celebration was given at Dunvegan Castle in honor of the MacLeod chief's birthday. Part of the celebration was a bagpipe competition, and its winner was declared the Piper to the Chief.

Donald MacCrimmon had been taking lessons from Mister MacSkirl, who was going to give him his old set of bagpipes. But when Mister MacSkirl realized that the boy had become the better player, he told Donald to forget about the pipes.

On his way home, Donald saw an old woman struggling to get out of the river. He scrambled down the bank and hauled her to safety.

The old woman took Donald to her home. When she heard his story about the bagpipes, she gave him the handsomest set of pipes he had ever seen. But she warned him that the bagpipes could be played only by him!

On the day of the gathering at Dunvegan Castle, Donald was up early, urging his family to hurry. Right after breakfast, Donald, his little sister, and his mother and father set off across the moor.

When the MacCrimmons arrived, the great fires were already roaring. Huge chunks of meat were roasting. All the clansmen had come with something for the feast—strings of fish, fresh-baked bread and cakes and scones, honey and jam. Donald felt hungry just looking at all the good things to eat.

In the harbor by the castle, many boats came bringing visitors. Across the road from the castle was a big open field where the games were already starting.

Donald munched on this and that while he wandered around the field, watching everything. All day there were competitions in racing and wrestling, caber tossing and hammer throwing.

Then, late that afternoon, Mister MacKenzie—who had been chosen because he had the loudest voice—shouted, "Pipers! Get ready!" and the contest Donald had waited for began.

Piper MacClure was first. Donald would be last, after O'Neil and Mister MacSkirl.

Donald waited happily, enjoying the music. He did not notice MacSkirl a few steps away. The old man stared at the boy from underneath his bushy eyebrows. He had a good set of pipes himself, but Donald's pipes were the best he had ever seen.

Finally, while O'Neil was playing, Mister MacSkirl spoke to Donald. "I'm sorry that I didn't fix up my old pipes for you," he said.

"Oh, that's all right, sir," said Donald happily. "I have a bagpipe set of my own now."

"So I see. But it's not a very good one. I'll tell you what I'll do, my boy. I'll trade with you."

And what did MacSkirl do then but jerk Donald's pipes from him and shove his own bagpipes at the boy! Then off he started. Of course, MacSkirl had not the least idea of how Donald had come by his set of bagpipes—he only wanted it for himself.

Donald started to race after the man. "No, no!" he called. "Please, Mister MacSkirl, I don't want to trade."

Just then MacSkirl's name was called, and he marched out on the field, leaving Donald weeping with anger.

Suddenly the boy heard such a strange noise that he stopped crying. What could it be? MacSkirl was playing, but it didn't sound like bagpipe music. It sounded like a cat fight!

There were squeals, shrieks, and gurgles. The bagpipe was wheezing and gasping like a sick cow. MacSkirl's fingers were slurring over every hoarse note.

At first the crowd listened in surprised silence. Then someone tittered and someone else giggled. And in a moment the whole crowd was rocking with laughter.

MacSkirl was bewildered. The pipes fell from his shaking hands. He pulled his bonnet down over his ears and fled.

Donald watched in amazement. Then he heard his own name called, "Donald MacCrimmon!" He ran out on the field, picked up his pipes, tucked them lovingly under his arm, and, puffing out his cheeks, began to play.

The laughter and hooting died as the people turned to listen to Donald. At first his music was as slow and sad and lonely as a single gull wheeling in a bleak sky.

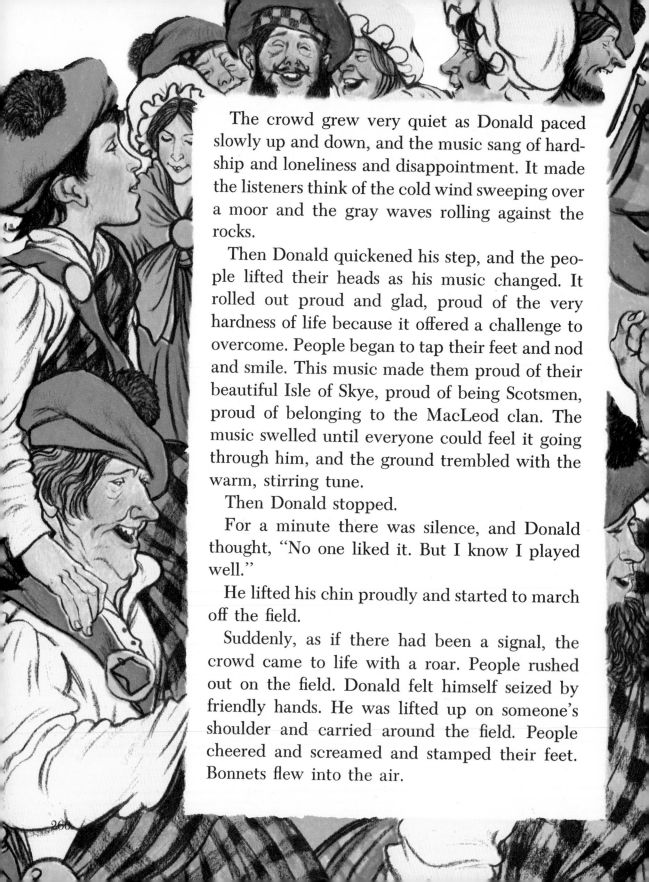

The crowd grew very quiet as Donald paced slowly up and down, and the music sang of hardship and loneliness and disappointment. It made the listeners think of the cold wind sweeping over a moor and the gray waves rolling against the rocks.

Then Donald quickened his step, and the people lifted their heads as his music changed. It rolled out proud and glad, proud of the very hardness of life because it offered a challenge to overcome. People began to tap their feet and nod and smile. This music made them proud of their beautiful Isle of Skye, proud of being Scotsmen, proud of belonging to the MacLeod clan. The music swelled until everyone could feel it going through him, and the ground trembled with the warm, stirring tune.

Then Donald stopped.

For a minute there was silence, and Donald thought, "No one liked it. But I know I played well."

He lifted his chin proudly and started to march off the field.

Suddenly, as if there had been a signal, the crowd came to life with a roar. People rushed out on the field. Donald felt himself seized by friendly hands. He was lifted up on someone's shoulder and carried around the field. People cheered and screamed and stamped their feet. Bonnets flew into the air.

Finally Donald was set down on his own feet in front of the MacLeod chief. The tall old man shook the boy's hand and said solemnly, "Donald MacCrimmon, that was the greatest piping I have ever heard. I am proud to call you Piper to the Chief."

And then Donald's parents were beside him. His father clapped him proudly on the shoulder, his mother hugged him, and his little sister jumped up and down with excitement.

Then followed feasting and toasting, and Donald had to play for the dancing as the long, happy day led into a long, happy night. And the happiest person in all that celebration was Donald MacCrimmon, Piper to the Chief.

Reflections

1. In what country is the Isle of Skye? Use clues from the story to answer this question.
2. Do you think MacSkirl deserved the crowd's ridicule? Explain.
3. What was so wonderful about the music that Donald played with his pipes? Why do you suppose the crowd was silent for a minute after he finished?
4. What musical instrument would you like to be able to play well? Why does that instrument appeal to you?

Music Makers
BURYL RED

LOUIS ARMSTRONG

Louis (Satchmo) Armstrong is credited with making jazz an accepted part of American culture. Born on July 4, 1900, in New Orleans, Louisiana, Armstrong's musical career as trumpeter and vocalist is permanently tied to the history of American jazz. Louis Armstrong took jazz out of the Negro quarter of New Orleans, where it was born, and introduced it as an art form around the world. He has become a legend in his own lifetime. Wherever New Orleans jazz is played, Satchmo is known and respected as one of the greatest jazz musicians.

DANNY KAYE

In recognition of the work he has done, UNICEF has given singer-actor-comedian Danny Kaye the title of "Ambassador-at-Large to the World's Children." Danny Kaye first began entertaining children for UNICEF in 1954. Since then he has made sick and unhappy children in countries throughout Africa, Asia, and Europe smile and laugh.

Born and raised in Brooklyn, New York, Mr. Kaye does not speak the many languages spoken in the countries he has visited. He communicates happiness with the universal language of music and his own natural warmth. He brings forth laughter by "double-talking"—running together nonsense syllables that sound like the native language.

Anyone who has been to see the movie *Hans Christian Andersen* has been exposed to Danny Kaye's way with children. Who else would have been a better choice to portray the famous author of children's fairy tales than Danny Kaye—Ambassador-at-Large to the World's Children?

LEONARD BERNSTEIN

Leonard Bernstein was the first musician born in the United States to become music director of the New York Philharmonic Symphony Orchestra. But Mr. Bernstein also won fame for conducting, composing, playing the piano, and lecturing on music.

It may seem hard to believe that the man who composed the score of *West Side Story* is the same one seen conducting and lecturing on television in the Young People's Concerts. On several occasions Mr. Bernstein has been able to combine his many musical talents. For example, he has performed the solo part in piano concertos while conducting the orchestra from the piano bench.

Born on August 25, 1918, in Lawrence, Massachusetts, Bernstein revealed his talents at an early age. At the age of fifty, he retired as music director to devote his time to composing and lecturing.

MARIA TALLCHIEF

Maria Tallchief's Indian name, Princess Wa-Xthe-Thonba (Princess of Two Standards), describes her life excellently. Born in Fairfax, Oklahoma, on the Osage Indian reservation, she became the prima ballerina with the New York City Ballet Company.

In the early 1930's when Maria was about seven, her family moved to Los Angeles. There she studied both concert piano and ballet. Right after graduation from high school in 1942, she made her dancing debut with the Ballet Russe de Monte Carlo. She joined the New York City Ballet Company when it was established in 1948 and became its prima ballerina in 1954. Shortly later she retired from dancing to devote her efforts to being a wife and mother.

Bola and the Oba's Drummers
LETTA SCHATZ

Bola had been allowed to leave his small village for the first time and to come with his mother to the market in the great town. At their stall in a far corner of the crowded West African marketplace, the deep sound of many drums reached Bola's ears. Then over the sea of bobbing heads, Bola saw the huge Royal Umbrella and the Royal Drummers, weaving and wheeling as they beat upon their drums. And in their midst, dancing as the drums commanded, was the Oba, the mighty king himself. But what truly held Bola's eyes were the two smallest drummers. They were boys about his own age. In that instant Bola knew he wanted to be a drummer, too, and to play at the Oba's palace. Without stopping to think about what he was doing, Bola followed the boy drummers through the palace gate to the veranda in the vast courtyard of the palace.

The Royal Drummers

One of the boys smiled. He had a merry, narrow face that folded into deep, smiling lines.

"Welcome," he said. "Greetings on our first meeting. I am Tunji. And this is my older brother, Bamiji. Are you new to the town?"

"I live in Ado-Ido village," Bola answered softly, still awed to be talking to one of the drummers. "My name is Bola. I came to market with my mother. Then I heard your drumming. Ah! How I would like to drum as you do! Is it hard to learn?"

"Hard?" the older boy, Bamiji, exclaimed. There was no mistaking that he and Tunji were brothers. Their faces were alike, but their expressions were different. Bamiji had a superior look. "One must be born a drummer," he said scornfully. "It has been the trade of our family for generations beyond remembering. Our father is Head Royal Drummer, and he has been teaching us since our hands could hold the stick. All of us bear the name Ayan, the name for drummers. My father is Ayanpeju. I am Ayanbamiji. My brother is Ayantunji. What of you, village boy? Who are your fathers? Are they named Ayan?"

As Bola sought words to answer, a deep imperious throbbing sounded, so near that it made him start.

gaw-GAWN   *gaw-GAWN*

gaw-gaw-GAWN   *gaw-GAWN-gaw*

The Head Drummer's bell-studded instrument thudded and thundered, and all the band quickly responded, making the courtyard resound.

gaw-gaw-gaw   *gaw-GAWN*

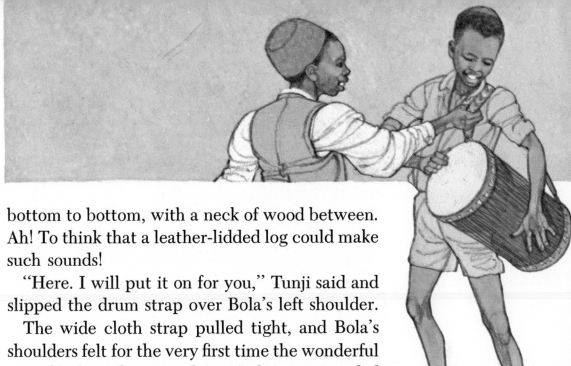

bottom to bottom, with a neck of wood between. Ah! To think that a leather-lidded log could make such sounds!

"Here. I will put it on for you," Tunji said and slipped the drum strap over Bola's left shoulder.

The wide cloth strap pulled tight, and Bola's shoulders felt for the very first time the wonderful tug of a drum hanging down. It hung suspended under his arm, its roundness just fitting into the hollow.

"Ayantunji! Ayanbamiji!" It was Father Ayan, the Head Drummer, calling.

"Yes, Father."

Tunji and Bamiji turned to go. "Come," Tunji said, beckoning to Bola as to an old friend. "We had better get back now."

Tunji ran after his brother. Puzzled, Bola followed the two boys, who were rapidly weaving their way through the people on the broad, dusky veranda.

"What is it? Why the hurry?" Bola asked.

"It is the chiefs," Tunji said over his shoulder. "They have come out of the king's chambers and are beginning to depart. Chief Adeyinka is going. And Chief Adeniyi. And now Chief Adepoju has come into the courtyard. . . ."

Bola was amazed. From the depth of the great dim veranda, they could not see the courtyard, yet Tunji and Bamiji knew exactly what was happening there.

"Haw-wu! Did the drums tell you all that?" Bola asked.

"Of course. Anyone with ears could hear it," Bamiji said. "Ah-ah! Now the Balogun is going! Come along, Tunji. Move your feet. Father will be very vexed if we are not there to drum the Balogun's praises!"

They passed between the pillars. The light of the courtyard struck their eyes after the darkness of the veranda. Bola looked up. The sun was beginning to dip low. He had not realized how long it had been since he left his mother's stall in the market. Mother's parting words clanged a warning in his head. How angry she would be if he were late.

Bola touched Tunji's arm. "I must go now," he said. "Thank you! Thank you many times!"

"Come again," Tunji said. "Any time you please. If you want, I will teach you to drum. I have never taught anyone before, but, if you wish, I will try."

"Truly?" Bola asked. "You do not joke?"

"Truly. It is a promise," said Tunji.

From the palace gate Bola waved back, then raced toward the market as if his feet were on wheels, stopping now and again to ask the way.

The First Lesson

The next week, as Bola reached the great wall, there was Tunji, sitting by the palace gate. Tunji jumped up and ran to greet Bola, a wide smile of welcome on his face.

"Greetings of the morning! Morning, did I say? Look. It is almost afternoon."

Bola smiled back, the friendly welcome settling the flutters inside him. "Greetings of the morning," he said.

Bola looked about. The palace seemed quiet. The drummers were seated at their place beside the gate. A few people waited patiently on the great broad veranda, hoping to see the Oba. But today the courtyard was almost empty.

"Where are all the people?" Bola asked. "Last week there were so many! And where is your brother? I do not see him."

"There is no council meeting today. Last market day the council met, and next market day it shall meet again. Today is just a day like all others. The chiefs came to greet the Oba, but they have gone now. As for Bamiji . . ." Tunji shrugged. "He is at school."

"How does it happen that you are not at school then?"

Again Tunji shrugged. "My father likes to keep one of us here with him. Next year, perhaps, he will send me. What of you? Do you not go to school?"

"No. Our village has no school. And besides, my father does not have money enough. But he says if the next cocoa crop is good, he will send me to school. There is one three miles from our home." Bola looked at Tunji's drum. "But if I could drum like you, I would not care if I never went to school. Last time you said . . . do you remember? You said, perhaps . . ." All week Bola had been boasting how Tunji would teach him to drum. Now suddenly he was afraid to say it. "You said, if I wished to drum . . ."

"Ah! Myself, I would rather go to school." Tunji said. "They have many books there with wonderful tales. And they play football on the school field. I would like to be a football player."

Bola looked at Tunji in amazement. Bola could not believe that anyone who could be a drummer should wish to be anything else!

"But if you want to learn," Tunji said, "let us get you a drum. Come."

The drummers sat in their shady spot on the veranda, talking to each other. They barely looked up as Tunji passed between them and opened a door in the palace wall. Bola had not even noticed this door before. Slowly he followed his new friend.

He was in a long room—dark except for the light from the open door—a long, narrow room, part of the hollow palace walls. The room was crowded with chairs and mats and even some pots, but this Bola barely noticed at all. It was at the wall he stared. The walls were studded with pegs from which hung drums of all sizes and shapes, big and small, old and new.

"My eyes! They will grow weak from looking!" Bola sighed. "This is like a treasure house. What do you do with so many drums?"

"Come on a festival day," Tunji said, "then you will see. Today only six drummers are here. But often there are twelve or even more. Some festivals use special instruments. And sometimes," Tunji grinned, "sometimes one of the men plays so hard, he splits the drum. We always keep some extra ones."

Bola's eyes roamed the drum-festooned walls. "Nnhn." There was one exactly like the one the Head Drummer played, a great leather-lidded tube surrounded by gleaming bells, its wide strap richly embroidered. Bola stared at it. He reached out, not quite daring to touch it.

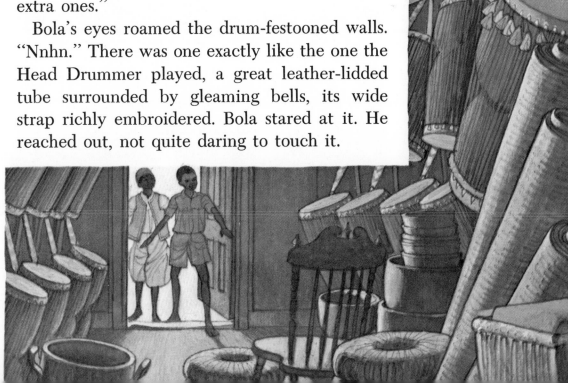

"Can you play this one, Tunji?"

"Iya Ilu?! The Mother Drum? Kai! My father would not let me use Iya Ilu. Nor Bamiji either. Mother Drum is the one that leads all the others and is played only by the most skilled of men. I am learning to play that one—Ishaju." There was pride in Tunji's voice as he pointed to a medium-sized cylinder hanging on the wall.

"Do all the drums have names?" Bola asked.

Tunji clicked his tongue. "Ttt! Does not each of us have a name of our own? Each drum has a different voice. Each has a part of its own to play. Naturally they have names." Tunji reached up. From a peg on the wall, he took down a small instrument, twin to his own, and from a peg beside it, a crook-shaped stick.

"Here," he said, handing them to Bola. "Kanango is the drum for learners. You can use this one for today."

"Ah-ah! Will your father not be angry?"

"Angry? Why? You will not take it away."

The two boys slipped quietly through the door, past the drummers, and down along the dusky veranda. They settled in a sheltered spot, close to the walls where the shadows were deepest.

Bola hugged the string-encircled drum to him. Kanango. Even its name was musical.

"Please, Tunji," he asked shyly, "will you show me how to make the drum speak?"

"Ah! You want to fly before you have feathers! To learn to make a drum speak takes much time. First . . ." Tunji beat out a simple rhythm.

"Listen. You must play exactly what I do." Tunji sounded very important, like a proper master.

"When you can copy rhythms, *then* you will be ready to copy speech."

GAWN-gaw-gaw—Tunji beat the simple rhythm.

GAWN-gaw-gaw—Bola copied it on his drum.

Then Tunji beat a more complicated rhythm: *gaw-GAWN-gaw gaw-gaw*. And Bola repeated it perfectly.

Tunji looked up and grinned. "Not bad. But let us see you play this one," he challenged: *gaw-GAWN-gaw GAWN-gaw-gaw gaw-gaw*.

Bola listened carefully. He began to play.

"No. That does not sound right," Tunji said. "The stick should be loose. Don't grab it with your fist. Let it hang in the loop between your thumb and first finger. Then it will strike lightly. Watch."

Bola watched and listened as Tunji again played the rhythm. Then Bola began again to

copy Tunji. He tried to hold the stick as Tunji did. How strange it felt, bobbing about in his hand, held only by the tips of forefinger and thumb.

"Better. Much better. Keep it loose," Tunji said.

Pleased with Tunji's praise, Bola loosened his fingers still more. The little crook suddenly took on a life of its own. It jumped from Bola's hand and clattered to the ground.

Tunji laughed. "Not quite so loose!" he said.

Bola reached for the stick, then glanced up at the sky.

The sun was beginning to move downward. His time at the palace was passing away.

"Please, Tunji. Now can you show me how to make the drum talk?"

"Ttt! How can you make it speak if your stick runs away?" Tunji asked, smiling a teasing smile.

"If you will show me, Tunji, I am sure I can do it properly. Let us try again. You will see," Bola pleaded.

This time Bola copied Tunji's rhythm perfectly. Tunji changed the pattern slightly, but Bola was not tricked. He repeated the new rhythm, beat for beat.

Again and again Tunji changed the rhythm. Each time Bola followed like an echo. Tunji tried longer, more difficult patterns. Repeatedly he challenged, "Ha! Listen, Bola! I bet you cannot play this!"

But Bola listened, putting all his being into his ears. The stick moved to his will as if it were part of him. Each time he echoed the rhythm Tunji played perfectly.

Several times the drums by the gate cried out, announcing the arrival and departure of important visitors. The quiet courtyard suddenly echoed with sound that rebounded from the palace walls and seemed even to shake the ground. One of the chiefs came, stayed awhile, then left again. Then another chief made a brief call. Two merchants came together. Then the Supervisor of Police came. Each time Bola looked up and listened closely to the drummers, the vivid throbbing echoing through him, setting him a-quiver. Would he ever be able to play like this?

The sun moved lower. Tunji beat out the longest rhythm yet. Bola repeated it.

"Well done!" Tunji exclaimed. "Ah, but you learn quickly. Now, if you wish to try to make Kanango speak . . ."

Bola flushed warm with pleasure. "Oh, please! Even just a word or two. How do you do it? How can a drum speak? I listen and listen. But I do not hear the words you hear when the drums sound."

"Ah! It seems hard to believe," Tunji said. "I suppose it is because your ears have not yet learned to listen properly. I hear it so plainly. It seems so simple.

"You know that in the Yoruba language, all words have tunes. If I wish to say your name, my voice must rise high, so all will know that *ola* means 'honor.' Otherwise, if we say the *o* and speak it low and the *la* in a middle tone, people will think your name means 'tomorrow.' Or if we say the *o* with a middle tone and then say the *la* very low, they will think your name means 'wealth.'

"Every word has its tune. The drum just copies the tune of the words. To make it speak high, we pull the strings tight. That tightens the drumhead and makes its voice high. Now listen. It will say 'Bola.' Watch."

Tunji seemed to be hugging his Kanango under his arm. His lower arm pressed down on its strings until they were squeezed tight against the body of the drum. Tunji tapped the drumhead with his stick, two quick, light taps. High and clear Kanango spoke out, two high, short sounds. Bola could hear it. Ah! It was truly speaking the tune of his name. Again Tunji tapped. But now the sound was different, not quite so high as before. Bola looked at the drum. How had Tunji changed the sound?

"See. If I loosen the strings that connect the drumheads," Tunji said, "if I loosen them just enough, then the drum speaks in a middle tone, halfway between high and low. And if I do not touch the strings at all—listen to it then."

Bola listened. "I hear it!" he exclaimed. "Now the voice is low! Wonderful! Truly wonderful! Let me try."

Bola pressed down on the leather thongs and felt them give, felt them bend toward the drum, their shape marking stripes on the flesh of his arm. He pressed until the pliant cords could give no more, then he tapped the drumhead lightly with his stick. Once. Twice. Again he plainly heard the tune of his name, two high syllables, "Bo-la." Again he played it. "Bo-la."

"Good!" Tunji exclaimed. "They must have won!"

Puzzled, Bola looked up at his friend. What was Tunji talking about?

"Won?" he asked.

Tunji nodded. "I can always tell just by looking," he said. "Bamiji's team won their football match today. See . . ." Tunji pointed toward the palace gate. Bamiji had just come trotting through the entrance, a grin on his face.

Bola was dismayed. Could school already be finished for the day? He tipped his head back. Kai! The sun had slid so much lower since last he looked. Bola jumped to his feet, slipping the drum from his shoulder as he rose.

"Ah-ah! I dare not be late!" he said.

"Too bad," said Tunji, taking Kanango. "When Bamiji tells of a match, you think you are seeing it. Will you come next market day?"

"I will try," Bola said.

"Till next time then," Tunji said, tapping his drum with the stick. An hour ago Bola would have thought it just an idle tapping, but now his ears could hear what they had not heard before.

"Till next time," sang the drum, echoing the tune of Tunji's words. "Till next time."

Reflections

1. Do you think Tunji was a good teacher? Explain why or why not. Would you like to have Tunji for a teacher?

2. What were the full names of Tunji and Bamiji? How were their names formed? If the same system were used in this country, what would be the name of each member of your family?

3. Do you think Bola will ever become a great drummer? Give reasons for your answer.

4. Here are three ways of expressing the idea that the ruler is approaching.
   a. A note with these words: "The king is coming."
   b. Someone saying, "The king is coming."
   c. A note with this drawing:

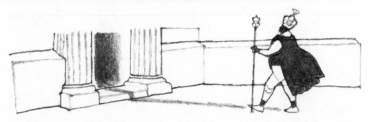

How else might someone who spoke the Yoruba language express this idea? Do you think that method would work with English? Explain why or why not.

Animals in Art

IRV BARNETT

THE DREAM (detail)

HENRI ROUSSEAU (1844–1910)

Man shares his whole world with animals, even his dreams. Rousseau imagined a jungle where a piper's notes draw wild animals to the source of the music.

THE MUSEUM OF MODERN ART, NEW YORK CITY. GIFT OF NELSON A. ROCKEFELLER

GROUP OF BULLS, HORSES, AND STAGS
PREHISTORIC CAVE PAINTING

This detail of a cave painting in Lascaux, France, was done some twenty thousand years ago. In 1940 two boys discovered the Lascaux Caves while they were searching for their lost dog. Perhaps prehistoric man wanted some way to control the herds of animals which he hunted, and the rock paintings were part of a magic ceremony created to influence the animal spirits.

PHOTO: HINZ, BASEL

AFRICAN DRUM FROM THE BAGA TRIBE
TWENTIETH-CENTURY CEREMONIAL DRUM

Sculpture is the most popular art form in Africa. Members of the Baga tribe in northwestern Africa carved one log to make this chieftain's ceremonial drum. It is as tall as a man and makes a deep booming sound when played. For each different ceremony the drum is redecorated with new patterns. But the little horse supporting the drum on his colorful saddle is kept the same.

ROYAL ONTARIO MUSEUM, TORONTO, CANADA

BUFFALO DANCE OF THE MANDAN INDIANS

KARL BODMER (1809–1893)

Karl Bodmer, a Swiss artist, visited the Mandan Indians of North Dakota in the mid-nineteenth century and painted this dance. The buffalo provided food, clothing, and shelter for the Indians. When the vast buffalo herds disappeared from the plains, the Mandans performed this dance to bring them back. The two bravest men in the tribe had the honor of wearing the entire head of the buffalo.

293

AKBAR PURSUING ELEPHANT
SIXTEENTH–CENTURY COURT PAINTING

Emperor Akbar, the greatest Mogul ruler of India, employed painters to illustrate scenes from his life. This painting shows Akbar advancing into battle. The men in the fortress are fleeing to their boats to escape from Akbar's thundering elephants.

PLOWMAN OF AREZZO
SIXTH–CENTURY B.C. ETRUSCAN BRONZE

The Etruscans were a rich and powerful people that lived in central Italy about twenty-five hundred years ago. This little bronze group shows an Etruscan farmer walking behind his two yoked oxen. Originally the farmer was holding on to the beam of the plow, which was fitted into his hands.

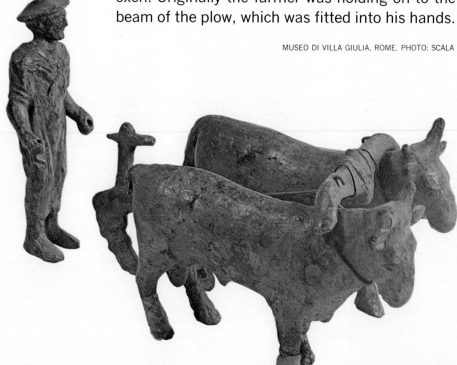

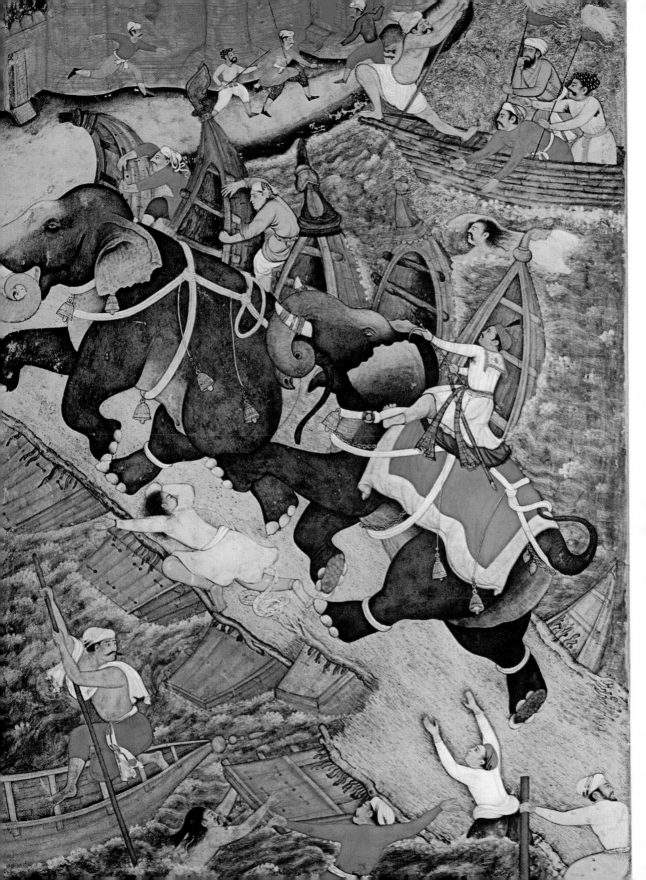

BOY TAKING FLEAS OUT OF A DOG
GERARD TER BORCH (1617–1681)

This boy and his dog lived in Holland in the seventeenth century. The boy is carefully grooming his pet so he will be clean and healthy, and the little spaniel is happy to stay just where he is.

THE HORSE FAIR
ROSA BONHEUR (1822–1899)

Rosa Bonheur's animal paintings are known for their remarkable accuracy. *The Horse Fair* is considered her masterpiece. It was originally called *The Horse Market in Paris* when it was begun in 1852. For a year and a half Rosa Bonheur went to the horse market twice a week to make sketches. She dressed as a man in order not to attract attention among the horse dealers and buyers. Looking at the painting, you almost hear the frantic sounds and sense the horses straining against the men.

THE METROPOLITAN MUSEUM OF ART, NEW YORK CITY. GIFT OF CORNELIUS VANDERBILT

THE UNICORN AT THE FOUNTAIN
FIFTEENTH–CENTURY TAPESTRY

This tapestry is one of a set made for the royal family of France. It is woven with wool, silk, and metallic threads. The unicorn, an imaginary animal, has always been thought to have magical powers. In this scene the hunters have sighted a unicorn by the fountain and are gathering around to watch him.

BABOON AND YOUNG
PABLO PICASSO (1881–1973)

Picasso was an artist with an extraordinary imagination. When he saw a child's toy car, he realized that it could easily become a part of his baboon sculpture. Can you see where?

THE MUSEUM OF MODERN ART, NEW YORK CITY. MRS. SIMON GUGGENHEIM FUND

THE METROPOLITAN MUSEUM OF ART, NEW YORK CITY. THE CLOISTERS COLLECTION, GIFT OF JOHN D. ROCKEFELLER, JR.

THE WINGED LION

JANET ANDERSON (1960–   )

Mrs. Lili Knize, art instructor for the New Canaan public schools, asked one of her classes to draw imaginary animals. Janet Anderson, a fourth grader, created this colorful animal for the assignment.

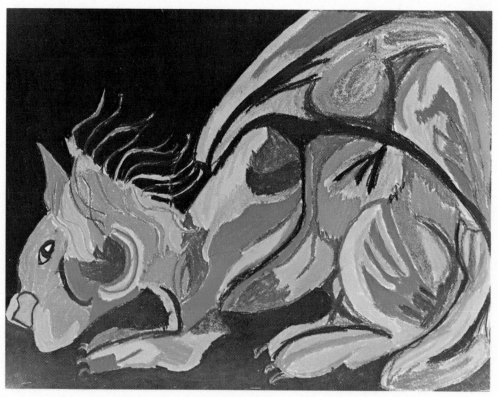

COURTESY MRS. LILI KNIZE, ART INSTRUCTOR, NEW CANAAN, CONNECTICUT, PUBLIC SCHOOLS

Time for Fun

PRISCILLA FITZHUGH

OLD STAGECOACH (detail)

EASTMAN JOHNSON (1824–1906)

People have always had time for fun. What they enjoy does not differ from century to century nor from continent to continent. If this were an abandoned bus instead of an old stagecoach, twentieth-century children would probably be climbing all over it just as these nineteenth-century boys are doing.

MILWAUKEE ART CENTER, LAYTON COLLECTION

ACROBATS

KATSUSHIKA HOKUSAI (1760–1849)

These Japanese drawings are actually woodcuts. They appeared in the *Manga*, a series of sketchbooks containing Hokusai's drawings. The acrobats are obviously enjoying themselves as they perform their warm-up exercises.

ONE HUNDRED CHILDREN AT PLAY
SOUTHERN SUNG DYNASTY (1127–1279)

This picture of Chinese children at play was done with ink and dyes on silk. If you look closely, you can see that children in the twelfth century played the same games that children the world over still play today: follow the leader, marching to music, and dressing up in costumes.

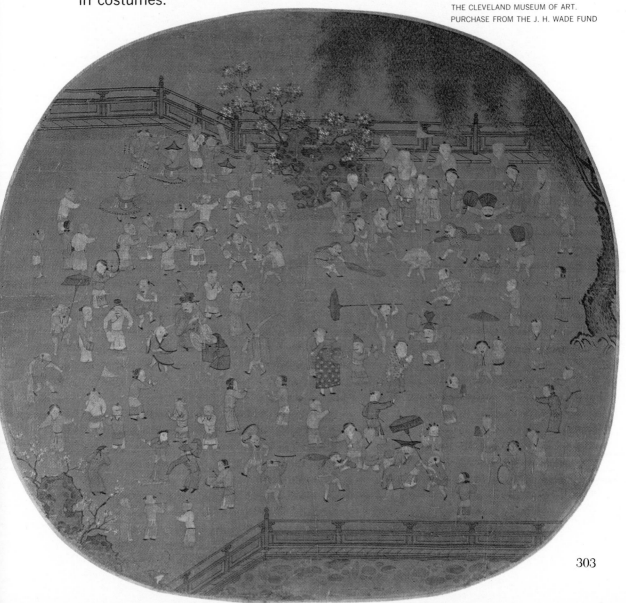

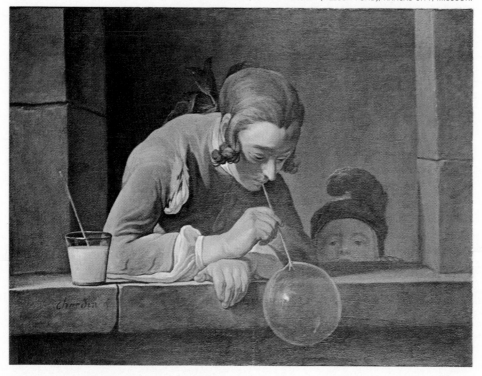

THE SOAP BUBBLE BLOWERS
JEAN–BAPTISTE CHARDIN (1699–1779)

The two French boys in this picture are having fun in an age-old way. If you've ever blown soap bubbles, you know that half the fun is seeing how big the bubble gets before it bursts or floats away. The younger boy is more interested in watching the older boy than he is in trying the game himself.

CHILD'S GAME
PAUL KLEE (1879–1940)

Sometimes an artist can have great pleasure himself by painting another person having fun. This painting seems to express the joy of being a little girl in the country on a sunny day.

FOOTBALL PLAYERS

HENRI ROUSSEAU (1844–1910)

These old-fashioned figures seem to be moving like marionettes on their tree-bounded stage. This football game is a product of Rousseau's imagination rather than a picture of an actual sporting event.

FOOTRACE

ROBERT DELAUNAY (1885–1941)

All you can see in this painting of a race are the five runners. The track, the spectators, the finish line are all left to your imagination.

YOUNG AMERICA

ANDREW WYETH (1917–   )

Born in Chadds Ford, Pennsylvania, Andrew Wyeth has painted the people and the land around there all his life. He was trained as a painter by his father, who was also a famous artist.

This boy on a bicycle was a close friend of the Wyeth family. His idea of fun was riding across the open farm country, the wind pressing against him and rustling the decorations on his bicycle.

HAMMERSMITH BRIDGE ON BOAT RACE DAY
WALTER GREAVES (1841–1930)

Incredible crowds have gathered on this bridge to watch the boat race on the Thames. The most daring of the spectators have climbed up on the cables for a better view. The boat race is not the only spectacle here. The crowd is also being entertained by the minstrels and dancers.

CHILDREN'S GAMES

PIETER BRUEGHEL THE ELDER (1520?–1569)

In this painting the whole town is a playground. A flood of people has filled every inch of this Flemish village. The children are using everything in sight for their game playing. As far as you can see, to the faint bluish church spire at the end of the long busy street, games are going on.

DREAM RIDE

WILLIAM JAMES GLACKENS (1870–1938)

The charming details in this painting could not have taken place except in someone's fantasy. This girl might be riding her rocking horse in the nursery. But anyone knows that when you are playing games and having fun, rocking horses and broomsticks can become dappled ponies and horseless riders get there just as fast.

The Mouse That Soared

HELEN LOUISE MILLER

Characters

ORVIE MOUSE

MAMMA MOUSE

FRISKY
WHISKERS } *mice who play the Three Blind Mice*
RISKY

SCAMPER, *a mouse who plays the Farmer's Wife*

LONG TAIL
SHORT TAIL
NIBBLER
SCRIBBLER } *other mice*
FLUTTER
FURRY
SQUEAKY
SQUEALY

BILL
JAKE } *boy rocketeers*

THOMAS CAT

ANNOUNCER (*offstage voice*)

REPRINTED FROM *EASY PLAYS FOR BOYS AND GIRLS* BY HELEN LOUISE MILLER, COPYRIGHT © 1963 BY PLAYS, INC., PUBLISHERS, BOSTON, MASSACHUSETTS.

Setting: Merry Mouse Meadow
(*At curtain rise the game Three Blind Mice is in progress.* FRISKY, WHISKERS, *and* RISKY, *who are blindfolded, join hands and go around in a circle, singing "Three Blind Mice."* SCAMPER, *as the Farmer's Wife, brandishes a cardboard carving knife and tries to break through the circle. When they finish the song, the Farmer's Wife chases the Three Blind Mice as they break the circle and run in all directions, until one is caught. During the game,* ORVIE *sits under a tree, ignoring the others, pretending to read a torn scrap of newspaper. Other mice stand around stage and watch the game.*)

FRISKY. That was fun! Let's play again.

WHISKERS (*as he takes off his blindfold*). Come on, Orvie, you play this time.

ORVIE. No, thanks. I want no part of that stupid game!

SCAMPER (*offering* ORVIE *the carving knife*). But it's fun. Take my part.

ORVIE. No, thanks.

NIBBLER. Oh, come on, Orvie. We need your voice. You're such a good squeaker.

ORVIE. I wouldn't sing that disgusting song!

SCAMPER. Disgusting! What's disgusting about it?

ORVIE. Everything! It makes us mice look silly and stupid.

LONG TAIL. I never thought of that.

ORVIE. Well, think about it. Actually, mice are very clever creatures. We have to be to stay alive.

SHORT TAIL. Maybe we could play Hickory Dickory Dock!

ORVIE. That's almost as bad.

FURRY. Hickory dickory dock,
>   The mouse ran up the clock.
>   The clock struck one,
>   The mouse ran down.
>   Hickory dickory dock!

RISKY. What's wrong with that?

ORVIE. Don't you see? The mouse was a coward. Afraid of a little old clock! He ran away.

WHISKERS. I never thought of that!

ORVIE. You're all too busy running away to think of anything. You're even afraid of old Thomas the Cat!

RISKY. Sh-h-h! Don't even mention him. He might hear you.

ORVIE. And what if he does? He's half blind and almost toothless. Yet you're all scared to death of him.

LONG TAIL. Mice are just naturally timid!

ORVIE. That's not true. Think of our great mouse heroes. Why doesn't anybody write songs about them?

SCRIBBLER. I don't know any mouse heroes.

ORVIE. Shame on you! What about our great ancestor who wasn't afraid of a lion?

SQUEAKY. Oh, I know about him. He even saved the lion's life.

ORVIE. And what about the brave mice who sailed with Columbus and came along with the Pilgrims on the *Mayflower?* Does anybody ever hear about them?

FURRY. No, never!

ORVIE. Take my own ancestor—Orville Mouse, the First.

SCRIBBLER. Tell us about him, Orvie. Maybe I could write a song about him.

ORVIE. He lived in the little bicycle shop where the famous Wright brothers built the first airplane. He was named for Orville Wright.

FURRY. How exciting!

ORVIE. You just wait and see! One of these days I'm going to make all you mice sit up and take notice.

SQUEAKY. I'll bet you would be a real mouse hero, if only you had the chance.

SQUEALY. But nothing exciting ever happens here in Merry Mouse Meadow.

(*There is a loud noise offstage. All the mice except* ORVIE *flee in terror.*)

ORVIE. Cowards! Cowards!

ALL (*ad lib*). What was that? (*Etc.*)

ORVIE. Don't you know?

FRISKY. It sounded like the end of the world.

ORVIE. It was a rocket taking off in the next field.

WHISKERS. A rocket! What rocket?

ORVIE. Don't you ever read the papers? Here, Scribbler. (*Hands him scrap of newspaper.*) Read this.

SCRIBBLER (*reading*). "The Junior Rocket Club meets every Saturday morning in Pleasant Acres near Merry Mouse Meadow where they have built a launching pad. The president of the club told reporters they are planning to send up a mouse in their next experiment."

SQUEAKY. Run for your lives! Run for your lives!

ORVIE (*as they start to run off*). Stop! Stop! Where are you going?

SHORT TAIL. I don't know, but I'm getting out of here fast.

LONG TAIL. You heard what it said. They're looking for a mouse to go up in a rocket!

ORVIE. There's nothing to be afraid of. You're all perfectly safe.

SCAMPER. How do you know?

ORVIE. Because they're going to take *me*.

RISKY. You!

ORVIE. Yes, me! I am going to volunteer.

FURRY. What!

ORVIE. This is my big chance. Just think, I'll be the very first mousetronaut!

NIBBLER. You wouldn't dare!

SCRIBBLER. You'll be blown to bits!

RISKY. What will your mother say?

ORVIE. She will be proud of me, and so will the rest of you when you see my name in headlines.

SCRIBBLER. "Orvie in orbit!" Yes, it has a wonderful sound.

WHISKERS. But you will be killed!

ORVIE. Nonsense! I'll live to tell even my great-grandchildren about my adventure in space.

SCAMPER. You will bring honor and glory to Mouseland.

RISKY. Do you really think you can do it, Orvie?

ORVIE. I know I can, but I will need all of your help.

ALL (*ad lib*). Tell us what to do. We'll help you. . . . (*Etc.*)

ORVIE. Good! Now first of all, I will need special equipment.

FLUTTER. I've heard there isn't any air in space. What will you breathe?

SQUEAKY. Couldn't we give him some cans of air to take along?

SQUEALY. It's not that simple. Orvie will need his own space suit.

NIBBLER. He will need a helmet.

SCRIBBLER. And gloves.

FURRY. And boots.

SQUEALY. What are we waiting for? Let's go round up the things he needs.

LONG TAIL. Come along, Orvie. You'll have to try them on for size.

(*All* MICE *except* SCRIBBLER *and* NIBBLER *exit.*)

NIBBLER. Do you really think he can make it?

SCRIBBLER. Other animals have done it. Remember that monkey who went up in 1961? What was his name?

NIBBLER. His name was Enos. His picture was in all the papers at the time.

SCRIBBLER. If a monkey can do it, so can a mouse.

NIBBLER. Anything apes can do, mice can do better!

SCRIBBLER. Sh-h-h! I hear somebody coming.

NIBBLER. Quick! Let's hide.

(NIBBLER *and* SCRIBBLER *hide as* BILL *and* JAKE *enter.*)

JAKE. Everything is set for the big test flight. All we need is our mouse.

BILL. We'll catch one. There are traps all around the base.

JAKE. But they're still empty. Those mice are getting smarter every day.

BILL. Maybe we could catch a field mouse right here.

JAKE. What do you think you are, Bill, a cat?

BILL. There's just one thing that bothers me, Jake.

JAKE. What's that?

BILL. I want to bring our mouse back alive. I don't want him to burn up on the way down.

JAKE. That's always the big re-entry problem, but I think we have it licked. The mouse will be safe in his little nose cone, and he will come down by parachute.

BILL. Sh-h-h! (*Pointing.*) Look! Look! Look over there.

JAKE. What? Where?

BILL. I thought I saw a mouse. Maybe we can sneak up on him.

JAKE. Oh, come on, Bill. We don't have time. We're due at the launching pad right now. Hurry up.

(*As* JAKE *and* BILL *exit,* NIBBLER *and* SCRIBBLER *creep out.*)

NIBBLER. What was all that talk about burning up on the way down?

SCRIBBLER. It has something to do with what scientists call friction. A fast-moving object falling through the atmosphere can burn itself up. That's what happens to a shooting star.

NIBBLER. Then it could happen to Orvie! We can't let him go!

SCRIBBLER. Simmer down. Every spaceman must face these dangers. But the scientists are finding new answers all the time.

NIBBLER. I hope those boys know what they're doing. Poor Orvie!

SCRIBBLER. Here he comes! And look! His mother is with him.

(ORVIE *enters wearing a space suit. He is accompanied by* MAMMA MOUSE *and other* MICE.)

MAMMA MOUSE. Oh, Orvie, are you sure you're all right?

ORVIE. I'm fine, Mamma. Now, don't worry.

SHORT TAIL. We'll go with you to the launching pad.

LONG TAIL. We'll see you off.

SCRIBBLER. No, we'd better stay here.

NIBBLER. We just found out there are mousetraps all over the base.

SCAMPER. How will we know what happens to Orvie?

WHISKERS. We can listen on the radio.

FRISKY. I brought my transwhisker!

MAMMA MOUSE (*throwing her arms around* ORVIE). Oh, Orvie! Orvie! I can't let you go!

ORVIE. Now, now, Mamma. Don't cry. When I come back, you'll be the proudest Mamma Mouse in all the world. Here, Squeaky, you look after her.

SQUEAKY. I'll take good care of her, Orvie.

ORVIE. And now I must be off. Thanks for all your help.

ALL. Good luck, Orvie. (ORVIE *exits, as* MICE *all wave and sing to the tune of "Good Night, Ladies."*)

Good luck, Orvie! Good luck, Orvie! Good luck, Orvie,

Come back here safe and sound.

MAMMA MOUSE. Oh, dear! I think I'm going to cry.

SQUEAKY. Now, now, Mamma Mouse, you must be brave.

RISKY. You come and sit by me, and we'll listen to the radio.

(MICE *form semicircle around* FRISKY *and radio.*)

FRISKY. It's too soon for any news.

FLUTTER. While we are waiting, I think we should plan a celebration for Orvie when he comes down.

FURRY. We'll give him a banquet.

SHORT TAIL. And call out the band!

LONG TAIL. We'll have music and speeches.

SCRIBBLER. I've already started a poem. Listen. It's called "Ode to Orville." (*Takes paper from pocket and reads.*)

Out by the Rocket Firing pad
The Meadow Mousie stands.
The mouse a mighty mouse is he
With large and venturesome plans,
And the courage of his tiny heart
Is strong as iron bands!

(*All applaud.*)

SCAMPER. Let's hear the rest of it.

SCRIBBLER. That's as far as I can go till I see what happens.

WHISKERS. Turn on the radio now, Frisky. It must be close to launching time.

(FRISKY *turns on the radio. There are static sounds from offstage. He pretends to listen closely.*)

FRISKY. I can't quite get the station, but I think they said they're starting the countdown.

ALL (*singing to tune of "John Brown Had a Little Indian"*).

One little, two little, three little seconds,
Four little, five little, six little seconds,
Seven little, eight little, nine little seconds,

Ten little seconds to go!
Ten little, nine little, eight little seconds,
Seven little, six little, five little seconds,
Four little, three little, two little seconds,
One little second to go!

(*Loud crash and whistling sound from offstage.*)

ALL (*ad lib*). He's off! He's off! (*They look up.*) Whee-ee! There goes Orvie! (*Etc.*)

MAMMA MOUSE (*jumping up in a frenzy*). Orville! Orville Mouse! You come back here this very minute! Do you hear me?

SQUEAKY. There, there. Take it easy, Mamma Mouse.

MAMMA MOUSE. He'll be killed! I know he will! Oh dear! Oh dear!

FRISKY. Sh-h-h! I think I'm getting something on the radio.

(*All crouch down and listen.*)

ANNOUNCER (*offstage, on loudspeaker*). A perfect takeoff! Everything is going just exactly as planned, and all precautions have been taken to bring our mouse passenger back to earth safely.

SQUEALY. Hear that, Mamma Mouse? There's nothing to worry about.

LONG TAIL. Orvie is going to be a hero for sure.

SHORT TAIL. We must give him a medal.

FLUTTER. Where will we get one?

RISKY. I know! I know! Let's give him Thomas Cat's bell!

WHISKERS. How would we get Thomas Cat's bell?

RISKY. If Orvie can be a hero, so can we! We'll take it right off Tom's neck. All in favor?

ALL. Aye!

FLURRY. Sh-h-h! I think I hear the cat coming. Quick, let's hide.

(ALL *hide behind bushes as* THOMAS CAT *enters.*)

THOMAS CAT. I smell something funny! Not a mouse in sight!

(MICE *dash out and attack* THOMAS CAT. *In the scuffle, two of them sit on* THOMAS CAT *as* SQUEALY *takes the bell from around his neck!*)

SQUEALY. We have it! We have it!

THOMAS CAT. Let me up! Let me up!

MICE. Promise to do us no harm.

THOMAS CAT. I promise. (*They let him up.*) Now what was that all about? Why did you take my bell?

NIBBLER. It's for Orvie.

SCRIBBLER. Orvie is a hero now. We want to give him a medal.

THOMAS CAT. Orvie has always been a hero. He was the only mouse who was never afraid of me. If you had told me the bell was for Orvie, I would have given it to you without all this fuss.

SCAMPER. Thanks, Thomas. You may join us at the radio for news of Orvie's return to earth.

THOMAS CAT. We don't need the radio for that. Orvie has already landed safe and sound.

MAMMA MOUSE. How do you know?

THOMAS CAT. I've just come from the field. Orvie is fit as a fiddle.

ALL. Hurrah! Hurrah! Hurrah!

THOMAS CAT. As soon as he has had his medical checkup, he'll be home.

FRISKY. Come on, everyone. We must get our band instruments and have a parade to welcome Orvie home.

MICE (*ad lib*). Yes, let's. Come on, hurry! (*Etc.*)

(FRISKY, WHISKERS, FURRY, FLUTTER, SQUEAKY, *and* SQUEALY *exit.*)

THOMAS CAT (*to* MICE *as they exit*). Bring me my fiddle. I want to take part in the celebration.

MAMMA MOUSE. Are you sure Orvie has not been hurt?

THOMAS CAT. He's as right as rain, ma'am.

SCRIBBLER. Dear me, I must finish my poem. (*Takes pad of paper from pocket and begins to scribble rapidly.*)

MAMMA MOUSE (*looking offstage*). Here they come with their instruments.

(MICE *return with sheets of paper and rhythm instruments, including fiddle for* THOMAS CAT.)

FRISKY. We're all tuned up and ready to go with "Three Blind Mice."

RISKY. But Orvie hates that song.

FLUTTER. We made up some new words, and here's a copy for each of you. (*Gives sheet to each one.*)

MAMMA MOUSE (*looking off left*). He's coming! He's coming! (*Running to meet* ORVIE *as he enters.*) Oh, Orvie, Orvie! Welcome home!

ALL (*singing to accompaniment of their rhythm instruments*).

One brave mouse! One brave mouse!
See how he soars! See how he soars!
He soars right up in the morning light,
Away he goes like a flying kite!
Did ever you see such a wonderful sight
As one brave mouse!

ALL (*ad lib*). Welcome home, Orvie! Are you all right? Congratulations! (*Etc.*)

ORVIE. Thank you. Thank you.

SCAMPER. As a small token of our admiration, we wish to present you with this medal. (*Hangs the bell around* ORVIE'S *neck.*) May you wear it with pride and honor.

ORVIE. But this is Thomas Cat's bell. How did you get it?

THOMAS CAT. They mobbed me and took it by
force.

ORVIE. But they've always been scared to death
of you!

SCRIBBLER. Not any more, Orvie. Some of your
courage must have rubbed off on us. All we
needed was a hero to look up to. Listen! (*Reads
poem.*)

> Our thanks to you, dear Orvie Mouse,
> For the lesson you have taught.
> In your brave deed each timid mouse
> Found courage that he sought.
> From this day forth, we sing your praise,
> O mighty mousetronaut!

(*Applause as curtain falls.*)

THE END

Reflections

1. In what ways does a play differ from a story? Give
as many ways as you can.
2. Would you prefer to read a play, see it performed,
or be an actor in it? Give the reasons for your
answer.
3. Why does Orvie think that mice are clever? Do you
agree with him? Why or why not?
4. What did the other mice learn from Orvie? How do
you know? Give evidence from the play.
5. What is a *mousetronaut?* What do you think a
transwhisker is? Since you cannot find these words
in a dictionary, how were you able to figure out their
meanings?

Unit 5
A WORLD OF WONDERS

Dream-Song

Sunlight, moonlight,
Twilight, starlight—
Gloaming at the close of day,
And an owl calling,
Cool dews falling
In a wood of oak and may.

Lantern-light, taper-light,
Torch-light, no-light:
Darkness at the shut of day,
And lions roaring,
Their wrath pouring
In wild waste places far away.

Elf-light, bat-light,
Touchwood-light and toad-light,
And the sea a shimmering gloom of gray,
And a small face smiling
In a dream's beguiling
In a world of wonders far away.

Walter de la Mare

The Goldfish

ELEANOR FARJEON

A Scrap of the World

There was once a Goldfish who lived in the sea
in the days when all fish lived there. He was perfectly happy and had only one care, and that was
to avoid the net that floated about in the water,
now here, now there. But all the fish had been
warned by King Neptune, their father, to avoid the
net. In those days they did as they were told.

So the Goldfish enjoyed a glorious life, swimming
for days and days in the blue and green water.
Sometimes he swam low down close to the sand
and shells and pearls and coral and big rocks. Here
the anemones grew like clusters of gay flowers,
and the seaweed waved in frills and fans of red,
green, and yellow. Sometimes he swam high up
near the surface of the sea, where the whitecaps
chased each other and the great waves rose like
mountains of glass and tumbled over themselves
with a crash.

When the Goldfish was as near the top as this, he sometimes saw swimming in the bright blue water far, far above him a great Gold Fish. This fish was as golden as himself but as round as a jellyfish. At other times, when that distant water above was dark blue instead of bright, he saw a Silver Fish. He had never met such a fish under the sea. She, too, was often round in shape, though at times, when she seemed to swim sideways through the water, he could see her pointed silver fins.

The Goldfish felt jealous of the other Gold Fish, but with the Silver Fish he fell in love at sight. He longed to be able to swim up to her. Whenever he tried to do this, something queer happened that made him lose his breath. With a gasp he sank down into the ocean, so deep that he could see the Silver Fish no longer. Then, hoping she might come down to swim in his own water, the Goldfish swam for miles and miles in search of her, but he never had the luck to find her.

One night as he was swimming about in very calm water, he saw overhead the motionless shadow of an enormous fish. One great long fin ran under its belly in the water, but all the rest of it was raised above the surface. The Goldfish knew every fish in the sea, but he had never before seen such a fish as this! It was bigger than the Whale and as black as the ink of the Octopus. He swam around it, touching it with his little nose. At last he asked, "What sort of fish are *you?*"

The big black shadow laughed. "I am not a fish at all. I am a ship," he said.

"What are you doing here if you are not a fish?"

"Just now I am doing nothing, for I am becalmed. But when the wind blows, I shall go sailing around the world."

"What is the world?"

"All that you see and more."

"Am I in the world, then?" asked the Goldfish.

"Certainly you are."

The Goldfish gave a little jump of joy. "Good news! Good news!" he cried.

A passing Porpoise paused to ask, "What are you shouting for?"

"Because I am in the world!"

"Who says so?"

"The Ship Fish!" said the Goldfish.

"Pooh!" said the Porpoise. "Let him prove it!" and passed on.

The Goldfish stopped jumping because his joy had been lessened. "How can the world be more than I can see?" he asked the Ship. "If I am really in the world, I ought to be able to see it *all*—or how can I be sure?"

"You must take my word for it," said the Ship. "A tiny fellow like you can never hope to see more than a scrap of the world. The world has a rim you can never see over. The world has foreign lands full of wonders that you can never look upon. The world *is* as round as an orange, but you will never see how round the world is."

Then the Ship went on to tell of the parts of the world that lay beyond the rim of things. He told of men and women and children and of flowers and trees. He also told of birds with eyes in their tails, of white and black elephants, and of temples hung with tinkling bells. The Goldfish wept with longing because he could never see over the rim of things. He could not see how round the world was, and he could not behold all at once all the wonders that were in the world.

How the Ship laughed at him! "My little friend," said he, "if you were the Moon yonder, or if you were the Sun himself, you could only see one half of these things at a time."

"Who is the Moon yonder?" asked the Goldfish.

"Who else, but that silver bit of light up in the sky?"

"Is that the sky?" said the Goldfish. "I thought it was another sea. And is that the Moon? I thought she was a Silver Fish. But who then is the Sun?"

"The Sun is the round gold ball that rolls through the sky by day," said the Ship. "They say he loves the Moon and gives her his light."

"I will give her the world!" cried the Goldfish. And he leaped with all his tiny might into the air, but he could not reach the Moon. He fell gasping into the sea. There he let himself sink like a little gold stone to the bottom of the ocean, where he lay for a week weeping his heart out. The things the Ship had told him about were more than he could understand, but they filled him with great longings—longings to possess the Silver Moon and to be a mightier fish than the Sun and to see the whole world from top to bottom and from side to side, with all the wonders within and beyond it.

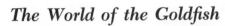

The World of the Goldfish

Now it happened that King Neptune, who ruled the land under the waves, was strolling through a grove of white and scarlet coral. He heard a chuckle that was something between a panting and a puffing. Peering through the branches of the coral trees, he beheld a plump Porpoise bursting its sides with laughter. Not far off lay the Goldfish, swimming in tears.

King Neptune, like a good father, preferred to share in all the joys and sorrows of his children. He stopped to ask the Porpoise, "What tickles you so?"

"Ho! ho! ho!" puffed the Porpoise. "I am tickled by the grief of the Goldfish there."

"Has the Goldfish a grief?" asked King Neptune.

"He has indeed! For seven days and nights he has wept because—ho! ho! ho!—because he cannot marry the Moon, be mightier than the Sun, and possess the world!"

"And you," said King Neptune, "have you never wept for these things?"

"Not I!" puffed the Porpoise. "What! Weep for the Sun and the Moon that are nothing but two blobs in the distance? Weep for the world that no one can behold? No, Father! When my dinner is nowhere, I'll weep for *that;* and when I see death coming, I'll weep for *that;* but for the rest, I say pooh!"

"Well, it takes all sorts of fish to make a sea,"
said King Neptune. He stooped and picked up
the Goldfish.

"Come, child," he said, "tears may be the
beginning, but they should not be the end of
things. Tears will get you nowhere. Do you really
wish to marry the Moon, be mightier than the
Sun, and possess the world?"

"I do, Father, I do!" cried the Goldfish.

"Then since there is no help for it, you must
get caught in the net. Do you see it floating
yonder in the water? Are you afraid of it?"

"Not if it will bring me all I long for," said the Goldfish bravely.

"Risk all, and you will get your desires," promised King Neptune. He let the Goldfish dart through his fingers. He saw him swim boldly to the net which was waiting to catch what it could. As the meshes closed upon the Goldfish, King Neptune stretched out his hand and slipped a second fish inside the net. Then, stroking his green beard, he continued his stroll among his big and little children.

And what happened to the Goldfish?

He was drawn up into the Fisherman's boat that lay in wait above the nets. In the same net a Silverfish was taken. She was a lovely creature with a round body and silky fins like films of moonlit cloud.

"There's a pretty pair!" thought the Fisherman. He carried them home to please his little daughter. And to make her pleasure more complete, he first bought a globe of glass and sprinkled sand and shells and tiny pebbles at the bottom. He set among them a sprig of coral and a strand of seaweed. Then he filled the globe with water, dropped in the Goldfish and the Silverfish, and put the little glass world on a table in his cottage window.

The Goldfish, dazed with joy, swam towards the Silverfish. He cried, "You are the Moon come out of the sky! Oh, see how round the world is!"

And he looked through one side of the globe and saw flowers and trees in the garden. He looked through another side of the globe and saw on the mantelpiece black and white elephants of ebony and ivory. Through another side of the globe he saw on the wall a fan of peacock's feathers, with eyes of gold and blue and green. Through the other side, on a bracket, he saw a little Chinese temple with many bells. He looked at the top of the globe and saw a man, a woman, and a child smiling down at him over the rim.

And he gave a little jump of joy and cried to his Silver Bride:

"Oh, Silverfish, I am greater than the Sun, for I give you, not just half, but the whole of the world! I give you the top and the bottom and all the way around, with all the wonders that are in it and beyond it!"

And King Neptune under the sea, who had ears for all that passed, laughed in his beard and thought:

"It was a shame to let such a tiny fellow loose in the vast ocean. He needed a world more suited to his size."

And ever since then, the world of the Goldfish has been a globe of glass.

Reflections

1. At the beginning of this story, what mistaken idea did the Goldfish have about the sun and the moon?
2. What happened to the Goldfish each time he tried to reach the Silver Fish?
3. How did the Porpoise feel about the news that there was a whole world he would never be able to see?
4. Why did King Neptune want the Goldfish to get caught in the net? Why did he slip another fish into it?
5. Do you think the Goldfish was brave to swim into the net? Explain.
6. How much of the world did the Goldfish finally get to see? How much did he think he saw? Why?

Once . . .

NATALIA M. BELTING

From the Hawaiian Islands

Once, when the sky was very near the earth,
a woman hoeing in her garden took off her
    necklace
and hung it in the sky.
The stars are her silver necklace.

From India

The dark gray clouds,
the great gray clouds,
the black rolling clouds are elephants
going down to the sea for water.
They draw up the water in their trunks.
They march back again across the sky.
They spray the earth with the water,
and men say it is raining.

From Siberia

When it storms,
a camel walks across the skies.
He has two riders.
One beats a drum. It is the thunder.
One waves a scarf. It is the lightning.

From Malaya

The rainbow is the fishing line of the king of
    dragons.
The king of dragons sits in the high places above
    the earth,
in places where no man has ever been.
He fishes in the waters below the earth;
And the rainbow is his fishing line.

The Snake Who Wanted to Fly

DAN STORM

A Snake once met two Buzzards sitting on a rock and said to them, "How fortunate you two are. You can travel through the air, while I go always with my stomach to the ground. How wonderful it must be to sail through the blue sky, flying, flying, looking down over the whole world. How unlucky am I, always crawling, crawling on the ground. It takes me all day to go even a short distance. But with you, *zzzsst*, you only have to think of being in some place to be nearly there."

The two Buzzards listened to the Snake and felt sorry for him, for they are kind birds who never kill anything and are a great help to animals and mankind in cleaning up the country. They tried to make this Snake more contented with his lot.

The younger Buzzard said, "Yes, flying seems pleasant enough. But there is nothing pretty to see. When we are up in the air, we are no closer to the blue sky than you are here on the ground."

"That is true," the older bird said. "Things are not always as pretty as they look. Sometimes it is tiresome living in the air. We are not welcome on the ground, you know. With you it is different. Everyone is afraid of you."

"Aha, yes," sighed the Snake, "but I am at heart like you two fellows. By nature I am really a bird. That is what I am. Oh, if I could only fly just once, it would be so wonderful."

The two Buzzards drew closer together on the stone where they were sitting on their heels like two cowboys and began to think very hard. "It is certainly impossible for you to fly," said one Buzzard. "That is certain. But there ought to be some way we could take you for a ride in the air."

"Yes, yes!" cried the Snake. "One of you take me on your back. I am not very heavy."

"You are too heavy for me," said one.

"Me, too," said the other. "We Buzzards are not very strong—mostly feathers. Feel . . ."

Now, indeed, it began to look as if the Snake would have to give up his idea of a trip into the air. Suddenly the older bird said, "Wait! There is one way we can take you for a little *paseo* into the sky. We will both carry you, Señor Snake, that is what we will do!"

So the two birds went nearby on the desert and brought back a dried-up yucca stalk. This stick was about six feet long, but very light and strong. Each bird took an end of the stick in his mouth, and they told the Snake to follow them up a small hill.

When all three were at the top of the little hill, the older Buzzard said, "Take a tight hold here in the middle of the stick, Brother Snake, with your mouth. We will each take hold of an end of the stick and will fly with it in our beaks, together. Hold on tight."

The Snake did as he was told, and the Buzzards shook out their wings. "Ready, Brother Snake! Here we go, taking off. *Cuidado!*" And with that the two birds went running down the hill, flapping their wings and shouting to each other, "Both together, *compadre.*"

The Snake dragged most of himself on the ground behind while he held on for dear life to the middle of the stick with his mouth. As they neared the bottom of the hill, the two Buzzards were at top running speed. With a strong beating of their wings, they rose together into the air, and the birds, Snake, stick, and all, were flying, flying higher and higher into the air.

The three had not gone far when a great crowd of all kinds of birds appeared behind them. They had come from afar to see what this strange group of fliers might be. The Snake was hanging onto the stick with his long teeth, swinging lightly back and forth high above the earth. This was what he long had wanted.

The Eagle, who was in the band of birds, flew over close to the Snake and began asking him all kinds of questions and saying things to make him angry. "Flap your wings, Brother Snake," he said. "Do I see feathers sprouting at your tail?"

The Eagle was about to say something more to the Snake, when the little Dove came and stood on the yucca stick right close to the Snake's head and said to him, "Don't answer the Eagle. He is trying to make you talk and open your mouth. If you did that, you would lose your hold on the stick and fall to the ground."

The little Dove did not want to see even its worst enemy have any trouble, but the Snake, with his new experience in flying, seemed to think that now he knew all about it. Seeing the Dove so close to him, he forgot for a moment that he was not a bird and opened his jaws to make a grab for the Dove.

No sooner had he done this than he dropped from the stick and fell through the air, turning over and over, down, down, down. He was flying, but he could go only in one direction, and that led him right into a prickly pear bush down on the plains. The breath was knocked out of him, and countless cactus thorns were knocked into him by his fall. Soon he gathered himself together and crawled back to his den in the rocks. And in the days that followed, every time he pulled a thorn out of himself, he cared a little bit less about his flying trip.

Reflections

1. Which characters in this story seem good-natured and kindhearted? Which one is stupid? Give reasons to support your opinion in each case.

2. A number of Spanish words are used in this story. They appear in *italic* type. Find them and reread the sentences that come before and after them (the *context*). What meaning do you think each foreign word has on the basis of its context?

3. What caused the Snake's downfall?

4. Pretend that one year after the Snake's sad experience, he was overheard asking two fish to take him swimming. Tell what you think might happen.

5. Have you ever wished to be someone else or to do something beyond your range? Tell about it.

Anansi's Hat-Shaking Dance

HAROLD COURLANDER

If you look closely, you will see that Kwaku
Anansi, the spider, has a bald head. It is said that
in the old days he had hair but that he lost it
through vanity.

It happened that Anansi's mother-in-law died.
When word came to Anansi's house, Aso, his wife,
prepared to go at once to her own village for the
funeral. But Anansi said to Aso, "You go ahead;
I will follow."

When Aso had gone, Anansi said to himself,
"When I go to my dead mother-in-law's house,
I will have to show grief over her death. I will
have to refuse to eat. Therefore, I shall eat now."
And so he sat down in his own house and ate a

huge meal. Then he put on his mourning clothes and went to Aso's village.

First there was the funeral. Afterwards there was a large feast. But Anansi refused to eat out of respect for his wife's dead mother. He said, "What kind of man would I be to eat when I am mourning for my mother-in-law? I will eat after the eighth day has passed."

Now this was not expected of him, because a man isn't required to starve himself simply because someone has died. But Anansi was the kind of person that when he ate, he ate twice as much as others and when he danced, he danced more vigorously than others and when he mourned, he had to mourn more loudly than anybody else. Whatever he did, he didn't want to be outdone by anyone else. And although he was very hungry,

he couldn't bear to have people think he wasn't the greatest mourner at his own mother-in-law's funeral.

So he said, "Feed, my friends, but as for me, I shall do without." So everyone ate—the porcupine, the rabbit, the snake, the guinea fowl, and the others—all except Anansi.

On the second day after the funeral, they said to him again, "Eat; there is no need to starve."

But Anansi replied, "Oh no, not until the eighth day, when the mourning is over. What kind of man do you think I am?"

So the others ate. Anansi's stomach was empty, and he was unhappy.

On the third day they said again, "Eat, Kwaku Anansi; there is no need to go hungry."

But Anansi was stubborn. He said, "How can I eat when my wife's mother has been buried only three days?" And so the others ate, while Anansi smelled the food hungrily and suffered.

On the fourth day Anansi was alone where a pot of beans was cooking over the fire. He smelled the beans and looked in the pot. At last he couldn't stand it any longer. He took a large spoon and dipped up a large portion of the beans, thinking to take it to a quiet place and eat it without anyone's knowing. But just then the dog, the guinea fowl, the rabbit, and the others returned to the place where the food was cooking.

To hide the beans, Anansi quickly poured them in his hat and put it on his head. The other people came to the pot and ate, saying again, "Anansi, you must eat."

He said, "No, what kind of man would I be?"

But the hot beans were burning his head. He jiggled his hat around with his hands. When he saw the others looking at him, he said, "Just at this very moment in my village, the hat-shaking festival is taking place. I shake my hat in honor of the occasion."

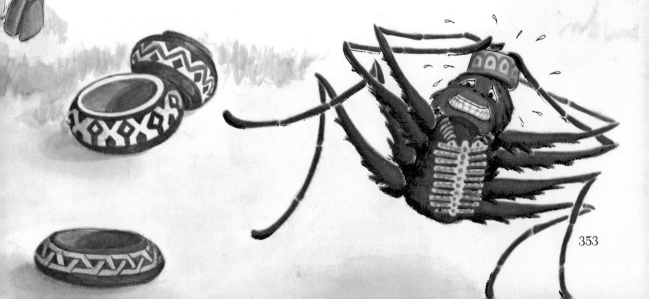

The beans felt hotter than ever, and he jiggled his hat some more. He began to jump with pain, and he said, "Like this in my village, they are doing the hat-shaking dance."

He danced about, jiggling his hat because of the heat. He yearned to take off his hat, but he could not because his friends would see the beans. So he shouted, "They are shaking and jiggling the hats in my village, like this! It is a great festival! I must go!"

They said to him, "Kwaku Anansi, eat something before you go."

But now Anansi was jumping and writhing with the heat of the beans on his head. He shouted, "Oh, no, they are shaking hats; they are wriggling hats and jumping like this! I must go to my village! They need me!"

He rushed out of the house, jumping and pushing his hat back and forth. His friends followed after him saying, "Eat before you go on your journey!"

But Anansi shouted: "What kind of man do you think I am, with my mother-in-law just buried?"

Even though they all followed right after him, he couldn't wait any longer, because the pain was too much, and he tore the hat from his head.

When the dog saw, and the guinea fowl saw, and the rabbit saw, and all the others saw what was in the hat, and saw the hot beans sticking to Anansi's head, they stopped chasing him. They began to laugh and jeer.

Anansi was overcome with shame. He leaped into the tall grass, saying, "Hide me." And the grass hid him.

That is why Anansi is often found in the tall grass, where he was driven by shame. And you will see that his head is bald, for the hot beans he put in his hat burned off his hair.

All this happened because he tried to impress people at his mother-in-law's funeral.

Reflections

1. What kind of personality did Anansi have? Give both his good and his bad points.
2. Do you think Anansi deserved what happened to him? Give reasons for your answer.
3. Describe how Anansi felt when his friends laughed at him.
4. What do you suppose Anansi's wife said to him on the first night they were both at home? Make up the conversation that you think they might have had.

The Wandering Minstrel
ALICE J. EVES

I met a wandering minstrel,
   A-strolling through the town;
He wore a shirt of lavender
   And breeches, russet-brown.

A gaily patterned kerchief
   Was knotted 'neath his chin;
Across his broad and burly back
   Was slung a mandolin.

His cheeks were lined and swarthy,
   His hair as black as night;
From one ear dangled jauntily
   A golden ear-ring bright.

And as he passed the corner,
   He flashed a smile at me
That made me think of sunny lands
   Beyond the rolling sea;

Of olive groves and vineyards
   Slow-ripening in the sun,
And of a gypsy-caravan
   When gypsy work is done.

I felt the urge to wander
  On some enchanted shore,
I longed to be a vagabond
  And roam the wide world o'er.

I followed close behind him
  And, as he went his way,
I saw him turn and wink at me,
  And this I heard him say:

"Oh! once I was a town-lad;
  My home I vowed to leave;
I yearned for far-off places, too,
  Until, one summer's eve,

I met a wandering minstrel,
  A-strolling through the town;
He wore a shirt of lavender
  And breeches, russet-brown."

Too Much Nose

HARVE ZEMACH

Three Gifts

Once there was a poor old father, who was both very poor and very old. He had three sons, and one day he called them to his side and said, "Sons, it is time for you to leave here and make your own way in the world. But before you go, I have some things to give you, some things of very great value."

The three lads were surprised to hear this. "What things, Father?" they asked, "and where are they?" The old man told them to pull the wooden chest out from under his bed and take what they found in it. They dragged out the chest and got it open, and what they found was an old broken hat, crushed on top and missing its brim; a ragged coin purse, full of holes; and a rusty horn.

"Now see what I've given you!" exclaimed the father to his eldest son.

The eldest son held up the hat and smiled sadly. "I see, Father," he said, "it was once a good hat, but now it is not even fit to sit on the scarecrow's head."

"So it seems," said the father, "but if you put it on, you can go wherever you care to go and do whatever you please to do, and no one will see you as long as you have it on." Then he turned

to his second son and said, "Now see what I have given *you!*"

The second son shook some dust out of the ragged coin purse. "If I had a coin to carry in it," he said, "it would soon fall out, there are so many holes. But no matter, since I haven't got a coin."

"So it seems," said the father, "but every time you put your fingers in, you'll find a silver coin there, and after that as many as you wish." Then he said to his third son, "And see what I have given *you!*"

"Father, it's a very nice horn," the third son said, "and when I am starving hungry, I shall blow tunes on it to make myself forget about eating."

"Silly boy! That's not what it is for," said the father. "Whenever you want anything, you need only to sound the horn, and Someone will bring you whatever you want."

Then the old father gave his blessings to his
sons, and they went their separate ways. The
second son tucked the coin purse under his belt
and headed for a nearby town. There, as he was
passing below the windows of a palace, a maid
looked out and called to him. "Can you play at
cards?" she asked him.

"As well as most," he replied.

"Good, then come up, for the queen wants
somebody to play with her."

The young man went in and up the stairs and
was shown where to sit at a table across from the
queen. She gave him a sharp look and began
dealing the cards. They played for an hour, and
the queen kept winning. Each time she won, she
cried, "The queen wins! Three silver coins for the
queen!" And when the game was over, she said,
"You unlucky man, you have lost thirty pieces of
silver. But never mind, I can see you are too poor
to pay."

"Oh, I can pay all right," said the second son. He opened his coin purse and reached into it thirty times and each time brought out a shiny silver coin.

The queen was amazed. "How is it possible," she asked, "that such a poor-looking fellow can find so much silver in that ragged old purse?"

"It is no ordinary purse," he answered proudly and told her the secret of his father's gift.

"I don't believe it. Here, let me see for myself," said the queen, and she snatched the coin purse from the young man's hands. Then, before he could say a word, she called the guards and ordered them to turn the fellow out.

When the guards had done with him, the second son went to find his elder brother. He told his brother about the queen and begged to borrow his hat, promising to return it shortly.

As soon as he got the hat, he put it on and became invisible. Then he went back to the palace. It was the dinner hour, and because of the hat no one was able to see the second son enter and sit down at the table right next to the queen. He waited until the queen was served her soup. Then, before she could eat the first spoonful, he lifted the bowl to his own lips and replaced it empty on the table.

The queen thought that very strange, and even stranger when the rest of her dinner disappeared the same way, each dish in turn. Finally she cried out, "Who are you, invisible one, and what do you want?"

"It is I who played cards," said the young man, "and I'll give you no peace until you return my coin purse."

"I would gladly return it," said the queen, "but how do I know it is you who speaks and not someone else? First you must let me see you; then I'll return your purse."

So the young man took off his hat and showed himself to the queen. "Now you see it is I," he said, "so give me my coin purse."

The queen went and got the ragged purse, but before giving it to him, she said, "Tell me, young man, how did you make yourself invisible?"

"Oh," he said, "it is this broken old hat that has the power. As soon as you put it on, no one can see you."

"I don't believe it," said the queen.

"But it's true," said he. "You just put it on and . . ."

"Impossible!" said the queen. "Here, let me see for myself." And she snatched the hat out of his hands and thrust it on her own head.

"There, just as I told you," said the young man. "Now you are invisible."

"So I am," cried the queen, and she rushed out of the room.

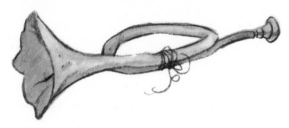

That Rusty Horn

Before the young man realized what had happened, she called for the guards and had him thrown out of the palace. The young man picked himself up and stumbled away to find his other brother. When he found him, he begged to borrow the rusty horn, just for a little while. His brother grumbled about it but finally agreed, and the second son hurried back to the palace.

He took a deep breath and blew the horn as hard as he could. At once Someone appeared, looming up before him, and asked in a mysterious voice, *"What is your wish?"*

"I want an army with cannons to overthrow the palace," cried the youth.

Instantly there was a sound of soldiers marching and a rumble of cannons. The soldiers surrounded the palace, closing in from all directions, and aimed the cannons. The queen and her company were terrified.

"What's this all about?" cried the queen as soon as she saw the second son standing under her window.

"Give me back my purse, and give me back my hat," said he, "or I shall overthrow the palace!"

"Wait," said the queen. "I have them right here. Just come inside, and I'll give them to you straightaway."

So the young man marched up to collect his things. The queen fluttered about the room, opening and closing cabinets and looking under chairs. "You gave me such a fright," she said, "that I can't remember where I put them. Are they behind that bench? No? Well, under the table in the corner?"

The young man went to look, and while he was looking, the queen said, "How did a poor fellow like you manage to call together such an army?"

"Because I've got this horn," said he, "and if you don't hurry up and find my things, I'll have the cannons batter down the palace in right earnest!"

"That rusty horn?" said the queen. "You won't make me believe it can even make a sound."

"Oh, yes, it can," said he. "You just hold it this way and blow very hard."

"Really?" said she. "Let me try!" And she grabbed it away from him and sounded it. And instantly Someone appeared and said to her, *"What is your wish?"*

"I want two stout men," cried the queen, "and I want them to drive that shabby-looking fellow out of the palace!"

It was done. And now the second son had nothing left and was ashamed to go back to his brothers. So he wandered away outside the town, and he wandered on and on. The sun set, and he could not see his way along the road. He finally stumbled into a vineyard, where he slept all night under a fig tree.

He woke up early the next morning and found the fig tree covered with ripe figs, though it was not yet the season for figs. "Some good luck at last," he thought, for he was hungry from his wanderings. He plucked some figs and began to eat. They were so delicious that he hardly noticed a certain tickling feeling in his nose. But suddenly he dropped the whole bunch and jumped to his feet.

His nose had grown to a terrible size!

Poor fellow! Now he could not even show himself to people and would have to spend the rest of his days wandering. He left the vineyard and hurried down the road. Before long he saw some cherry trees. One of them was all covered with ripe cherries. He was still hungry, so he plucked some and began to eat. And with every cherry that he ate, his nose got an inch smaller. By the time he was done, it was back to its regular size.

"Aha!" he said out loud. "Now I know what to do!"

First he filled a bottle with juice squeezed out of the ripe cherries. Then he ran back to the

vineyard and collected a basketful of figs. Then he returned to the palace, going around to the back door. "Figs for sale!" he cried. "Delicious ripe figs!"

The queen's servants bought the whole basketful. They sent word to the queen of their luck in finding figs for sale at this time of year, and the queen said to serve them right up. Everyone in the palace feasted on the figs, and the queen, of course, ate more than anyone else.

Well, it happened to them, just the way it happened to the second son when he had eaten the figs. Their noses grew and grew.

There was a terrible fuss in the palace. They sent for doctors, and all the doctors for miles around came hurrying to the palace and tried all their medicines, one after another. But nothing did any good.

Meanwhile the second son waited until all the doctors had given up and gone. Then, with a beard pasted on his chin and a hat pulled down over his eyes, he came to the palace again and called out, "Noses! I can heal noses! Whoever has got too much nose, let him come to me!"

The queen and her servants rushed to the window. "A doctor!" exclaimed the queen. "Maybe he can help us." They called him inside and begged him to heal their noses.

"All right," said he. "I have a special medicine, just for healing noses like yours. But it is very strong stuff. I'm afraid it may be too strong for a queen."

"Nonsense," said the queen, "if it really heals noses, then I must have some. I shall pay you anything you ask."

"Oh, yes," said he, "you'll have to pay a lot, because it is the only medicine of its kind in the world. But I do think that it's terribly strong stuff to give to a queen."

"Well, then, start by healing the noses of my servants," said the queen. She thought she ought to see if the medicine worked before she paid anything for it.

So the second son held up the bottle of cherry juice and gave each of the queen's servants just enough to make each nose return to its ordinary size. "There! You see!" he said. "Isn't it wonderful medicine! One drop . . . two drops . . . and *presto!* the nose is healed."

The queen looked on. She saw how well the medicine worked, but it made her jealous to hear the doctor boast about it. "You think yourself very clever," she said, "but you are not the only one who can work wonders. I've got even greater wonders than yours."

"Is that possible?" said the pretended doctor. "What could be more wonderful than my medicine for noses?"

"Why, I have a hat," said she, "that makes you invisible when you put it on. I also have a purse

369

that gives you a silver coin every time you reach into it and a horn that calls forth Someone, who brings you anything you need."

"You are joking," said he. "Such things don't exist."

"Yes, they do. I have them right here!" said the queen, showing him the coin purse and the hat and the horn.

Quick as a wink, the second son flipped the hat onto his head, snatched up the purse and the horn, and vanished from the palace. Then he went and found his brothers and gave them back the hat and the horn. And he lived comfortably for the rest of his life by means of his magical coin purse.

As for the queen, you can be sure she was furious. But nobody could tell what made her more angry—losing the treasures she had taken from the second son or being left forever with too much nose!

Reflections

1. At first, why were the three sons disappointed in the things their father gave them? What did he tell them that made them feel better?

2. What kind of person was the queen? Tell why you think so.

3. If you could choose, which one of the three gifts would you pick for yourself? Why?

4. If you were the queen, what would you have done when everyone's nose became longer?

5. Do you think this experience will change the queen? If so, how?

6. Do you think "Too Much Nose" is a good title for this story? Explain.

If You Had a Wish

CHARLES J. FINGER

The Way Things Go

In the old days in France, and very good days they were, there was a hardworking, cheerful fisherman, but never did a good fellow have worse luck. If a storm blew up, it was his nets which were carried away. If he caught no fish, the market for fish would be good. If he caught many, there would be no market at all. Yet he never complained.

"It's the way things go," he said with a hearty laugh. "Why, Wife, I believe if I had been brought up to be a barber, the whole world would have been as bald as an egg."

But his wife would not look at things in any happy way. She was sour-tempered, always frowning, always scolding.

"I see nothing to smile for," she grumbled when he came home empty-handed. "You bring nothing with as merry a look as though you had brought a boatload."

"Why not sing?" he asked. "Look at things this way. The longer bad luck lasts, why, the nearer we are to good luck, since nothing lasts forever."

"Bah!" she answered. "Every time you come home, a fool enters the house."

"Well, well," said he, trying to calm her. "With health and hope a man is lucky, and I have both in plenty."

"You cannot live on hope," said she.

"You cannot live well without it," said he.

One day his luck changed. There had been much talk among the fishermen in the village of a certain big fish which had been seen often. The rich man of that place offered a purse of gold to the one who would catch it. So, of course, every fisherman tried, but what should happen but that that particular fish leaped into the poor fisherman's boat when the man was looking another way and, striking its head on the mast, fell dead!

"After all," said the fisherman, "a man does not seek his luck, but his luck seeks him. Good luck reaches farther than long arms."

So he cleaned the fish, put it on a wooden dish, put a lemon in its mouth to make it look happy, and then went on his way, carrying the dish carefully through the forest to the rich man's castle. When he was halfway there, he came upon a poor man dressed in ragged clothes. The man was sitting on a stone by the wayside, groaning sadly.

"Now, what ails you?" asked the good-hearted fisherman.

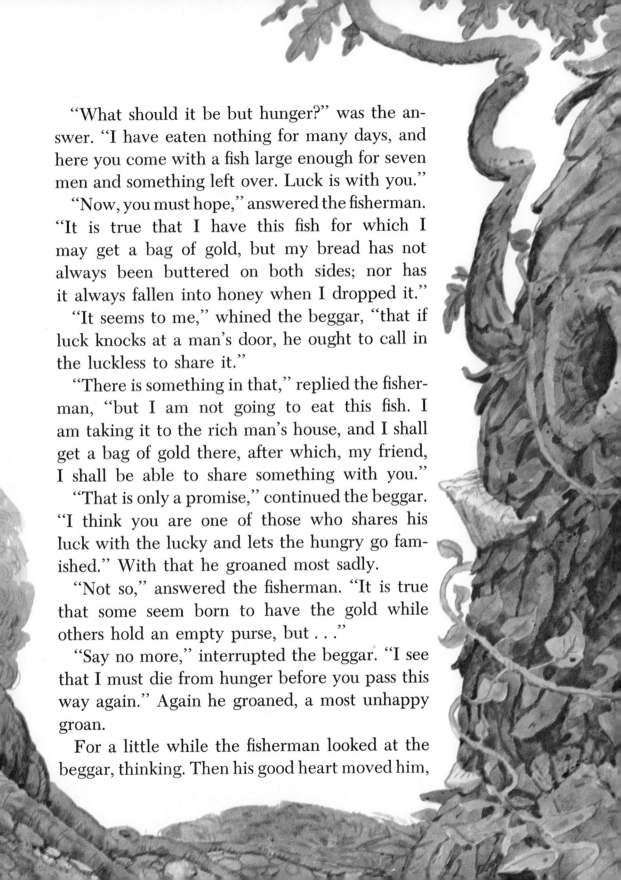

"What should it be but hunger?" was the answer. "I have eaten nothing for many days, and here you come with a fish large enough for seven men and something left over. Luck is with you."

"Now, you must hope," answered the fisherman. "It is true that I have this fish for which I may get a bag of gold, but my bread has not always been buttered on both sides; nor has it always fallen into honey when I dropped it."

"It seems to me," whined the beggar, "that if luck knocks at a man's door, he ought to call in the luckless to share it."

"There is something in that," replied the fisherman, "but I am not going to eat this fish. I am taking it to the rich man's house, and I shall get a bag of gold there, after which, my friend, I shall be able to share something with you."

"That is only a promise," continued the beggar. "I think you are one of those who shares his luck with the lucky and lets the hungry go famished." With that he groaned most sadly.

"Not so," answered the fisherman. "It is true that some seem born to have the gold while others hold an empty purse, but . . ."

"Say no more," interrupted the beggar. "I see that I must die from hunger before you pass this way again." Again he groaned, a most unhappy groan.

For a little while the fisherman looked at the beggar, thinking. Then his good heart moved him,

and he said, "Now, friend, if you are in such a
bad case, the fish is yours for the asking. It was
easily got. It is easily gone."

Thereupon the beggar man stood up and
clapped the fisherman on the shoulder in high
delight. "Never yet," said he, "did a good deed
go unrewarded. I have a strange power. This
moment, whatever you wish for shall be yours.
Name the wish."

"Now that is a hard matter to decide," replied
the fisherman.

"You have until I count to twenty—slowly—to
say what you want," said the other.

"There are so many things," answered the
fisherman.

"I am to seventeen in my count," said the
beggar. "And now eighteen."

"Well, then, for the rest of this day I wish that
I (and maybe with my wife helping) could have
everything I wish for."

"You are a clever fellow," replied the beggar
man. "It shall be so. But see to it that in your
wishing you wish good for others. And now go.
Until midnight you can wish and wish, and what
you wish shall come to be."

This Nonsense About Wishing

With that the beggar went his way, carrying the fish. The fisherman turned his steps toward his cottage, very busy with his thoughts. But the way was long, and the wind was cold, and without thinking of his gift, he said to himself, "I wish I were at home and on my stool in front of a blazing fire with a bowl of hot fish stew on the table."

No sooner had he said the words than he found himself on his stool before the fire, and his wife sprawling in the corner saying hard things to him, for she had been sitting in that corner and on that stool.

"What silly jokes are these?" she screamed, believing he had come in quietly and pushed her from the stool where she had been nodding, half asleep. "Did I not say that every time you come home, a fool enters the house?"

"Peace, good woman," he replied. "I did but wish thoughtlessly, and the beggar man warned me to be careful. But I see now that wishes may well be dangerous. Also, I did not think of others, meaning you."

"What is this nonsense about wishing?" she asked. "Are you mad, or have you become more foolish than usual?"

"Peace, woman. Listen to this," he replied.

So he told her the tale of the fish and the stranger, how the beggar man had repaid him,

and how the wishing would end at midnight. After that they argued for a long time, for although his wife wanted to do all the wishing, the promise was only that she might help. But he remembered the warning that he should keep the welfare of others in mind.

"But wish something for ourselves first," said his wife.

"No. We ought to finish wishing for others first," he said. Then he fell to thinking, while his wife kept an eye on the clock and warned him that time was passing.

"I am sure I can wish one wish that will help others," began the good fellow. "It is that every neighbor in the village had a house twice as large, with the richest of furniture and the best that there is to eat in all the world."

The words were hardly spoken when a great uproar arose. The two ran to the window to look. They saw a strange sight. Where there had been cottages, each with a garden, now were buildings that they had never seen before. Houses had spread to crowd one another. Some were pushed up sideways. Some were tilted forward, and some were tilted backward. Some bulged; some were bent; some were crooked. There were windows that were too high and doors that were too big. Of course, the people who lived in them were much disturbed and were running about like ants, crying that the place was bewitched.

Within the houses, too, things were all upset. The fisherman, in his kindness, had wished that people would have the finest foods in the world. But people's tastes for fineness are different. Some people found boiled camel's meat on the dishes, a food of which they had never dreamed. Some had whale meat, others seal fat, others sherbet. Some found food strangely changed on its way from plate to mouth, and some even found the meat change into something unfamiliar as they ate it!

The furnishings they had been used to were changed or gone altogether, with new things in their places. There were great beds (high and wide), carved benches, couches, thrones, Eskimo furs, draperies of silk, iron holders for torches,

seven-branched candlesticks of gold, and rugs of great richness. There were many articles for which the good people had no use and which they had never even seen before. As a result, every man, woman, and child was comfortless.

"Now, see what you have done!" cried the fisherman's wife. "Here is everyone rich, with great houses, and we are in our old cottage, the poorest of the poor, fool that you are. If I had the wishing, I would wish you three thousand miles away."

"That would not be so bad," murmured the fisherman, thinking that then he would be free from her scolding. "But I did but wish for the welfare of others. It begins to look as if wishing brings grieving."

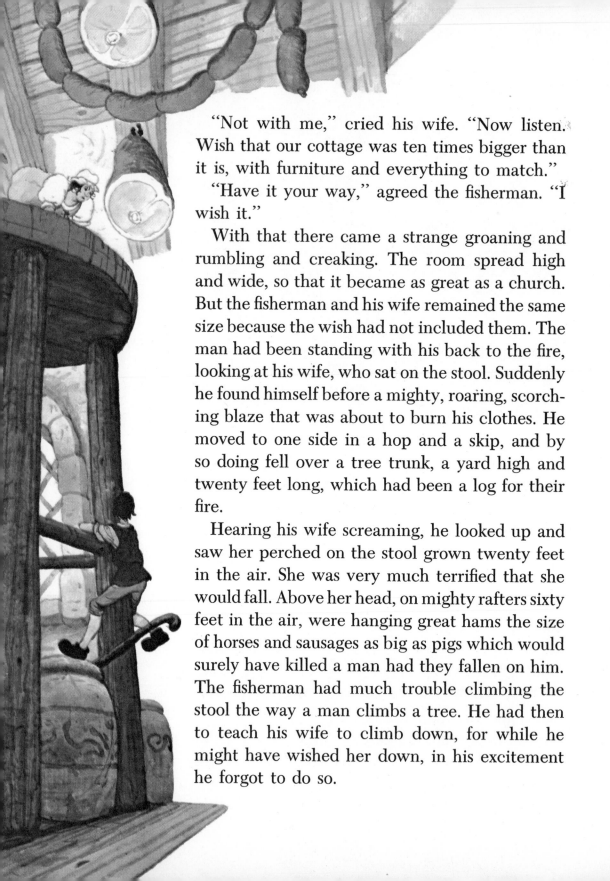

"Not with me," cried his wife. "Now listen. Wish that our cottage was ten times bigger than it is, with furniture and everything to match."

"Have it your way," agreed the fisherman. "I wish it."

With that there came a strange groaning and rumbling and creaking. The room spread high and wide, so that it became as great as a church. But the fisherman and his wife remained the same size because the wish had not included them. The man had been standing with his back to the fire, looking at his wife, who sat on the stool. Suddenly he found himself before a mighty, roaring, scorching blaze that was about to burn his clothes. He moved to one side in a hop and a skip, and by so doing fell over a tree trunk, a yard high and twenty feet long, which had been a log for their fire.

Hearing his wife screaming, he looked up and saw her perched on the stool grown twenty feet in the air. She was very much terrified that she would fall. Above her head, on mighty rafters sixty feet in the air, were hanging great hams the size of horses and sausages as big as pigs which would surely have killed a man had they fallen on him. The fisherman had much trouble climbing the stool the way a man climbs a tree. He had then to teach his wife to climb down, for while he might have wished her down, in his excitement he forgot to do so.

With Wishing Comes Grieving

When they were safely on the floor again, they could not see the tabletop, for the table was as huge as a rich man's barn. They could not reach the shelves. They could not see out of the windows. They could not unlatch the door, for the lock was far above their heads. And the fireplace—why, it was a fearful, roaring, blazing cave of flame near which they dared not go.

Then they saw the cat!

It was a monstrous creature, fearful to behold, with a head that stood higher than theirs, green, glaring eyes and terrible whiskers, long white teeth, and a body like a tiger's. Across the floor the great beast crept toward them, its eyes glaring pitilessly, its tail waving fearfully from side to side. It crouched to spring.

"Wish something!" cried the woman in great fear, as she clung to her husband, who was standing by one of the table legs.

"Oh! I wish we were in the middle of the table," said he.

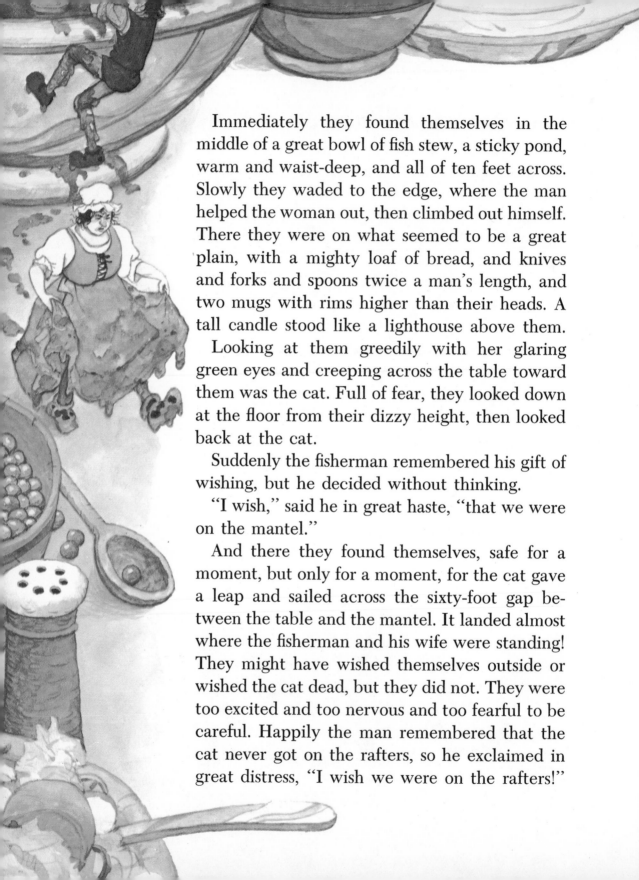

Immediately they found themselves in the middle of a great bowl of fish stew, a sticky pond, warm and waist-deep, and all of ten feet across. Slowly they waded to the edge, where the man helped the woman out, then climbed out himself. There they were on what seemed to be a great plain, with a mighty loaf of bread, and knives and forks and spoons twice a man's length, and two mugs with rims higher than their heads. A tall candle stood like a lighthouse above them.

Looking at them greedily with her glaring green eyes and creeping across the table toward them was the cat. Full of fear, they looked down at the floor from their dizzy height, then looked back at the cat.

Suddenly the fisherman remembered his gift of wishing, but he decided without thinking.

"I wish," said he in great haste, "that we were on the mantel."

And there they found themselves, safe for a moment, but only for a moment, for the cat gave a leap and sailed across the sixty-foot gap between the table and the mantel. It landed almost where the fisherman and his wife were standing! They might have wished themselves outside or wished the cat dead, but they did not. They were too excited and too nervous and too fearful to be careful. Happily the man remembered that the cat never got on the rafters, so he exclaimed in great distress, "I wish we were on the rafters!"

Almost immediately they landed there in dust way up to their knees. As they looked down at the floor from that great height, they realized they would be killed if they fell. They were weary. They were miserable. They were frightened. Their clothes were wet and heavy with the fish stew. But they were safe from the cat, and they felt even safer when they walked along the rafter to the wall and rested a while in the dark.

Then a new thing came to distress them. From a black hole that smelled terrible, there shone evil eyes. Out from the dark came a pair of claws onto the rafter: first one, and then another long, thin, hairy leg; and then—a spider bigger than a man's head! For a moment it stood looking at them, swaying back and forth a little; then it began to walk toward them.

With a scream, the woman fled along the rafter, the man following. Although the way seemed long, they did not stop until they came to a great rope, as thick as they were tall, that held one of the hams. Over this they had to climb, and, to make matters worse, there were other such ropes farther along.

"These wishes are terrible," wailed the woman, wringing her hands. "If things are ever right again, I shall never make another wish, but be satisfied with what I have."

"How can things ever be right again?" asked the man. "We are undone. And we have undone

everyone else. We shall perish before midnight comes."

"Ah, with wishing comes grieving!" sighed the woman. "And as we make our bed, so we must lie in it."

"Not at all," said the fisherman. "Not liking it, one gets up and makes it again. Listen, I wish we were in a far-off land where things are right and that our neighbors were with us and that we could begin all over again."

And that is how there came to be very contented people living in Gaspé, at the mouth of the St. Lawrence River. Suddenly the villagers found themselves in this place, a good land where fish are plentiful, where there are no rich lords, and where fields are green. Here men know that if they cannot make the thing they wish for, they must wish for the thing they can make.

Reflections

1. What kind of person was the fisherman? What kind of person was his wife?

2. What arguments did the beggar use to get the fisherman to give him the fish?

3. Why did the beggar say that the fisherman was clever? Do you think he was?

4. Why did the fisherman's wishes turn out badly?

5. This story contains many *proverbs*—common sayings that people often use. Find each of the following proverbs in the story. Then think of another situation or happening when someone might say each of them:
   a. "Nothing lasts forever."
   b. "Good luck reaches farther than long arms."
   c. "My bread has not always been buttered on both sides."
   d. "Easily got . . . easily gone."
   e. "Wishing brings grieving."
   f. "As we make our bed, so we must lie in it."

6. Reread the last proverb above. What do you think it means?

388

The Witch of Willowby Wood

ROWENA BENNETT

There once was a witch of Willowby Wood,
and a weird wild witch was she, with hair that
    was snarled
and hands that were gnarled, and a kickety,
    rickety
knee. She could jump, they say,
to the moon and back, but this I never did see.
Now Willowby Wood was near Sassafras Swamp,
where there's never a road or rut. And there
    by the
singing witch-hazel bush the old woman builded
her hut. She builded with neither a hammer or
    shovel. She
kneaded, she rolled out, she baked
her brown hovel. For all the witches' houses,
    I've oft heard
it said, are made of stick candy and fresh
gingerbread. But the shingles that shingled
    this old
witch's roof were lollipop shingles and
    hurricane-proof, too
hard to be pelted and melted by rain.
(Why this is important, I soon will explain.)

One day there came running to Sassafras
        Swamp a dark little
shadowy mouse. He was noted for being a
        scoundrel
and scamp. And he gnawed at the old woman's
        house where the
doorpost was weak and the doorpost was worn.
And when the witch scolded, he laughed her to
        scorn.
And when the witch chased him, he felt quite
        delighted. She
never could catch him for she was nearsighted.
        And so,
though she quibbled, he gnawed and he nibbled.
The witch said, "I won't have my house
take a tumble. I'll search in my magical book
        for a spell
I can weave and a charm I can mumble to get
        you
away from this nook. It will be a good warning
        to other
bad mice, who won't earn their bread
but go stealing a slice."
"Your charms cannot hurt," said the mouse,
        looking pert.

Well, she looked in her book and she
waved her right arm, and she said the most
      magical
things. Till the mouse, feeling strange,
looked about in alarm, and found he was
      growing some
wings. He flapped and he fluttered the longer
      she muttered.
"And now, my fine fellow,
you'd best be aloof," said the witch as he
      floundered
around. "You can't stay on earth and you
can't gnaw my roof. It's lollipop-hard and
      it's
hurricane-proof. So you'd better take off
from the ground. If you are wise, stay in the
      skies."
Then in went the woman of Willowby Wood,
in to her hearthstone and cat.
There, she put her old volume up high on the
      shelf, and
fanned her hot face with her hat. Then she
      said,
"That is that! I have just made a bat!"

A Tale of Stolen Time

EVGENY SCHWARTZ

translated by LILA PARGMENT and ESTELLE TITIEV

Plenty of Time

Once there lived a boy called Peter Zubov. He was a lazy boy and was way behind all the other children in his class. He didn't do his arithmetic homework or his spelling homework. Even in singing he was behind all the others. But Peter didn't worry. He would always say, "There's plenty of time. I'll catch up next week." But when the next week came, he would say again, "There's plenty of time. Next week I'll catch up."

One morning Peter came to school, late as usual. As he ran to the cloakroom, he called, "Aunt Natasha, take my coat."

From behind the coat hangers came a voice, "Who is it?"

"It's I—Peter," answered the boy.

"Why is your voice so hoarse today?"

"I don't know. I just suddenly became hoarse."

Aunt Natasha's head peered out from among the hangers. She took one look and gasped in surprise.

"What's the matter?" Peter asked.

"What's the matter indeed!" Aunt Natasha answered. "You told me you were Peter, but you must be his grandfather!"

"What do you mean—grandfather? *I'm* Peter Zubov. I'm in the fourth grade."

"Just look at yourself in the mirror."

Peter looked, and what he saw made him shake. He had turned into a thin, pale old man with a long gray beard and a moustache! His face was *covered* with wrinkles. He stood and stared at himself. His gray beard began to quiver. He turned and ran out of the room.

He ran straight home, thinking, "Surely Mother will recognize me." At last Peter reached his house, and he rang the bell quickly three times. The door opened, and there was his mother, who stood looking at him without saying a word. Peter, too, remained silent. His gray beard shook. He was ready to burst into tears.

"Whom do you want to see, sir?" asked Peter's mother.

In a faint whisper Peter asked, "Don't you know me?"

"I'm sorry, but I don't," answered his mother.

Peter turned away and walked off, thinking, "Maybe I'm not really Peter any more. I guess I'm just a lonely old man. I'm all alone, with no mother and no friends. How can I get along? Old people are usually doctors, lawyers, or teachers— but I have learned to be none of them. I've only gone as far as the fourth grade, and I certainly haven't learned very much—not as much as I should have. What will become of me?"

Peter kept walking and thinking, thinking and walking. He didn't notice that he had left the town behind him and that he was now in a forest. He walked on and on until darkness fell.

Peter began to feel tired. "It would be nice to rest a while," he thought. Just then he spied a tiny white house among the trees. He went in and looked about. No one was there. In the middle of the room stood a table with a lamp hanging over it. Four stools had been placed around the table. On the wall was a clock with a pendulum that said, "Tick-tock, tick-tock," as it swung to and fro. In one corner of the room, there was a pile of hay.

Peter crawled deep into the hay. He made himself a cozy, warm nest and cried for a while. Then he wiped the tears with his long gray beard and fell asleep.

Some time later he awoke. The lamp was shining brightly, and around the table sat four children, two boys and two girls. A large abacus lay before them. The children were counting on it, softly sighing and mumbling:

"Two years plus five years plus seven plus three.
This is for you and this is for me."

"What strange children," thought Peter. "Why are they mumbling and sighing like old people? Why are they here at night in this lonely little forest hut?"

Peter lay as still as he could—not moving a muscle, scarcely breathing. He was trying to hear everything that the children were saying. Suddenly he realized that these were not real children.

These were not two little boys and two little girls sitting together around a table. They were four sorcerers who knew a terrible secret. They could change children who wasted their time into old people. They were always hunting for children who wasted their time. They had found Peter and another little boy and two little girls and had

turned them all into old people. Then they took
the time they had stolen from the children, and
now the sorcerers were the children and the
children were old, old people.

The sorcerers had counted up all the time and
were ready to put away the abacus when one of
them, who seemed to be the leader of the group,
picked up the abacus and went up to the clock.
First he turned the hands; then he pulled the
weights and listened carefully to the tick-tock of
the pendulum.

Once again he calculated on the abacus, counting until the clock struck the hour of midnight.
He shook the abacus, and again he counted. Then,
calling the others to him, he said in a very low
voice, "My fellow sorcerers, you know that the
children whom we transformed into old people
still have a chance to become young again."

"How?" asked the sorcerers.

"I'll tell you in a moment, but first I'll make
sure no one is listening to us." The sorcerer went
out of the house on tiptoe, walked around and

around, and then came back and locked the door with a key. He took a large stick and stirred through the hay where Peter was hiding. But the lamp gave only a poor light in the corner, and the sorcerer didn't find Peter.

"Now, come close to me," called the leader to the others. In a low voice he continued, "The world is so made that any person can save himself from trouble if he tries hard enough. If the children whom we transformed into old people meet here tomorrow at exactly midnight and turn the hands of the clock seventy-seven times, then they will become children once again, and—*we* will die."

All were silent. Then one sorcerer, a girl, said, "But how will they find out what they have to do?"

Another mumbled, "They won't get here exactly at midnight. They'll be at least one minute late."

The third one added, "They can't even count to seventy-seven. They'll get mixed up."

"Just the same," warned the leader, "look sharp and listen carefully. If the children so much as touch the hands of the clock, we will become motionless—unable to move a finger. Now, let's not waste any time—to work, to work!"

The sorcerers hid the abacus and ran off like children, though they moaned and sighed just like very old people.

No Time to Waste

Peter waited until the sound of their steps had died away. Then he ran out of the house as fast as he could. Hiding behind bushes and trees from time to time to see if he was being followed, he finally reached the town. Now to find three old people who were really schoolchildren!

The town was still asleep. No lights shone in the windows; no people walked in the streets. Only a policeman stood on the corner. Daylight was just beginning to break. In the distance a streetcar began to clang.

After some time Peter noticed an old woman who came hobbling down the street with a large basket over her arm. Peter ran to her and asked, "Tell me, Granny, are you a fourth grader?"

"What? What?" shrieked the old woman.

"Aren't you really a little girl?" Peter whispered.

The old woman stamped her foot and flung her basket at Peter. He dodged the blow and ran off.

By now the town was awake. Buses were running, people were dashing to work, and trucks were grinding their gears. Peter had seen this happen many times before, but it was only now that he understood that people hurried because they didn't want to waste time. He looked around him. He saw a number of old people coming down the street, but he could tell at a glance that they were really old people, not children who had been transformed by witches.

Here comes an old man carrying a briefcase. He's probably a teacher.

Here comes an old man with a brush and pail—a painter.

There goes a red fire engine with the fire chief in it. Surely *he* never wasted a minute.

Peter walked up and down without seeing a trace of young old men or old young children.

By now it was noon, and Peter decided to walk over to the square to rest a bit. Just then he noticed an old woman sitting on a bench crying bitterly. Peter wanted to go up to her, but he thought he had better wait a while.

After a bit the old woman dried her tears and sat swinging her legs as she took a piece of raisin bread out of her pocket. She kept picking out the raisins and eating them, but she threw the bread away. Then her eye fell on something lying in the snow—a ball that someone had forgotten. She picked it up, and, turning it round and round, she wiped it carefully with her handkerchief and began to play with it, throwing it up into the air and catching it.

Peter ran up to her saying, "I bet you're really a fourth grader."

The little old woman jumped up and down. "I am. I'm in the fourth grade. I'm Maria Popova. What's your name?"

Peter told her who he was and told her, too, all that had happened to him. Then off they went together to look for two more schoolchildren. After searching and searching for a long time, they came upon a big house with a large backyard that had a woodshed at one side. Not far from the shed was a little old woman playing hopscotch. Peter and Maria looked at each other, and then together they ran as fast as they could towards the little figure, crying, "Granny, are you a schoolgirl?"

"Schoolgirl? Yes, I'm in the fourth grade, and my name is Nadya. What are your names?"

Peter and Maria told Nadya all that had happened, and then the three of them, holding hands, ran off to find the fourth child. They looked everywhere, in gardens, in the movies, in the Children's Theater, but not a trace of him could they find.

Meanwhile, time was running out. It was beginning to get dark. People were turning on the lights in their houses. Daytime was almost gone. Would they never find the fourth child and become young again? Were they doomed to remain old people?

Suddenly Maria called out, "Look, look up there!" pointing to the top of a passing trolley car. High up on the very top of the trolley sat an old man. His hat was pulled over one ear, his beard was waving in the wind, and he whistled as he rode along. The three children were very tired after all their searching. There, without a care in the world, sat the one they were looking for. There was nothing to do but run after the trolley. Luckily, the traffic light turned red just then, and the trolley stopped.

Up the children clambered and pulled the old man down. "You're a schoolboy, aren't you?" they demanded.

"Of course I am—third grade. What do you want?"

They told him the whole story, and since the trolley was going in the right direction, they all

got in. When the trolley came to the woods, the four old people jumped out and ran off in search of the little house. Once again, they were in trouble. They lost their way. It became darker and darker. They wandered about, stumbling and falling.

"Oh dear," said Peter. "Yesterday I was in such a hurry and so afraid to lose a minute that I didn't look carefully enough to remember the road to the house. Now I see that sometimes it's wisest to take time in order to save trouble later."

The children were very tired and very unhappy. At that moment a gust of wind chased the clouds from the sky and let the full moon shine down on the woods. Peter climbed up into a tree to look around, and there, not more than a few

yards away, stood the little white house, its windows shining through the fir trees.

Peter climbed down, whispered to the others to follow him, and quietly they went toward the sorcerers' house. Through the window they could see the clock—it was five minutes before twelve. The sorcerers were sleeping in the hay, guarding the time they had stolen.

Softly, ever so softly, the children opened the door and crawled on hands and knees toward the clock. When it was just one minute before twelve, they stood up. Exactly at midnight Peter stretched out his fingers to the hands of the clock and began turning them back from right to left, counting, "One, two, three . . ."

The sorcerers jumped up with a shriek—but they could move no further. They were rooted to that spot. And as they stood there, they began growing taller and taller, until they were as big as grown people. Wrinkles covered their faces, and their hair had turned gray.

"Lift me up, lift me up," cried Peter. "I'm getting smaller and smaller, and I can't reach the hands of the clock!"

The children lifted him up, and he went on counting, ". . . thirty-one, thirty-two, thirty-three." When he got to forty, the sorcerers had turned into bent, old people. Now they were getting shorter and shorter, bending closer and closer to the ground.

On the seventy-seventh turn of the clock's hands, the wicked sorcerers gave a horrible shriek and then disappeared completely.

The children looked at one another and jumped for joy. They were themselves. They were children once more.

Reflections

1. What serious fault did Peter have? What excuse did he always give?
2. What made Peter realize that he had turned into an old man?
3. This story is set in Russia, not America. One of the clues is the fact that the cloakroom at Peter's school has an attendant whom the children call "Aunt" Natasha, even though she is not related to them. Where else does Peter follow the Russian custom of calling a stranger by a relative's title?
4. The title of this story is "A Tale of Stolen Time." Who stole time in the story and from where?
5. How did Peter know that the "old people" were really children?
6. What do you think Peter learned about the value of time? What is the difference between "wasting time" and "taking time"?

PICTURES FROM WORDS

In any story you read, words are used to describe the setting, or the place where the events of the story happen. Writers use words to describe people and things. We have to use our own imagination with words when we read sentences. For example, in these sentences, watch the word *carriage*. Think of the pictures you get as you read.

1. Mother left the baby *carriage* by the door.
2. George Washington rode in a *carriage* from Alexandria to his home, Mount Vernon.
3. You should see my dad's new car. What a *carriage!*
4. That's some *carriage* you have there. Did you make it?

Which picture below do you match with each of the sentences above? Would the third picture be suitable for the first, second, or fourth sentences? Why or why not?

Word Pictures

Good writers use certain ways to help you understand what they mean. Here is one way.

1. The girl was chattering away *like an excited monkey.*
2. Tony sailed into the room *like a great eagle.*
3. She sat down *like a tired elephant.*

In each of these sentences, a person is described as similar to, or like, something else. How do you think an excited monkey chatters? How does a boy sail into a room like a great eagle? Do you think he walks swiftly? Is he silent? If you sit down like a tired elephant, do you sit on the edge of your chair, or do you drop heavily and rest your arms on the arms of your chair?

When we say one thing is like another, or similar to another, we call *like* or *as* and the words following it a simile (sim'ə lē). Writers often use similes. Your everyday speech is full of similes. You can easily make up some. Copy each of the following sentence starters; then complete each one. See how your similes are different from or similar to those your classmates write.

1. I am the air in a balloon, and I am going to come out like ——.
2. I am an egg being tossed into an electric fan, and I am going to smash like ——.
3. I am a great spotlight, and I shine as ——.
4. I am a shooting star, and I speed through the night like ——.
5. I am hungry enough to eat like ——.

Discuss the different word pictures your words made in the sentences above. Writing similes gives you a chance to use your imagination. Were some of your similes funny? Were some sad? Were some surprising?

Changing the Meaning of Words

Sometimes people make their language more interesting by changing the meaning of a word or group of words. The words define one thing in a way that is like a simile but without *like* or *as*. This is how it works.

1. John's head is a computer.
2. He is a regular adding machine.
3. Tina is a walking encyclopedia.

As we read, we know that in fact John's head is not a computer, that no boy is an adding machine. We know a girl is not a walking encyclopedia. But we accept these words because they are a good, clear way of describing, or defining, one thing in terms of another. When we say to our best friend, "Gee, what a nut you are!" we know in fact that he is not a nut. If we said this to a stranger, we might get into trouble.

This use of words, calling someone or something by another name, is called metaphor. You make a metaphor by letting one word, or group of words, name something else.

Use a metaphor to complete each word group that follows the sentences below. The first one is done for you.

1. Mr. Demos has a cold way of being unfriendly.
   His heart is an iceberg.

2. Mrs. Demos has a warm way of being friendly.
   Her heart is ——.

3. Mrs. Jenkins, the librarian, knows dozens of stories.
   She is ——.

4. The dog knows a dozen tricks.
   Old Rover is a ——.

5. The car squeaks, rattles, pops, and wheezes.
   The car is ——.

How are your metaphors in the sentences above alike?

Which one of the sentences below has a metaphor and which one a simile?

1. Her skin is like marble.
   Her skin is marble.

2. The car squeaks like a dozen mice.
   This car is a nest of squeaking mice.

3. Old Rover is like a clown.
   Old Rover is all clown.

As long as you speak or read, you will use similes and metaphors. Know how words used in these two ways work to help you break the reading code.

Unit 6

TO CATCH THE HIGH WINDS

Roads Go Ever Ever On

Roads go ever ever on,
  Over rock and under tree,
By caves where never sun has shone,
  By streams that never find the sea;
Over snow by winter sown,
  And through the merry flowers of June,
Over grass and over stone,
  And under mountains in the moon.

                              J. R. R. Tolkien

The Day Jean-Pierre Went Round the World

PAUL GALLICO

Plans and an Accident

For weeks and weeks Cecile Durand had been dreaming of her family's annual two-week holiday in Paris and telling her pet guinea pig, Jean-Pierre, all about it.

Most children, when they think of a holiday, look forward to going to the country and playing in the woods or to paddling at the seashore, finding shells, and digging in the sand. But Cecile lived in the country, not far from the sea. Her father owned a flower farm near Nice, which is on the Mediterranean. Her holiday was just the

other way round. It was to journey to a city to visit her aunt, Louise Tissaud, who lived in a tall, old house in Paris.

There had been great excitement when it came to the preparations, like finding and purchasing a suitable box for Jean-Pierre. Cecile held long conversations with the guinea pig, telling him all about what Paris was like.

There was only one small thing to mar Cecile's happiness. She had thought she would be able to carry Jean-Pierre's box on her lap, or Jean-Pierre himself in her pocket, as she often did. Monsieur Durand explained it was a rule of the airlines that no animals were permitted inside the cabin. Jean-Pierre would have to go with the luggage. But since the flight to Paris was very short, he would not mind.

With this Cecile had to be satisfied. But she decided to take her own precautions. She prepared special instructions in both French and English.

Dear Anyone,

Please, this is my own guinea pig, Jean-Pierre, whom I love better than anyone, except my parents. He is an Abyssinian guinea pig. He is special. He is also magic and can understand. If he is lost or misses the plane, or anything should happen, please do not leave him in this box, but take him out and give him love.

He is used to being cuddled at night and spoken to. He drinks milk but likes it made a little warm for him, please. He eats anything from the garden, like carrots, lettuce, cabbage, radishes, pieces of marrow, bits of apple, pear, and grapes—also crumbs of bread or cake or a little cheese. But best of all he likes pomegranate seeds, if you have any. If not, it does not matter. Please do not give him too much, as he will make a pig of himself if you let him.

He should be kept warm. If he sneezes, it is not because he has caught a cold but because he is excited. His big meal is at suppertime. That is all I have to say, except do not forget to give him lots of love and hugs and do not let him be lonely.

Thank you very much,
Jean-Pierre's mother,
Cecile Durand

To this she added her address, care of Madame Tissaud. Cecile put the two letters in separate envelopes, addressed one in French and the other in English, "To Whom It May Concern." These she quietly attached to the inside of Jean-Pierre's traveling box the morning they left.

They were driven to the airport by the head gardener who looked after things during Monsieur Durand's absence.

The loudspeaker went, "Plank, plonk, plink," and a voice announced, "Passengers for Paris on Flight 1200, proceed to Gate 5. Please have your boarding cards ready."

There were many planes parked on the apron of the airport, but Cecile knew the Caravelle at once, for she had flown before. She was allowed to run ahead and up the stairs into the aircraft so she could occupy a seat by a window. Soon they were all strapped in and the sweets offered by the air hostess popped into Cecile's mouth. They taxied to the end of the runway, and with a great roar the jet plane thundered away and climbed into the sky.

In less than an hour they would be in Paris, over six hundred miles away. Cecile gave herself up to dreaming about being reunited with Jean-Pierre, safe and sound in his little traveling box somewhere in one of the luggage compartments of the giant Caravelle that was carrying them to Paris.

Only, alas, he wasn't! An airline official had seen Jean-Pierre's box sitting on the loading bay. By mistake he had picked up the box, and it was soon on a plane bound for Bangkok, Thailand!

After landing and discovering that Jean-Pierre wasn't among the baggage, it began to seem to Cecile as though she were in a nightmare. Instead of happily proceeding in a taxi to Aunt Louise's house, here they were at the airport, and no Jean-Pierre. There was much talk and confusion. No one seemed to know what had happened. Finally the chief of the airline promised to call the Durands the first moment he heard of Jean-Pierre's whereabouts.

And with that the Durands had to be satisfied. They collected their bags and took a taxi to Aunt Louise's.

A Surprise from Thailand

Cecile sat by the telephone all the next day, except when called to meals. She had slept very badly. Once, dreaming that she heard the telephone, she had leaped out of bed. There were also false alarms when friends of her aunt rang during the day.

On the third morning she had the surprise of her life. And it did not come over the telephone, after all. It arrived in a letter addressed to Cecile.

Her aunt handed it to her, saying, "My goodness, Cecile, you have friends in strange places!"

Cecile took it and ran to her father. "Look, Papa, look! I've got a letter! It's such a funny-looking one. It must be from Jean-Pierre."

There was a beautiful stamp on the envelope, showing it came from Thailand. The handwriting was small, delicate, and easy to read. In perfect French it began:

Dear Mademoiselle Durand,

I am writing to tell you of your little guinea pig, who was entrusted to my care until we were able to put him on a TWA plane for Paris, to be returned to you. You must be a very kind little girl to love your pet so much and leave such perfect instructions in case he should become lost.

He was given to me because I, too, own many pets. My name is Sirima Desjardins, and I am Siamese. My husband, Marcel, is French. He is Chief European Assistant to the Royal Forestry Department and is in charge of more than one hundred elephants.

I am sure you would be interested in my pets. I have a python (he is sweet—and also likes to drink warm milk) and a dwarf deer, a ruffed lemur who would make you laugh, he looks so funny, and a honey bear. Jean-Pierre visited my python and played with the lemur. I also have my favorite elephant on which I ride.

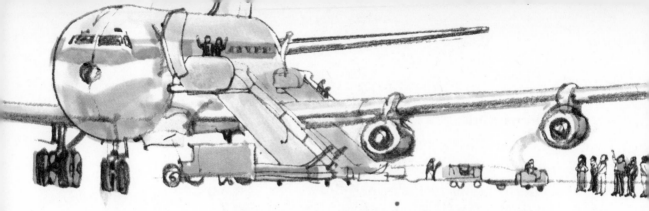

Her name is Nang-Hiaw, which means "Old Wrinkled-Skin," and indeed her gray hide looks like the map of a thousand rivers.

Yesterday morning, after I fed Jean-Pierre, I took him on Nang-Hiaw (for some twenty of my husband's elephants are working on the edge of the airport here), and I think he liked it. I held him tightly to my cheek all the time. He wasn't frightened even when Nang touched him with the sensitive tip of her trunk. He only wrinkled up his nose and sneezed.

When we returned to the airport, the king and queen of our country had just flown in from the north, and Jean-Pierre saw them both. As they came down the steps from the airplane, we all cheered, and Nang-Hiaw saluted them with her trunk. They waved to us and to Jean-Pierre, too.

Then I returned Jean-Pierre to the director of the airport, who put him aboard a TWA airliner bound for Paris. Perhaps you will have him back safe in your arms even before this letter arrives. But I thought you would like to know how he spent his time in our lovely country.

Wishing him a safe journey and a happy arrival,

Yours in distant friendship,
Sirima Desjardins

A Circus Guinea Pig

But Jean-Pierre's adventures weren't over. Because of bad weather and other complications, instead of going to Paris, he landed in Australia! A few days after the letter from Thailand, the phone rang, and Cecile was very surprised when she picked it up and an operator said, "Hello, Mademoiselle Cecile Durand on the line? Go ahead, Sydney."

A man said in French: "Hello, Cecile, can you hear me?"

Cecile replied that she could, for it was just as plain as if it were from across the street.

"This is Monsieur Flippo speaking. Perhaps you have never heard of me, but I am a famous circus clown. I have your little guinea pig, Jean-Pierre, right here with me, safe and sound.

"When Jean-Pierre arrived in Sydney, nobody knew where he was from or where he was going or what to do with him. But when they read your clever little letter inside the cage, they knew that someone would have to look after him until they found out. And who do you think they went to? Old Monsieur Flippo, the circus clown, with his educated kangaroos and his trained pigs.

"Our circus is playing in an amusement park not far from the airport. So they sent the little fellow over to me. I fed him and gave him his warm milk, and then, where do you think he spent the night?"

"Where?" Cecile asked, prepared for almost anything but certainly not for what he said next.

"In Angelique! Angelique is one of my kangaroos. You see, my Angelique's baby died, and she was unhappy. Jean-Pierre was lonely and cold, so that's exactly where I tucked him. They got on fine. And do you know what happened the next day?"

Cecile was almost breathless with excitement by now but managed to say, "No, what?"

"He looked so funny, the guinea pig, with his head sticking out of Angelique's pouch, that I put him in the act."

"You mean Jean-Pierre was in the circus!" Cecile gasped.

"Right! He was a sensation! Three thousand children laughed, cheered, and clapped when I took him out of Angelique's pouch and showed him to them. (I shall have to get a guinea pig of my own.) Oh, he was marvelous! Such stage presence! Like an old trouper. Well, then, the next day they came from the airport to say that they had found out where he belonged and that he must go home. They said they would put a call through to you so I could tell you all about it. If you like, you can speak to him, Cecile."

"Oh, Jean-Pierre, Jean-Pierre, Jean-Pierre!" Cecile cried into the telephone. "Jean-Pierre, can you hear me?"

For a moment there was a silence from the other end of the line, and then—could it be possible? She heard a faint little chirrup, followed by the tiniest noise of small teeth clicking together. They were actually Jean-Pierre noises that Cecile knew so well. And then, best and most wonderful of all, in quick succession came three small but unmistakable Jean-Pierre sneezes.

"There you are!" It was Monsieur Flippo again. "He said hello to you. Tonight he will sleep in Angelique for the last time, and early tomorrow, that's Monday morning, he is starting his journey back home to you. How's that?"

"Oh, thank you, thank you, thank you, Monsieur Flippo!" said Cecile.

Then there was a click at the other end of the line, and it was over.

The next news Cecile received of Jean-Pierre was this cablegram.

YOUR GUINEA PIG JEAN-PIERRE STOPPED OFF
HERE INTERNATIONAL AIRPORT HONOLULU EN
ROUTE PARIS VIA SAN FRANCISCO NEW YORK
STOP IN ADDITION TO THINGS YOU WROTE HE
LIKED TO EAT HE ALSO GOES FOR PINEAPPLE
PAPAYA COCONUT BREADFRUIT YAMS MALAY
AND CUSTARD APPLES AVOCADOS POI MANGOES
GUAVA POHA TAMARIND PASSION FRUIT LICHEE
MACADAMIA NUTS AND SUGARCANE ALL
PRODUCTS HAWAIIAN ISLANDS STOP HE ENJOYED
SOME OF EACH ONLY HOPE NOT GIVE HIM
STOMACHACHE STOP DEPARTED HERE OKAY
GOOD WISHES SAFE ARRIVAL Y A CHIN TRAFFIC
SUPERINTENDENT INTERNATIONAL AIRPORT
HONOLULU

If Jean-Pierre could be said to have a fault, it was that he was a bit greedy. If allowed, he would eat until his sides swelled out and one was afraid he would burst.

Unhappily he did get a bad stomachache. When he finally arrived in New York, his nose was hot. His eyes were watery. He huddled in a corner of his cage, shivering miserably. No one knew what to do. Then the airport officials remembered a Professor Jones, who had hundreds of guinea pigs. If there was one man who knew all about what might be the matter, it was this professor.

Hurried phone calls were made. Then, in a special ambulance with police escort, Jean-Pierre was rushed to the laboratory of Professor Jones in downtown New York. Fortunately Cecile knew nothing of this.

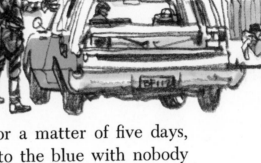

And so once more, for a matter of five days, Jean-Pierre vanished into the blue with nobody able to trace hide nor hair of him.

Strange to say, Cecile took even this calmly and occupied herself with enjoying the rest of her holiday. For she was certain that a guinea pig who was magic enough to telephone her from Australia would come safely home to her.

And then the day for the Durands' return to the south of France was at hand. The holiday was over. They were all packed and ready to leave for the plane back to Nice. Aunt Louise came to the cab to see them off and listened to the final instructions from Cecile as to exactly what to do and how to look after Jean-Pierre, should he arrive after they had departed.

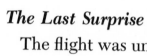

The Last Surprise

The flight was uneventful. The Caravelle made its gentle landing on the airstrip. People arose and made their way out through the rear of the plane and down the stairs. The Durands were the last ones off.

At the same time a big Pan American four-engined Boeing jet had landed just before them. The passengers had already left it, and the luggage was being unloaded. But four officials were standing uneasily by one compartment door that had not been opened.

Out from the airport building came a procession of three big cars. They drove up and came to a halt beside the huge airplane.

From the first car stepped an important-looking man in civilian clothes. With him were four others in uniform, covered with gold braid. From the second car came two men who were doctors, for they carried little black bags. And from the third car marched three airline hostesses and a nurse.

"Goodness," said Monsieur Durand, "there must be someone very important and very ill aboard that plane."

Cecile said, "Oh, Papa, let's stay and watch a moment!"

As the important-looking man in civilian clothes approached the plane, the four attendants waiting there snapped to attention. The doctors stepped up closer. The hostesses and the nurse stood ready. The man motioned for the compartment door to be opened. Up it flew. From inside it a hand passed out—a small box—well, a kind of cage. It had so many stickers on it, the wood could hardly be seen, but at one end was a square of wire mesh, and poking his pink, healthy nose up against it was . . .

"Jean-Pierre! Jean-Pierre!" screamed Cecile at the top of her lungs. She ran to the plane and threw her arms about the little box, hugging it to her.

"Jean-Pierre, you've come back to me! I knew you would!" She opened the cage, reached inside, and took him out. The guinea pig was overcome with joy at being back with Cecile again. He squealed, clicked, chirruped, shrieked, and sneezed all at the same time, and then snuffled his way into her neck.

The important-looking man went over to Monsieur and Madame Durand and asked, "Are you Monsieur Durand, and is this Cecile?"

"Yes, of course," said Monsieur Durand. "Would you like to see my passport to prove it?"

"No, no," said the man, "take the animal. They were so nervous in New York, they put him on the wrong plane again, the one that flies directly from New York to Nice. But we were told about the mistake and were going to send him on to Paris. You're lucky to have Jean-Pierre back."

Cecile held Jean-Pierre up in her two hands and looked into his golden-yellow eyes and cried, "Oh, Jean-Pierre, no other girl has ever had such a splendid guinea pig!"

Jean-Pierre sneezed happily six times in a row to celebrate the happy end to his adventures.

Reflections

1. On a map or a globe, trace Jean-Pierre's route around the world. Approximately how many miles did he travel?

2. Why was it fortunate that Cecile wrote her instructions in both French and English? What do you think might have happened to Jean-Pierre if Cecile had put just her name and address on his cage?

3. What animals did Sirima Desjardins have as pets? Which animal would you most want to have as a pet? Give reasons for your answer.

4. Since no punctuation is used in cablegrams or telegrams, how is the end of a sentence indicated?

5. Suppose Jean-Pierre were entrusted to your care for a day. Write a letter to Cecile, telling her how you cared for him.

International Mail

H. ALEXANDER FRAENKEL

How easy it is to mail a letter to almost anywhere! Drop an addressed and stamped envelope
into a mailbox, and, as if by a miracle, it reaches
its destination. But it has taken more than two
thousand years for a system that anyone can use
to be developed.

Back in 559 B.C., in Persia, only a lucky few
enjoyed the postal system that King Cyrus set up.
He stationed riders a day apart throughout his
kingdom, and messages were relayed from rider
to rider. Sometimes very private messages were
written on a man's scalp. When his hair grew
back, he was sent on his postal errand. When he
reached his destination, his head was shaved once
more so that the message he carried could be
read.

During the next 2,200 years, more modern postal systems were developed in many parts of the world. By the 1830's most countries of Europe had methods of getting letters from one place to another. But mailing letters still was not easy. Each country had different rules. Sometimes the sender had to pay a fee to get his letter sent, and sometimes the receiver had to pay if he wanted the letter. Rates varied, and many people could not afford to post letters.

An English postmaster named Rowland Hill thought that everyone should enjoy inexpensive mail service. In 1840 he set a single postal rate when he designed the first prepaid postage stamp.

Thanks to the one-penny stamp, people could send mail more easily. But still they had trouble in sending mail beyond the borders of their own country. International mail was highly taxed because every nation that a letter passed through wanted payment to cover the costs of handling the mail. Unless the rate was reduced, many people would not be able to afford international mail service.

In 1874 representatives from the United States and twenty-one other countries met in Berne, Switzerland, to try to solve the problems of the high rates. At first disagreement prevailed. Small countries argued to keep taxes high. They insisted that they had to handle more letters from larger countries than they sent out. They said that for

this reason postal services cost them more. Only high taxes could cover their expenses. Other countries argued that as many letters were sent out of small countries as passed through. Everyone present was finally convinced that the costs of handling mail were about the same for each country, large or small. With this and other disagreements ironed out, the attending nations formed the General Postal Union.

The Union, later called the Universal Postal Union, made some rules that all could follow. Every member nation promised to transport the mail of every other member nation. The rates to be charged for mail of different kinds would be set up by the Union. The sender of a letter would prepay the charges for the letter by buying a stamp, just as he did for domestic mail. The Union would also settle any disagreements which might arise between its members.

Today the Universal Postal Union numbers about 125 members. Each nation takes its membership seriously. If one country should refuse to transport the mail of another country, all the members could refuse to handle the mail of that nation. But there have been very few disagreements between members, and these have been settled in a friendly way.

Progress often means growth. At first there was only the English one-penny stamp. Today, because almost every country in the world produces stamps, there are hundreds of thousands of different stamps. On the stamps are pictured a very wide range of subjects—people, plants, animals, paintings, sporting events, buildings, spaceships, organizations, bridges, maps, and airplanes—to mention a few. Because of this great variety of stamps—and because of the great beauty of many of them—stamp collecting has become a universal hobby.

But also because of the great variety and number of stamps, a collection should be limited to certain fields. It is best to collect stamps from only one or a few countries or only those that are devoted to a certain subject. Otherwise, it would be an impossible task to have a meaningful collection. Look at the next two pages to see what a sample collection might look like.

Reflections

1. How many years ago was the year 559 B.C.?
2. What would the Universal Postal Union do if a country refused to transport international mail?
3. Look up the Pony Express in an encyclopedia. How did this American postal system resemble the one that King Cyrus set up?
4. What do you think would happen to everyday life and commerce if there were no mail services?
5. If you could design a new U.S. stamp, what would the stamp look like? In what category would it be? Explain the reasons for your choice.
6. What things might a person learn about other countries just from collecting foreign stamps?

CHILDREN

Monaco

Maldive Islands

GREAT MEN

United States

Gambia

SPORTS

Japan

Dominican Republic

NATURE

Czechoslovakia   Austria

RED CROSS

Israel

German Democratic Republic

SPACE

England

Nigeria

Wilbur Wright and
Orville Wright

ROSEMARY and STEPHEN VINCENT BENÉT

Said Orville Wright to Wilbur Wright,
"These birds are very trying.
I'm sick of hearing them cheep-cheep
About the fun of flying.
A bird has feathers, it is true.
That much I freely grant.
But, must that stop us, W?"
Said Wilbur Wright, "It shan't."

And so they built a glider, first,
And then they built another.
—There never were two brothers more
Devoted to each other.
They ran a dusty little shop
For bicycle-repairing,
And bought each other soda-pop
And praised each other's daring.

They glided here, they glided there,
They sometimes skinned their noses,
—For learning how to rule the air
Was not a bed of roses—
But each would murmur, afterward,
While patching up his bro.
"Are we discouraged, W?"
"Of course we are not, O!"

436

And finally, at Kitty Hawk
In Nineteen-Three (let's cheer it!),
The first real airplane really flew.
With Orville there to steer it!
—And kingdoms may forget their kings
And dogs forget their bites,
But, not till Man forgets his wings,
Will men forget the Wrights.

The Would-Be Cowboy

ILSE KLEBERGER

Where the Indians Live

"What are the names of the German tributaries of the Danube?" asked Ingeborg.

Jan drawled in a bored voice, "Iller, Lech, Isar, Inn, thingummy, Nab, and Regen."

"What's thingummy?" Ingeborg asked her brother.

Jan yawned. "I've forgotten."

"But you must remember. When your teacher asks you tomorrow and you don't know, you'll get a bad mark again. Look at your atlas and find the rivers for yourself."

Unwillingly Jan took the atlas out of his satchel. When Ingeborg came back a quarter of an hour later, he was studying a map with glowing eyes.

"Have you found them?"

"Yes, here's Oklahoma and here are the Rocky Mountains, where the big reservations are."

"What sort of reservations? I thought you were looking for the tributaries of the Danube."

"Oh, I don't care a button about the Danube. I'm looking for the territories where the Indians live in America. Look here."

Ingeborg pushed the atlas aside and scornfully said, "And I don't care a button about your Indians, and I don't suppose your teacher does either. If you go on being so lazy and learning nothing, you'll stay in the same class *again*."

Jan looked tearful. "Why should I learn all that? I want to go to America and be a cowboy," he sobbed.

"A fine cowboy you'd make, crying like a girl!" jeered Ingeborg and left the room, slamming the door after her. She went to join her mother and her grandmother, Oma.

Jan dried his tears. She was right; cowboys shouldn't cry. But she was all wrong about cowboys needing to know the names of the tributaries of the Danube. He tucked a book called *As Cabin Boy to America* under his arm and withdrew to the goat shed, where no one would disturb him until the evening milking. He sat on a stool and settled down to read.

Suddenly they sighted land. It was America! The little cabin boy's heart beat faster. Now he would see the country where the cowboys and the Indians lived, the country of skyscrapers and Niagara Falls.

Jan looked up from his book and gazed thoughtfully at the goat, which was rubbing against his leg. If only *he* were a cabin boy! But why not?

A Traveling Companion

Early on Sunday morning Jan dressed quickly, packed his bag, and sneaked out of the house. He did not breathe freely until he got on the train. There he took a seat by the window and looked out. When the train was on its way and the roofs of the village had disappeared, his heart felt heavy. He decided he would come home one day, when he had become rich or famous in America, or perhaps both. Then he would bring his mother a new dress and his father a watch and for his grandmother, Oma . . .

"Good morning!" said Oma cheerfully, sitting down opposite him.

Jan blinked, but there was nothing wrong with his eyesight. Oma was really there, in her black dress with the lilac straw hat on her head. In her right hand was the bird cage with Paul, the parrot, prattling gaily. On her left arm were her handbag and umbrella.

"Where . . . where are you going?" stammered Jan.

"To America," Oma replied.

"America?" Jan gasped for breath. "You want to go to America?"

"Yes, why not?" Oma said. "I've always wanted to go to America. I wanted to go once a long time ago when I was a little girl, but then I got chicken pox, and after that something else always stopped me. When I heard yesterday that you wanted to go to America, I decided to come with you."

Jan stared out of the window in dismay.

"Or don't you like the idea?" asked Oma.

"Oh, yes," answered Jan quickly.

"Well then, everything's all right." Oma took out her knitting, and soon the needles were clicking. She said nothing more.

"How are you going to get to America?" asked Jan timidly.

"Just like you," answered Oma.

"But you can't be a cabin boy!"

"I will peel potatoes in the galley and earn my passage that way," Oma said.

"And what will you do when we finally get to America?"

441

"Perhaps I can work as a cook on the ranch where you're a cowboy."

"Then you could make me macaroni pudding sometimes."

"Of course."

Jan began to be enthusiastic about the idea of Oma traveling to America with him.

"Eberbach—all change!" shouted the guard. Oma jumped up and took her handbag, the umbrella, and Paul's cage.

"Perhaps you would carry my suitcase."

Jan took the suitcase off the rack and followed her out of the train. Outside, in front of the station, they looked at each other.

"Now what?" asked Oma.

"I was going to hitchhike," said Jan.

"All right, let's hitchhike."

They stood on the edge of the broad road. The first three cars Jan tried to stop went racing past.

They waited for half an hour without success.

"I guess we'll have to walk," said Oma.

They set off, but after a few steps Oma stopped. "Are we going the right way?"

Jan shrugged his shoulders uncertainly.

"Where is Hamburg?" asked Oma.

"In—in the north," stammered Jan.

"Northeast or northwest? I'm afraid I was very bad in geography at school."

"Me, too," said Jan in a small voice.

Paul, who had recovered from the shock of the railway trip, shook his feathers and called, "Northwest."

"Paul says northwest," said Oma. "But which way is northwest?"

Jan felt that he couldn't go on making a fool of himself, so he pointed straight ahead.

Oma marched firmly off, singing, "Oh, you'll take the high road . . ."

Jan tried to join in, but soon lost his breath. His Sunday shoes hurt, and Oma's suitcase seemed to grow heavier and heavier.

"What have you got in your suitcase?" he asked.

"Is it too heavy for you?" Oma asked. "There are only a few odds and ends in it. A nightdress, toothbrush, soap, a cookbook, some birdseed, and my roller skates." Oma said that roller-skating kept her young. "That's all. Do you want me to carry it instead?"

"No, no, it's quite light," Jan assured her quickly.

"And what did you pack?"

"My Indian headdress, my water pistol, my comic, a packet of chewing gum, a clothesline . . ." Jan glanced at Oma. "I need a lasso, you see."

"Of course, you need a lasso. And what about some soap and your toothbrush?"

"Oh, I forgot all about them."

Oma nodded her head. "That's easily done. You can borrow my soap, and the Indians clean their teeth with twigs, so I read in a book."

Jan was astonished that Oma knew anything about Indians. His respect for her increased enormously. Now he was really glad that she wanted to come to America with him.

Oma and the Bull

It had grown very hot. Jan was sweating. His right arm was numb, and he felt that a blister was forming on his left heel. Yet Oma walked on, still cool and collected. Jan did not want to be the first to suggest a rest.

All at once Oma said, "Now we'll have lunch."

"Where shall we get the food?" asked Jan in astonishment.

"In here." Oma slapped her handbag.

Jan felt much happier. Oma was sure to have something good in her bag, perhaps cakes or sandwiches or even potato salad. His mouth watered at the thought.

Oma looked around for a shady spot. There was a chestnut tree growing on a hill in the middle of a meadow in which two cows and a bull were grazing. Oma began to climb through the barbed wire fence.

"What about the bull?" asked Jan.

"If we leave him in peace, he'll leave us alone," said Oma, stumping across the meadow towards the hill. She was right. The bull and the cows took no notice of them. They sat down in the shade. Oma took a paper bag of birdseed out of her handbag and filled Paul's dish. Then she drew out a napkin and spread it over her knees. Next she took a thermos bottle and a small package out of the bag. Jan watched her greedily. His stomach was rumbling. Next she unpacked a few biscuits.

"What do you think of this?" she asked proudly. "It's real, genuine ship's biscuit, the sort we'll have to eat if our ship is in distress and drifts about for weeks without a rudder. When all the provisions are eaten up, there's always ship's biscuit. It's a good idea for us to get used to the taste."

Jan was rather disappointed. But a cabin boy couldn't be fussy. He began to chew. The biscuit was very hard.

"Tastes a bit like mothballs."

Oma nodded. "Yes, they have been lying next to the mothballs in the drawer for a couple of years, but that's just as it should be. Ship's biscuit always tastes of something else, tar or salt water or shoe polish."

"What's in the thermos bottle?" asked Jan hopefully.

"Water," replied Oma.

Jan drank a little. It was lukewarm and did not taste very good. When his hunger and thirst were barely satisfied, he lay down in the grass. Oma chewed her biscuit with enjoyment and took a sip from the flask. Then she got out her knitting and began to knit. As Oma sang to herself, Jan read his comic.

When he began to fumble in his own bag, Oma borrowed his comic and arranged it on her knee so that she could read while she went on with her knitting. Soon she was so deep in what she was reading that she did not notice that Jan was unraveling the clothesline. Behind them the bull was grazing peacefully.

In America Jan would have to rope lots of wild bulls with his lasso. He felt lucky to be able to practice here! He made a noose and sauntered towards the bull, which took no notice of him. Jan threw the rope, standing a little behind so that the bull could not see him. He wanted to rope the horns and jerk the bull's head backwards, but his throw fell short. Next Jan tried from the side, and this time the bull turned its head and glared at him. Jan threw the lasso again. It touched a horn, but slid down and hit the bull sharply on the nose. The bull stretched and gave a bellow that sent shivers down Jan's spine.

"Oma," he shouted, "Oma!" and ran as fast as his legs could carry him to the tree where Oma was knitting. Behind him he could hear the bull thudding along and snorting. When Oma saw them both coming, she threw knitting and comic aside and grasped her umbrella. As Jan reached her, she opened the umbrella and pointed it at the bull.

"Shoo, shoo, go away, you brute!" she cried.

The animal stopped short. As soon as he moved again, Oma shut the umbrella and then opened it quickly. The confused bull watched this strange game rather nervously.

"Take the luggage," whispered Oma.

Jan grabbed Paul's cage, Oma's suitcase and handbag, and his own bag. As Oma kept opening and shutting the umbrella in the direction of the bull, they retreated.

They were panting as they squeezed through the fence at last. With a furious bellow the bull suddenly charged the fence. When he found the way barred, he rushed back to the tree. He trampled Oma's knitting and the comic, which had been left behind, into the ground. Jan and Oma watched with horror. He could so easily have been trampling *them!*

"Ugh!" Oma said. "We came out of it all right that time. But life is full of dangers. I'm sure it would be best if we went back home again now, before we go any farther. I must fetch some more knitting. What do you think?"

Jan could not speak. The shock had taken his voice away. He only nodded.

As they were walking down the road side by side, Oma said, "I think we'll postpone our journey for a while. Maybe it would be better if we learned some more geography and English first."

Jan's heart suddenly felt much lighter. Only one thing worried him—what would they say to him at home?

To his surprise no one said anything. They arrived just before supper, and the table was already set. Mother asked a strange question: "Well, did you enjoy yourselves?"

No one noticed that Jan was quiet during the meal because his brother and sisters made so much noise. He was very tired and went to bed right afterwards. When he was lying stretched out on the soft mattress, he thought with a shudder of where he might be sleeping now if Oma had not had the idea of coming home.

Oma was helping Mother do the dishes.

"Did you have a nice excursion?" asked Mother.

Oma nodded. "Please, will you give me back the note I left on the table for you this morning? There is something on the back of it that I want."

Mother took a piece of paper out of her apron pocket and handed it to Oma. It said, "I'm going out for the day with Jan. We'll be back in time for supper. Oma."

Reflections

1. What is a *tributary?* What rivers in the United States have tributaries? Name some of them.

2. How did Jan prepare for his trip and future life in America? Compare his preparations with Oma's. Do you think Oma was well prepared for the kind of journey she was taking? Explain.

3. Why do you think faraway places often seem so desirable? What lands have you wished you could live in? How do you think you might be able to get there?

4. When Jan and Oma returned, why wasn't Jan scolded for running away?

5. What "lessons" do you think Jan learned from his day's outing? How would you like to have someone like Oma as a teacher? Explain your answer.

Night Train
ADRIEN STOUTENBURG

A train at night
is yellow lights running
across the darkness
with a sound of many
black doors slamming
in a long hall,
one after another,
but softer,
and softer,
until the last one
whispers
and closes.

Navigation

HAL HELLMAN

Every time you go from one place to another, you are navigating. Whether you go to the store around the corner or to your friend's house on the other side of town, you still have to find your way there.

Perhaps the first time you went to the store, someone made a simple map for you. It might have showed that you had to turn right when you came out of the house. Then you had to go five blocks to the church and turn right again. And finally you had to look for the big white house on your right. The store was just after that.

We call objects like the church and the big white house *landmarks*. They "mark the land" and tell you exactly where you are at any moment.

A ship's captain doesn't have landmarks like houses and churches and streets to mark his way. Yet, surprisingly, the simplest and oldest method of navigation on water did depend on landmarks.

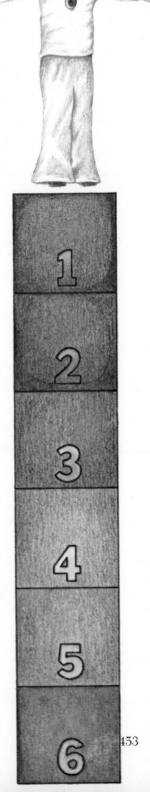

For example, a Roman galley setting out from Rome's port of Ostia for Alexandria, Egypt, two thousand years ago sailed along the Italian shore from Ostia to Sicily. Then it sailed west along Sicily to Africa, and finally it sailed east along the African coast to Alexandria. Thus, the navigator was rarely out of sight of land and could use landmarks all the way.

This type of sailing has been given the official name of *pilotage,* but was better known as "hugging the shore." It was a slow and dangerous way of navigating. The ship could easily run onto rocks, sailing so close to the land.

In good weather some of the braver and more capable mariners sometimes took shortcuts out of sight of land. When the captain of the vessel felt he was nearing land, he would command that *soundings* be taken to find the depth of the water. A weighted line was dropped over the side until it hit bottom. Then the line was measured in fathoms. A *fathom* is six feet, the approximate span of a man's outstretched arms.

Some early mariners had to learn to navigate without the use of landmarks. The Polynesians, for example, are a people who live on groups of islands that are spread across a large part of the South Pacific Ocean. Often they found their way across hundreds of miles of open sea without modern navigational tools. At least two of their earliest recorded voyages covered over a thousand miles of sea—without any landmarks. How did they find their way across that giant ocean?

In 1947 six men decided to find out if the Polynesians could have found their way from South America to the islands in the Pacific. They sailed on a log raft called the *Kon-Tiki* from the coast of Peru in South America to a small island in Polynesia—more than four thousand miles away. The *Kon-Tiki* was a copy of the rafts which were used by certain South Americans many hundreds of years ago.

The men on the *Kon-Tiki* discovered that much of the work of propelling the raft was done by the Humboldt Current. This current, which is like a river in the ocean, flows along the west coast of South America. Then it turns due west across the Pacific Ocean. Once the *Kon-Tiki* had picked up the current, it rode it clear across the ocean.

Few mariners can depend on currents for power and navigation. For one thing, a current cannot tell mariners exactly how far it has carried them and in what direction. In Columbus's time, most mariners depended on landmark sailing and another process, called *dead reckoning*, to determine speed and direction. Dead reckoning is a kind of guessing game—at which Columbus was a master. The navigator would guess how fast he was going, for there were no speedometers on board his ship to tell him his speed. Then he would multiply this figure by the length of time he had traveled. He could figure out, for example, that if he had been at sea for eight hours, and he had sailed five miles every hour, he must have gone forty miles (five times eight). He knew his course pretty well, so he put a small circle on his chart to indicate where he thought he was at that moment.

There was an even older method the mariner could use to help him navigate—especially during a long voyage at sea. This method relied on the position of the sun and stars in the sky.

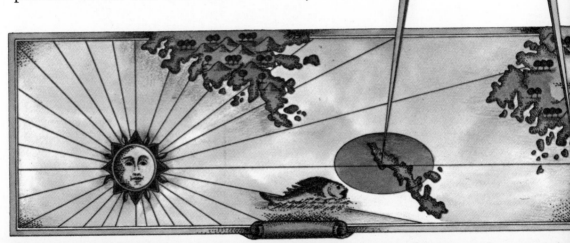

Ancient man noticed that the sun always went down in about the same place and always came up from about the same place. So even if he were traveling in a strange land, he could still use the sun as a kind of landmark. If he wanted to travel due west, for instance, all he had to do was keep the sun at his back in the morning and head toward it in the afternoon.

It didn't take ancient man long to observe that stars seemed to rise and set pretty much as the sun did, although not at the same time. After a

while, he gave names to some of the stars and got to know which ones rose and set over the places he wanted to travel to.

Early man noticed something else, too. Not all stars rose and set. Some just seemed to circle around in the sky. And at the center of these circling stars was one which seemed to be pinned to the sky and to be hanging right over the North Pole. The reason for this, as we now know, is that the axis, or pole around which the earth spins, points almost exactly at that star. So it is called the Pole Star, Polaris, or the North Star. To travel west by night, it is only necessary to keep the North Star over your right shoulder.

Today's mariners, even with their modern equipment, still rely on landmarks, water currents, and the sky to direct them over vast stretches of water. However, navigating today is no longer a guessing game, but an exact science. It has developed to such a point that a captain can guide a submarine underwater and be able to surface it exactly at the North Pole.

Reflections

1. What is a *landmark?* What outstanding landmarks are there in your area?

2. Suppose a stranger who could not read street signs wanted to go from your school to the public library at 4:30 P.M. Using landmarks, what directions would you give him?

3. Trace the probable path for a voyage from Ostia, Italy, to Alexandria, Egypt, two thousand years ago. Then trace the probable route for the same voyage today.

4. What is *dead reckoning?* How might ocean currents, such as the Humboldt Current and the Gulf Stream, affect a captain's estimate of his present position?

5. Using the sun, how would you tell in which direction your classroom faces?

He Did It

MARY BRITTON MILLER

Said the dangerous sea,
"You'll not conquer me,
Try as hard as you can.
You are not a whale,
You are not a shark—
You cannot walk
On the waves, young man."

So he made a boat
That was able to float.
"Ho, ho!" said his foe,
"It floats all right
And it's watertight,
But you can't make it go."
"Oh yes I can,"
Replied the young man.
And he made some oars
And learned how to row.

When the sea saw
The boats and the oars
And all the rowers,
He said, "Young man,
They make a fine show,
But what will you do
When they venture out
Where the deep sea swells
Can take them up
And toss them about
Like cockleshells?"

"You can't stump me,"
Said the bright young man,
And cut down a tree
And made a tall mast
And rigged it with sails
To catch the high winds
And weather the gales.

When the ships set out
With their sails unfurled
To cross the Atlantic
And discover the world,
The sea looked them over
From stern to stem
And when he saw,
With considerable awe,
That Columbus himself
Was on one of them,
He said, with a show
Of humility,
"I admit, young man,
You have conquered me."

The Sailmaker and the Sea Captain

ESTHER M. DOUTY

The early morning sun splashed brightly through the window. James Forten could barely see the outline of the mainsail he had chalked on the floor of the sail loft.

It was the spring of 1793. Young James had come a long way. The son of a sailmaker, James had been one of the first Negro children in Philadelphia to attend school at a time when few schools accepted black children. When he was fifteen, during the American Revolution, James signed on a privateer called the *Royal Louis* as a powder boy. The ship was captured by the British, and James found himself held a prisoner on the prison ship *Jersey* for seven months.

When James was seventeen, he signed on another ship bound for England. There he worked for a shipping company as a stevedore. In the English harbors he saw the slave ships which transported kidnaped Africans to America. He met and became friendly with men who deeply believed that this evil practice should be fought.

Returning to Philadelphia a few years later, James brought with him a firm belief that slavery must be done away with and that free Negroes had a right to have first-class citizenship.

In the next two years James rose from apprentice to foreman in one of the largest sail lofts in Philadelphia. This was a record few twenty-two-year-olds could match.

There were forty sailmakers in the loft, half of whom were white, and half Negroes. Only James could cut sails all day, stopping only for lunch. It was James, too, who most quickly grasped the principles of sailmaking. He could take a sail from the drawing stage to the great canvasses, all sewn and roped and ready to be bent (fastened) to the mast. No wonder that his employer praised him for his "skill, energy, and good conduct."

Now, as James was leaving the loft to do an errand at the waterfront, he noticed a ship anchored near the public landing. He stopped short and stared. There was nothing unusual about the ship. It was a smallish schooner named *Mary*, of Westport, Massachusetts, and it reeked of whale oil and bone. But on the deck he could see the captain and the crew. All were Negroes.

Before nightfall James had managed to meet the captain, Paul Cuffe. Captain Cuffe was a tall, broad, kindly looking man of thirty-four. The captain had just returned from a successful whaling trip to Newfoundland. With him was his cargo of whale oil and bone that he wished to sell in Philadelphia.

During the next few days the two men saw much of each other. Although the New England sea captain was modest, James learned his story.

Paul Cuffe's father was a poor farmer who had been born in Africa. He had been brought as a slave to Massachusetts. In time he worked out his purchase price and bought his freedom. Paul's father and mother moved to Cutterhunk Island, where they raised their family.

At thirteen Paul was barely able to read and write. But he kept at his studies, teaching himself and occasionally getting help from white friends on the mainland. Since he lived in a region that made its living mostly from the sea, he decided to learn the art of navigation.

In 1775, when he was sixteen, Paul became a seaman on a whaling vessel. On his third voyage, made at the height of the American Revolution, he was captured by the British and was imprisoned for three months.

After his release he decided to build and sail his own boat, and he spent every spare minute studying arithmetic and navigation. At first he

was unlucky. He built and sailed two boats, but both were attacked and stolen by pirates. But then his luck changed, and soon he was making a nice profit from his ventures. Cuffe finally had enough money to be able to build the forty-two-ton schooner *Mary,* which lay now at the Philadelphia wharf.

Sailmaker Forten was particularly interested in Captain Cuffe's account of what had happened on the *Mary*'s first voyage. The schooner, accompanied by two boats, and with a crew of ten men—all Negroes and Indians—had gone on a whaling expedition to the whaling grounds off Newfoundland. When they reached the Strait of Belle Isle, Cuffe found four other whaling ships already there. They were fully equipped with boats and harpoons.

The usual custom was for whaling ships to share their equipment. But these four New England captains grew angry and tried to drive the *Mary* away. They thought that Cuffe and the *Mary*'s crewmen were not experienced whalers and that the vessel did not have proper equipment.

Captain Cuffe decided that he and his crew would go it alone. His harpooning activities alarmed the other whalers. They seemed to fear that Cuffe's group would drive the whales away. But when Cuffe's group caught its first whale, the other captains changed their minds and decided to share their equipment and to include the *Mary* in the whale hunts. Seven whales were taken, six of them by the crew of the *Mary*—and two of these harpooned by Cuffe himself!

James Forten and Paul Cuffe admired each other at once, and the two men became good friends. Both men became important figures in the American Negro's struggle for equal opportunity, but each in a different way.

Paul Cuffe, gaining wealth as a very successful sea captain, believed that free American Negroes could find greater opportunity in Africa, the continent of their ancestors. At his own expense, he took thirty-eight free Negroes on his ship to Africa. He had hoped to transport many, many more, but he died before he could make another voyage. At the time of his death, there were two thousand people waiting for Cuffe to take them to Africa.

James Forten, too, wanted to fight for Negro rights, but he could not be convinced that American Negroes, many of whose families had been in this country for generations, should have to go to Africa to find happiness. Instead, he devoted his efforts and his considerable fortune to changing the lives of Negroes around him. He held classes where Negro children, who were not legally permitted to go to school, could learn to read and write; he hid runaway slaves in his home; he donated vast sums of money to *The Liberator*, the famous newspaper dedicated to the idea of Negro freedom; and in countless other ways, Forten used his wealth and influence to make conditions better for American Negroes.

James Forten and Paul Cuffe each came to believe in a different course of action for Negroes to follow in their search for equality and fair treatment. But at their first meeting they agreed on one thing. Both men felt that they must "cultivate a love to all mankind."

Reflections

1. What is an *apprentice?* What is a *foreman?* How long did it take James Forten to rise from apprentice to foreman?

2. Why did the New England captains at first want to drive the *Mary* away? What made them change their minds?

3. Suppose Paul Cuffe and his crew really had been inexperienced and ill-equipped. Do you think the New England captains would have been right in refusing to cooperate? Be prepared to take either side of the argument.

4. How did Paul Cuffe and James Forten differ in their ideas of what was best for American Negroes? How did each man try to carry out his ideas?

5. If James Forten and Paul Cuffe were alive today, what might each be doing in the struggle for equal opportunity? Be sure to consider each man's character and actions in preparing your answer.

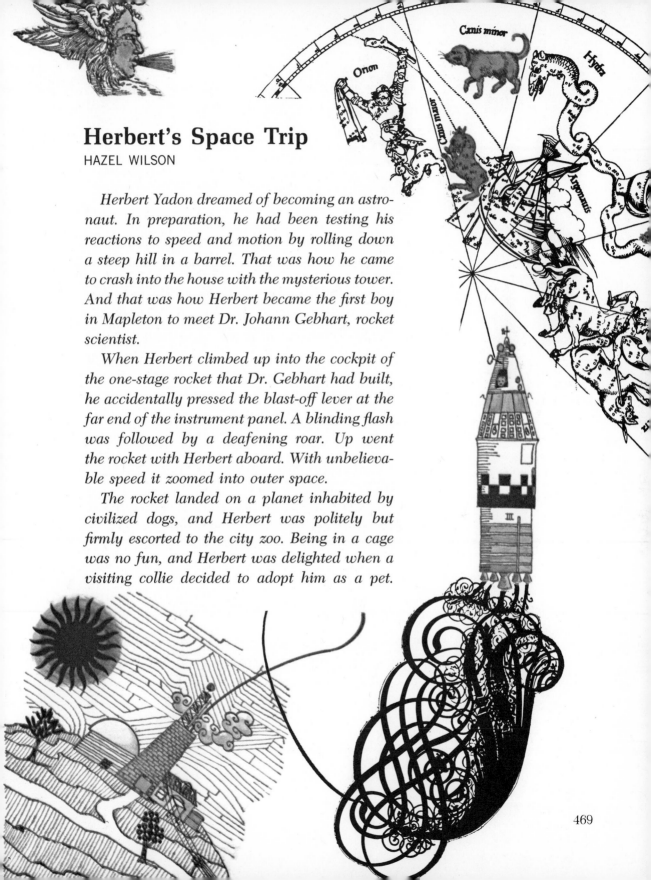

Herbert's Space Trip

HAZEL WILSON

Herbert Yadon dreamed of becoming an astronaut. In preparation, he had been testing his reactions to speed and motion by rolling down a steep hill in a barrel. That was how he came to crash into the house with the mysterious tower. And that was how Herbert became the first boy in Mapleton to meet Dr. Johann Gebhart, rocket scientist.

When Herbert climbed up into the cockpit of the one-stage rocket that Dr. Gebhart had built, he accidentally pressed the blast-off lever at the far end of the instrument panel. A blinding flash was followed by a deafening roar. Up went the rocket with Herbert aboard. With unbelievable speed it zoomed into outer space.

The rocket landed on a planet inhabited by civilized dogs, and Herbert was politely but firmly escorted to the city zoo. Being in a cage was no fun, and Herbert was delighted when a visiting collie decided to adopt him as a pet.

Breakthrough

Herbert woke up the next morning determined to prove to the collies that he was not just a tame animal but a civilized being. When Prince (Herbert called the young collie Prince because he lived in a house like a palace and had something princely about his character) took his human pet to the kitchen for breakfast, Herbert refused to eat from a dish on the floor. He picked up the dish, took it to the kitchen table, got out a knife, fork, and spoon from the drawer where he had noticed they were kept, and drew up a chair and sat down. He was more careful about his table manners than he sometimes was at home because he wanted to make an especially good impression.

Pleased and astonished at this show of civilized behavior, Prince ran to get his parents to come and see Herbert eating breakfast like a super-dog.

They were pleased and astonished. Before they had finished barking about it, however, it was time for Prince to go to school, and the first of the twelve eminent doctor-dogs and scientists coming to study Herbert was at the door.

Prince's father waited until the twelve eminent doctor-dogs and scientists were seated in his spacious library before he led Herbert in. He motioned Herbert to a chair, and all the very eminent doctors and scientists were surprised to see an animal of a strange species sitting in a chair. They all looked pleased as well as surprised, except the mean-eyed mongrel who had examined Herbert at the zoo. He growled deep in his throat, and the look in his eye would have frightened Herbert if Herbert had been the kind to be easily frightened.

"I'm glad the zoo director did not let *you* take me home, you bad-tempered, evil-eyed, surly, ill-begotten cur," Herbert said to the wolfish-looking dog, and perhaps it was fortunate for Herbert that his words were not understood by any dog there.

In a kindly manner, Prince's father made Herbert understand that he was to submit to a very thorough examination by the twelve eminent doctor-dogs and scientists. The contents of Herbert's pockets had been taken from him at the zoo but had been returned when the collies took him home with them. Now each item was passed from paw to paw and scrutinized with great care. There was a stick of gum, the wrapper from a candy bar, a jackknife, a piece of chalk, a shark's tooth, a pencil with a broken point, three marbles, a paperback baseball handbook, and a dime and three pennies. The eminent doctors and scientists were especially interested in the dime and three pennies and took turns looking at them through a microscope.

Then Herbert had to undergo another physical examination. None of it hurt until the wolfish dog jabbed him cruelly with a blunt instrument and pricked him with a sharp one. He also flashed an intense, bright light in Herbert's eyes. He was just getting a pair of pincers out of his doctor's bag when Prince's father strenuously objected. Apparently the noble-faced collie was king-dog

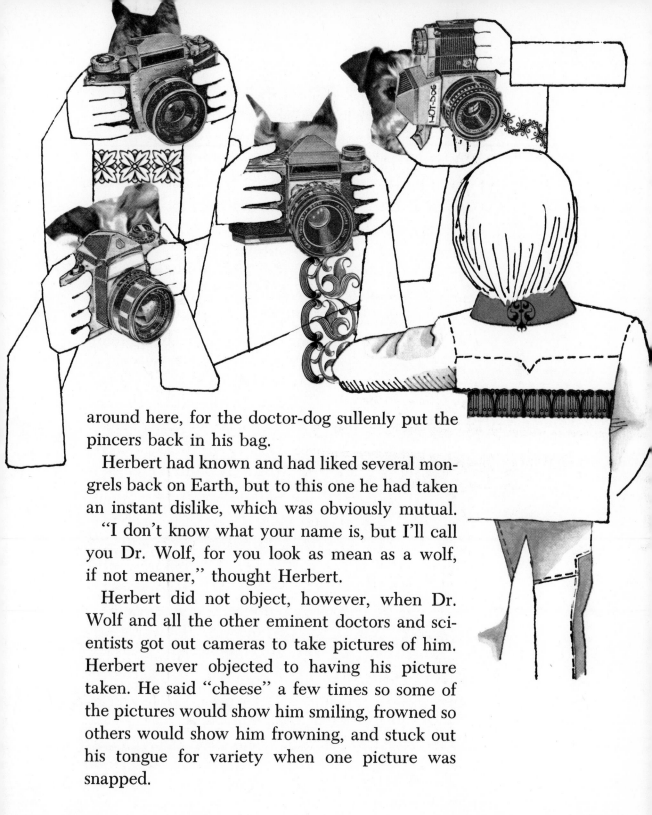

around here, for the doctor-dog sullenly put the pincers back in his bag.

Herbert had known and had liked several mongrels back on Earth, but to this one he had taken an instant dislike, which was obviously mutual.

"I don't know what your name is, but I'll call you Dr. Wolf, for you look as mean as a wolf, if not meaner," thought Herbert.

Herbert did not object, however, when Dr. Wolf and all the other eminent doctors and scientists got out cameras to take pictures of him. Herbert never objected to having his picture taken. He said "cheese" a few times so some of the pictures would show him smiling, frowned so others would show him frowning, and stuck out his tongue for variety when one picture was snapped.

After the picture-taking the eminent doctors and scientists made tape recordings of Herbert's voice. When Herbert was made to understand what was expected of him, he obliged by reciting all he remembered of Lincoln's Gettysburg Address, gave the salute to the flag while standing at attention, and gave one word for each letter of the alphabet, hesitating only over a word beginning with Z before he remembered *zero*.

Herbert was almost out of breath by then, but he rested only a moment before he recited four television commercials, counted up to five hundred by fives, and said the multiplication tables beginning with the ones and ending with the sixes. And, by then, Herbert really was just about out of breath.

When urged to continue, Herbert sang the Marine Hymn, always a favorite of his. Then, deciding that he had been serious long enough and that doggerel was appropriate to recite to dogs, he spoke a silly poem he had recently learned.

"I wish I were a little egg
Away up in a tree,
Rocked about by every breeze,
And rotten as can be.
And then I wish some little boy
Would climb up after me.
I'd up and bust my little self,
And spatter him with me."

Herbert knew that *bust* was not good usage, but he thought that, since the dogs did not understand the words, it did not matter. Of course, nobody but Herbert found the verse funny.

By this time Herbert was tired of tape recording and was relieved that nothing more in that line was expected of him.

While all this examination had been going on, all the doctors and eminent scientists had been taking notes. Now Herbert was able to make one of them (a handsome greyhound) understand that he wanted a piece of notepaper. The greyhound gave Herbert a pencil and paper, and he and the other doctors and scientists intently watched what Herbert did with them.

First Herbert tried to express himself in pictures. He was no artist, but he really exerted himself. He drew the almost round globe of Earth and a stick figure representing himself seated in the cockpit of a landing rocket and stick-figure dogs capturing him.

"This will show you that I remember what happened to me," Herbert said, passing the paper around.

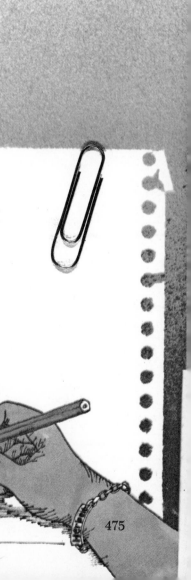

475

Then Herbert wrote a short note to his Uncle Horace.

Dear Uncle Horace,
 I wish you were here. This is an interesting planet, but one might say that I have gone to the dogs.

Your loving nephew,
Herbert

This used up the sheet of notepaper, and Herbert passed the letter around.

"This will show you that I know how to write," Herbert told the eminent doctors and scientists, who, with the exception of Dr. Wolf, looked impressed but not yet convinced that Herbert was a civilized being.

Herbert next picked up the paperback baseball handbook and began to read from it.

He read aloud that the New York Yankees had been champions in the American League far more often than any other team. He read a list of home-run leaders. "Babe Ruth," he read, "hit sixty home runs in the year 1927." Then he read a long list of no-hitters and the number of perfect games pitched in major league championship play from 1880 to the previous baseball season. "Now you know that I can read," said Herbert, closing the paperback baseball handbook.

All the eminent doctors and scientists, with the exception of Dr. Wolf, looked impressed and almost convinced that Herbert was an intelligent being. Herbert realized, however, that he still had not quite convinced them.

Herbert searched his mind for some further means of communication. If only he could find a bridge between the two cultures—something which would be the same on both planets. His eye fell on a large clock on the wall. It was not unlike clocks on Earth except that the numbers denoting the hours were different. Herbert's mind raced as he came up with an idea.

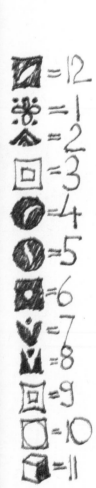

Again Herbert made it known that he wanted paper and a writing implement, which were given to him. Sitting down at the library table facing the clock, Herbert drew a clock face. Only, instead of copying the numbers as they were on the clock here, Herbert wrote the clock numbers from one to twelve, like those on clocks on Earth. Then he drew another clock face and carefully copied the numbers on the large library clock. The next step was to list the numbers in two rows, with a *12* matching a corresponding numeral, according to the large library clock.

Rapidly Herbert did a few simple sums in arithmetic, never using a number above twelve. He then wrote down the answers in both the numerals he was accustomed to and the numerals used on the dog planet.

Herbert passed this paper around, and every dog examined it. Then dog after dog rose to his feet and made a speech. Herbert could tell that they were speeches about him and that most of them were admiring and flattering. Only Dr. Wolf still looked unimpressed. He made an angry speech and seemed to be in disagreement with every other dog there.

When all the dogs had finished speaking, Prince's father did something which would have made Herbert weep for joy if he had been a weeping-for-joy boy. The noble-faced collie unbuckled and removed the collar from Herbert's neck. Then he cordially reached out a paw and shook Herbert's hand while every dog there (with the exception of Dr. Wolf) applauded by clapping his paws vigorously.

Herbert could tell that he must have convinced the super-dogs that he was an intelligent being. And he was thankful that, from that time on, he would not be wearing a leather collar.

Herbert's Diary

Several weeks after having been accepted as an intelligent being, Herbert remembered that Arctic and Antarctic explorers and other discoverers of new lands on Earth often kept diaries in which they recorded the weather, meetings with strange tribes, and other observations they felt would be of interest. So Herbert decided to do the same. Maybe after he got back to Earth (and Herbert had by no means given up hope of getting back to Earth), some publisher might want to print Herbert's diary. In his mind's eye, Herbert could already see *"Life on the Dog Planet* by Herbert Yadon"* on a book cover. Herbert thought he would choose to have the cover either red or green—he rather favored red.

Here are Herbert's entries for the five days from July 12 to July 16, after he had been on the dog planet nearly four weeks.

July 12. It rained for the first time since I have been here. Rainfall is controlled, and it only rains when a poll shows that a majority of super-dogs feels that rain is needed. The super-dogs do not have umbrellas. If caught in the rain, they just put on dry clothes and throw away their wet ones. Clothing is so cheap, it is worn only one day and can be bought in vending machines. Male and female dogs dress alike, except that the robes of the lady dogs have ruffles.

July 13. Sunny and pleasant. The temperature on this planet is also controlled, but I haven't yet found out how that is done. I'm not sure, but I think it never snows here. Can't be dead sure of that unless I am still here during the winter, and I'd rather not be here that long.

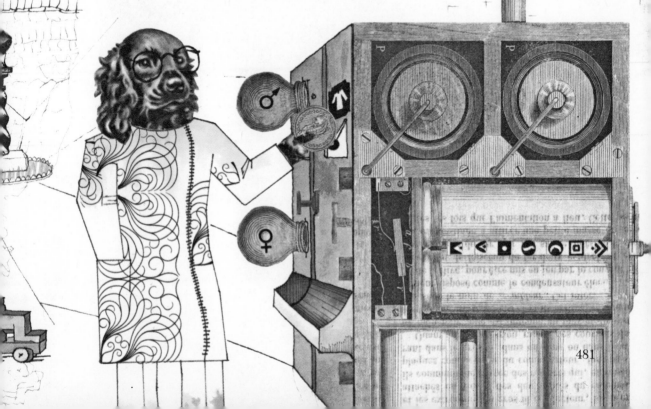

481

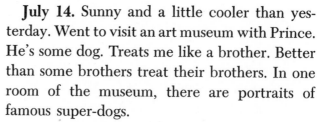

July 14. Sunny and a little cooler than yesterday. Went to visit an art museum with Prince. He's some dog. Treats me like a brother. Better than some brothers treat their brothers. In one room of the museum, there are portraits of famous super-dogs.

July 15. Cloudy and cool but not too cool. The super-dogs like variety in their weather, but so far there has been no fog. Visited another museum and saw my space suit on exhibit. Hope I can get it back when I need it again. The curator of the museum says it is the most popular exhibit there.

July 16. I should have described the geography of this place before. Some of the facts I've only known recently. I'm on a planet much, much smaller than Earth. Probably that's why there's nothing about it in the astronomy books. I'm not dead sure, but I think it's not much bigger than the state of Ohio. It is inhabited by dogs in a high state of civilization and by wolves and wild dogs, who are still barbarians. The city I am in is the capital city of the super-dogs, at least that's what I call them.

Herbert was less regular about writing in his diary after that week, but he never failed to record the weather. He also listed the flora and fauna of the planet, which he knew meant plant and animal life. Herbert had never kept a diary for nearly as long before. Usually he stopped writing in a new diary after a few days. But now

he had things to describe which had never been described before, not even by Jules Verne. Herbert felt it his duty to tell the world about them, and he still dreamed of having his diary published as a book with a bright green or, preferably, red cover.

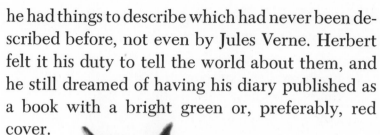

Herbert spent about another month on the dog planet. It was his Uncle Horace who arranged his timely rescue. Unfortunately his diary was never published, not even as a school composition, "How I Spent My Summer Vacation."

Reflections

1. What do you think is the difference between a "tame animal" and a "civilized being"? between *intelligence* and *civilization?*

2. How would you like to be some animal's pet? If you had a choice, what kind of master would you choose?

3. What were some of the things that Herbert did to show that he was an intelligent being? Which do you think were the most clever?

4. Suppose the collies' clock had had seventeen numerals on the face. What else might Herbert have then done to prove he was an intelligent being?

5. Why do you suppose diaries and journals are kept? If you keep a diary, would you want it published? Explain.

Where Do I Go from Here?

MARY BRITTON MILLER

Land and sea and earth and sky,
I'm not a bird but I can fly
With the greatest of ease,
I'm not a boat but I can go
Under and over the seven seas,
I'm not a goat but with my skis
I can take a slide down a mountainside,
And also at my very best
Climb to the top of Everest.
Earth and sky and land and air,
I have conquered all of these—
Tell me, children, if you please,
Where do I go from here?

WORDS, MEANINGS, AND FEELINGS

Beat the eggs.

Toss the salad.

Put out the lights.

Dust the table.

Measure one cup of beans.

Dress the turkey.

Read the directions under each picture above. Are the directions being followed? How would you beat the eggs? How would you toss the salad? How would your mother dress the turkey or measure a cup of beans? These pictures show that words may have several meanings. Your meaning for a word always depends on your own understanding of it.

The Meaning of Words

Words stand for things, people, animals, actions, and feelings. Written words themselves are only groups of letters. They suggest the sounds which the word stands for. We bring meaning to words. What makes the pictures on the opposite page funny is that the wrong meanings have been brought to the words.

Words may be tricky. Many words have a number of meanings. What a word means depends very much on the other words near it in a sentence. Think of words in a sentence as you think of colors in a shirt or dress. Often the colors are in a careful pattern or design. The colors and the pattern are woven or dyed into the cloth. In much this way words are woven and dyed into sentences.

Context is a word which we borrow from two Latin words. In Latin cum means "with," and texere means "to weave." We cannot get the meaning, or context, of a sentence until we weave all the words in it together. What a word means in a sentence may depend on the other words that give clues to its meaning. Here is how this works.

1. Spring is my favorite season.
2. The spring is the source of the brook.
3. The pipe may spring a leak.
4. Spring over the hedge and into my yard.
5. A spring in my watch is broken.

How do you define spring in each sentence above? How do the other words in each sentence help you make your definition? If spring could mean only "a season of the year," could you use spring in sentences 2 through 5?

Use the word *scene* in sentences to tell the following:

    a.   where you are

    b.   a favorite part of a TV show

    c.   a temper tantrum

Use the word *legs* in sentences about the following:

    a.   part of your body

    b.   part of a table

    c.   part of a pair of blue jeans

Look at the five meanings for the four words below. Then see if you can make up a sentence for each meaning.

eye	**wing**
my eye	a wing chair
the eye of a needle	a single-wing formation
the eye of a hurricane	the wing of an airplane
the eye of a potato	the wing of a bird
my mind's eye	the wings of thought

root	**air**
the root of a tree	air I breathe
the root of a tooth	a friendly air
the root of a word	on the air
to root for the team	they sang an air
the root of the trouble	walking on air

Discuss the different meanings of *eye, wing, root,* and *air.* Could you thread the *eye of a potato* or *my mind's eye* or *the eye of a hurricane?* Of course not. Often we must weave words together with the words near them before their meanings become clear. Context clues will help you break the reading code.

Discuss the following sentences. Tell why or why not each sentence is true or false.

1. The words we read bring their meaning to us.
2. We bring meaning to the words we read.

Words and Feelings

Words are threads that tie us to other people. The same threads tie others to us. Without our spoken language, we would be very lonely. The written words of a story, a poem, or an essay give us a way to know what a writer is saying to us. As we read aloud, we use our voices to show that we understand the words. How we speak, how we pronounce words, what syllables we stress, our tone of voice, our facial expressions, and the movement of our bodies are all ways to show feelings.

Read this dialogue between a father and his son.

FATHER.   I see you finally got home. You know it's almost nine o'clock, past your bedtime.

SON.   I had dinner at Bobby's house.

FATHER.   So you had dinner at Bobby's house, did you? I am sure his mother and father were pleased about that.

SON.   We watched TV and played some records.

FATHER.   What a fine way to spend the evening. Run along to bed. I'll see you later.

Now read the dialogue aloud, pretending that the father is very angry and that the son is very ashamed. Imagine that the father does not like Bobby's parents, does not enjoy TV or records. How would you read the dialogue?

Now pretend that Bobby is the son of the father's closest friend. Imagine that the father likes to have his son and Bobby play together. Read the dialogue aloud again.

The good reader uses context clues to help him find the meanings of words. The good oral reader uses his voice to help him get the meaning of an author's sentences.

GLOSSARY

FULL PRONUNCIATION KEY

The pronunciation of each word is shown just after the word, in this way: **ab bre vi ate** (ə brē′ vē āt). The letters and signs used are pronounced as in the words below. The mark ′ is placed after a syllable with primary or heavy accent, as in the example above. The mark ′ after a syllable shows a secondary or lighter accent, as in **ab bre vi a tion** (ə brē′ vē ā′ shən).

a	hat, cap	j	jam, enjoy	u	cup, butter
ā	age, face	k	kind, seek	ů	full, put
ã	care, air	l	land, coal	ü	rule, move
ä	father, far	m	me, am	ū	use, music
b	bad, rob	n	no, in		
ch	child, much	ng	long, bring	v	very, save
d	did, red	o	hot, rock	w	will, woman
e	let, best	ō	open, go	y	young, yet
ē	equal, be	ô	order, all	z	zero, breeze
ėr	term, learn	oi	oil, voice	zh	measure, seizure
f	fat, if	ou	house, out		
g	go, bag	p	paper, cup	ə represents:	
h	he, how	r	run, try		a in about
i	it, pin	s	say, yes		e in taken
ī	ice, five	sh	she, rush		i in April
		t	tell, it		o in lemon
		th	thin, both		u in circus
		ŦH	then, smooth		

FROM *THORNDIKE-BARNHART JUNIOR DICTIONARY* BY E. L. THORNDIKE AND CLARENCE L. BARNHART. COPYRIGHT © 1968 BY SCOTT, FORESMAN AND COMPANY. REPRINTED BY PERMISSION.

ab a cus (ab′ ə kəs) device, used for doing calculations, which has a frame with rows of beads that can slide back and forth

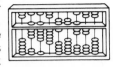

a bil i ty (ə bil′ ə tē) skill; power to do something

ab sence (ab′ səns) state of being away

ab sent mind ed (ab′ sənt mīnd′ əd) not paying attention; paying attention to something else

ab so lute (ab′ sə lüt) complete; unlimited

Ab ys sin i an (ab′ ə sin′ ē n) from Abyssinia, now called Ethiopia, a country in northern Africa

ac cent (ak′ sent) **1.** particular way of pronouncing a language; speech habits. **2.** force or stress on the loudest or most important syllable of a word

ac cord ing (ə kôr′ ding) used with *to:* based on

Ac cra (äk′ rä *or* ä krä′) capital city of Ghana

ac ro bat ics (ak′ rə bat′ iks) difficult turns and twists; tricks

A de ni yi (ä′ dä nē′ yē)

A de po ju (ä′ dä pō′ jü)

A de yin ka (ä′ dä ying′ kä)

a *dieu* (ə dū′) French: good-by

ad just (ə just′) to make right; to correct

ad lib (ad′ lib′) stage direction meaning without instructions; made up on the spot

Ado- Ido (ä′ dō ē′ dō) small village in southwest Nigeria, a state in west Africa

a dopt (ə dopt′) to take on as one's own

ad ver tise ment (ad′ vər tīz′ mənt) notice that gives information about a sale, a contest, etc.

af fect (ə fekt′) to influence

af fec tion ate ly (ə fek′ shən it lē) kindly; in a friendly way; fondly

ag ile (aj′ l) able to move quickly and easily

air strip (ãr′ strip′) runway used by planes for landing and taking off

aisle (īl) space between rows of seats

Ak bar (ak′ bär) Mogul emperor in the late sixteenth century

al fal fa (al fal′ fə) plant grown as a food for livestock

al le giance (ə lē′ jəns) loyalty and duty to one's country

all spice (ôl′ spīs′) spice made from the berries of a West Indian tree, similar to cinnamon and nutmeg

am a ryl lis (am′ ə ril′ is) plant with large, usually red, pink, or white flowers

a maze ment (ə māz′ mənt) wonder; great surprise

am bu lance (am′ byə ləns) special automobile for carrying sick or injured people

a mi a ble (ā′ mē ə bl) pleasant; friendly; good-natured

an ces tor (an′ ses tər) any of those from whom one is descended; a parent, grandparent, etc.

an chor (ang′ kər) to keep a boat in one place by throwing a heavy spiked weight attached to a chain overboard

a nem o ne (ə nem′ ə nē) sea animal that looks like a flower

An gel ique (än zhe lēk′)

An glo- Sax on (ang′ glō sak′ sən) Old English; language spoken in England from about 450 to 1100; parent language of Modern English

an ti bi ot ic (an′ tē bī ot′ ik) medicine that kills bacteria

a part ment (ə pärt′ mənt) group of rooms for one person or family to live in; part of a larger building

---

hat, āge, cãre, fär; let, bē, tėrm; it, īce; hot, gō, ôrder; oil, out; cup, pùt, rüle, ūse; ch, child; ng, long; th, thin; ŦH, then; zh, measure; ə represents *a* in about, *e* in taken, *i* in April, *o* in lemon, *u* in circus.

ap pa ra tus (ap′ ə rāt′ əs *or* ap′ ə rat′ əs) machinery; equipment; any tool used to carry out some purpose

ap pear (ə pēr′) to come into sight

ap pli ance (ə plī′ əns) small machine or tool used for cooking or housework, such as a stove, refrigerator, or vacuum cleaner

ap pro pri ate (ə prō′ prē it) suitable; right for the occasion

ap prox i mate (ə prok′ sə mit) nearly exact or right

apt (apt) likely to

a quar i um (ə kwãr′ ē m) building or glass container filled with water in which live fish and water animals are kept

A rez zo (ä ret′ sō) town in central Italy southeast of Florence

ar gu ment (är′ gyə ment) reason for a way of thinking; way to persuade someone

ar ma dil lo
(är′ mə dil′ ō) small animal with a very hard shell, found in the Southwest and South America

Arm strong (ärm′ strông) Louis (lü′ ē)

ar row root (a′ rō rüt′) edible root that grows in the tropics

ar ti cle (är′ tə kəl) thing; object

as sume (ə süm′) to take on as one's own

as sump tion (ə sump′ shən) belief

as sure (ə shùr′) to guarantee; to convince

as ton ish (ə ston′ ish) to surprise greatly

as ton ish ment (ə ston′ ish mənt) great surprise; amazement

as tron o my (ə stron′ ə mē) study of stars, planets, and other heavenly bodies

a sun der (ə sun′ dər) apart; not together; away from: *The ax split the log asunder.*

ath lete (ath′ lēt) person who is good at sports or exercise

at mos phere (at′ məs fēr) air around the earth

at tend ant (ə ten′ dənt) person who waits on another; a servant

Aus tra lia (ô strāl′ yə) island continent southeast of Asia

au thor (ô′ thər) one who writes books, stories, or articles; a writer

au to bi og ra phy (ô′ tō bī og′ rə fē) one's life story written by himself

av er age (av′ r ij *or* av′ rij) usual; like most others of the same kind

av o ca do (a və käd′ ō) tropical fruit with dark green or black skin, soft green pulp, and a large pit

axis (ak′ sis) central line around which an object turns

Ayan (ä′ yan) surname used for Nigerian drummers

A yan ba mi ji (ä′ yan bä mē′ jē)

A yan pe ju (ä′ yan pā′ jü)

A yan tun ji (ä′ yan tün′ jē)

bac te ri a (bak tēr′ ē ə) one-celled plants, so small they can only be seen through a microscope

bac te ri ol o gist (bak tēr′ ē ol′ ə jist) scientist who studies bacteria

baf fle (baf′ l) to confuse

Ba ga (bä′ gä) tribe in Africa

bag pipe (bag′ pīp′) musical instrument having a cloth bag filled with air which the player squeezes to force air through the pipes, making the sound

bal ance (bal′ əns) standing steadily and not falling over

bal co ny (bal′ kə nē) platform coming out from an upper story of a building

Ba lo gun (bä lō′ gün) title given to brave African war chiefs

Ba mi ji (bä mē′ jē)

Bang kok (bang′ kok) capital city of Thailand, a country in Asia

ban ter ing (ban′ tər ing) joking; teasing

bar bar i an (bär bär′ ē n) one who is not schooled or well mannered

ba sis (bās′ is) main part; foundation: *His wide reading formed the basis of his knowledge.*

Bat te ry Park (bat′ r ē pärk) park in New York City at the southern end of Manhattan Island

be calmed (bi kämd′) unable to sail because of a lack of wind

be drag gled (bi drag′ əld) wet and soiled

be fud dle (bi fud′ l) to confuse; to make someone seem stupid

be lit tle (bi lit′ l) to make less important; to insult

bel low (bel′ ō) loud roar; threatening noise

Bern stein (bėrn′ stīn) Leonard (len′ ərd)

be wil der ing (bi wil′ dər ing) confusing; puzzling

be witch (bi wich′) to put under a spell

bi ol o gist (bī ol′ ə jist) scientist who studies living things

bi plane (bī′ plān′) earliest airplane, which had two sets of canvas wings, one above the other

bit ter sweet (bit′ r swēt′) both bitter and sweet

bless ing (bles′ ing) prayer or wish for someone's luck or happiness

blue bot tle (blü′ bot′ l) large bluish fly

boast (bōst) to praise oneself or rave about something one owns

Bod mer (bod′ mər) Karl (kärl)

Boe ing (bō′ ing) name of company that makes airplanes; airplane made by this company

boil er (boil′ r) machine that produces steam: *Old fire engines used a steam boiler to run the water pump.*

Bola (bō′ lä)

Bon heur (bō nėr′) Rosa (rōs′ ə)

bon net (bon′ it) kind of woman's hat, tied under the chin with a string or a ribbon

bow sprit (bou′ sprit) pole sticking out from the front of a sailing ship with ropes attached to it that help to steady the sails

BOWSPRIT
BOW

brack et (brak′ it) shelf that comes out from the wall

braid (brād) trim made by weaving together three or more strands of thread, cord, hair, etc.: *The general's uniform had gold braid on the shoulders.*

bram ble (bram′ bl) thorny bush

bread fruit (bred′ früt′) large starchy South Pacific fruit

brief case (brēf′ kās′) box-shaped leather bag for carrying books and papers

brook (brùk) small flow of running water; small stream

Brue ghel (broi′ gəl) Pieter (pēt′ r) the Elder

bue no (bwā′ nō) Spanish: good

bulge (bulj) to balloon outward; to swell

bull doz er (bùl′ dōz′ r) large tractor used for moving earth

Byz an ti an (bi zan′ ti n) of or like the ancient city of Byzantium

ca ber (kā′ bər) tree trunk or large heavy pole weighing about 180 pounds, used in throwing contests

cab i net (kab′ ə nət) piece of wooden furniture that holds such things as books, clothing, dishes, etc.

ca ble gram (kā′ bl gram′) telegraph message sent under the ocean through a cable made of many wires twisted together

---

hat, āge, cãre, fär; let, bē, tėrm; it, īce; hot, gō, ôrder; oil, out; cup, pùt, rüle, ūse; ch, child; ng, long; th, thin; ŦH, then; zh, measure; ə represents *a* in about, *e* in taken, *i* in April, *o* in lemon, *u* in circus.

cac tus (kak′ təs) desert plant with sharp spines

cal a bash (kal′ ə bash) hard tropical gourd

cal cu late (kal′ kyə lāt) to figure out by arithmetic

can dle nut (kan′ dəl nut′) oily tropical nut

Car a velle
(kar′ ə vel) brand name for a small jet airplane

ca ress (kə res′) to stroke; to pet

car pen ter (kär′ pən tər) worker who makes wooden objects

casa (kä′ sä) Spanish: house

cat e gory (kat′ ə gô rē) group of things that are alike; class

cat tail (kat′ tāl′) tall plant that grows in marshes and swamps

cel e bra tion (sel′ ə brā′ shən) special event honoring some person or past event

ce les tial (sə les′ chəl) heavenly

cell (sel) smallest complete unit of living matter

cen sus (sen′ səs) official counting of the people in a country or area

cen tu ry (sen′ chə rē) period of a hundred years

cer e mo ny (ser′ ə mō nē) act or acts done on special occasions

Char din (shär dan′) Jean-Baptiste (zhän′ bap tēst′)

chem i cal (kem′ ə kəl) substance made up of two or more natural elements, often used for a specific purpose

chick en house (chik′ n hous) small building in which chickens are kept

chick en pox (chik′ n poks) childhood disease that causes a rash and itching

Chi nese (chī nēz′) 1. language spoken by natives of China. 2. a native of China

choc o late (chôk′ lit *or* chôk′ ə lit) candy or flavoring made by roasting and grinding cacao seeds and mixing them with sugar

cin na mon (sin′ ə mən) reddish-brown spice made from the bark of an East Indian tree

cir cuit (sèr′ kit) complete path of wires and plugs for electricity

cit i zen (sit′ ə zən) one who is a member or native of a nation, state, city, or town

civ il (siv′ l) having to do with the citizens of a country: *A civil war is fought between groups of citizens of the same country.*

ci vil ian (sə vil′ yən) private; not having to do with the armed forces

clam ber (klam′ bər) to climb; to scramble up

clans men (klanz′ mən) members of a clan, which is a group of related families

clo ver (klōv′ r) low plant with leaves arranged in threes

clue (klü) item of information that points to the solution of a problem

clus ter (klus′ tər) group of things; clump

coast al (kōs′ təl) along or of the coast; very near the ocean

co co nut (kōk′ ə nut′) large round tropical fruit that has edible hard white flesh and nourishing liquid in the center

co coon (kə kün′) case which a caterpillar spins around itself and in which it turns into an adult butterfly or moth

col li sion (kə lizh′ n) crash of several objects: *There was a three-car collision on the highway.*

col o nist (kol′ ə nist) one who starts or lives in a colony or new community

com mu ni cate (kə mūn′ ə kāt) to talk; to exchange news, feelings, beliefs, etc.; to share thoughts or ideas

com pa dre (kom päd′ rā) Spanish: friend; pal

com part ment (kəm pärt′ mənt) part of a whole, separated from the rest, meant to hold something

com pli ca tion (kom′ plə kā′ shən) something that makes things more confused or harder to settle

com pos er (kəm pōz′ r) one who writes music

com put er (kəm pūt′ r) machine that does arithmetic or calculations

con cer to (kən chär′ tō) musical work played by a solo instrument accompanied by an orchestra

conch (kongk *or* konch) large spiral seashell

con coct (kon kokt′) to prepare; to make something out of many ingredients

Con gress (kong′ gris) the lawmaking body of the United States of America, made up of the Senate and the House of Representatives

con ser va tion (kon′ sər vā′ shən) protection of natural resources such as forests, lakes, rivers, wildlife, etc.

con stant ly (kon′ stənt lē) all the time; without stopping

con trast (kon trast′) to point out differences between two items

con trib ute (kən trib′ ūt) to add something; to help

coop (küp) pen for chickens, geese, etc.

cor al (kôr′ l) tiny sea animals with hard skeletons that band together to form branches or reefs

cor dial ly (kôr′ jəl ē) warmly; sincerely

coun cil (koun′ sil) group of wise men who advise a king or leader

cozy (kō′ zē) comfortable; snug

crab (krab) water animal with a hard shell, eight legs, two of which end in large claws

crook ed (krùk′ id) not straight; bent

crouch (krouch) to stoop down with bent legs

crys tal (kris′ təl) clear stone or mineral that looks like glass

cud (kud) food brought back up to the mouth of a cow and chewed for a long time

cui da do (kwē dä′ dō) Spanish: care; used as a command meaning look out or take care

curb (kėrb) raised edge between sidewalk and street

cus to di an (kus tōd′ ē n) janitor; one who takes care of a building

Dan ube (dan′ ūb) river in Germany and Austria

dap pled (dap′ əld) spotted

dazed (dāzd) confused; stunned; not thinking clearly

ded i cat ed (ded′ ə kāt əd) set apart for a special purpose

De lau nay (de lō nā′) Robert (rō bãr′)

de li cious (di lish′ əs) good tasting

de serve (di zėrv′) to earn; to be worthy of

des ti na tion (des′ tə nā′ shən) place to which someone or something is going or being sent

de vel op (di vel′ əp) to grow; to become more complicated

de vise (dē vīz′) to describe fully; to reflect

di a ry (dī′ ə rē) book in which one writes his thoughts or feelings about what has happened during each day; an account of each day's events

di fí cil (dē fē′ sēl) Spanish: hard; difficult

dis cov er (dis kuv′ r) to find out; to learn

dis pute (dis pūt′) to argue

dog ger el (dôg′ r l) bad poetry; worthless rhymes; senseless verse

do nate (dōn′ āt) to give

drawl (drôl) **1.** slow drawn-out way of talking. **2.** to talk in a slow drawn-out way

driz zly (driz′ lē) misty; like a gentle rain

Du bois (dü bwä′)

dune (dün) hill or mound of sand

Dun veg an Cas tle (dun′ vāg′ n kas′ l) home of the MacLeod clan on the western coast of the Isle of Skye

---

hat, āge, cãre, fär; let, bē, tėrm; it, īce; hot, gō, ôrder; oil, out; cup, pùt, rüle, ūse; ch, child; ng, long; th, thin; ᵺH, then; zh, measure; ə represents *a* in about, e in taken, *i* in April, o in lemon, *u* in circus.

dwin dle (dwin′ dəl) to become smaller; to fade away

ear nest (ėr′ nəst) real; serious

ear wig (ēr′ wig) harmless insect with slender antennas

Eb er bach (ā′ bėr bäk′) town in West Germany near Heidelberg

e lec tric i ty (i lek′ tris′ ə tē) kind of energy in the form of a current, used to produce light and heat, run motors, etc.: *Lightning is a natural form of electricity.*

em broi dered (em broid′ ərd) decorated with fancy stitches

em i nent (em′ ə nənt) important; outstanding; having a high position

en dur ance (en dùr′ əns) strength or power to last

e nor mous (i nôr′ məs) very big; gigantic; huge

en to mol o gist (en′ tə mol′ ə jist) scientist who studies insects

en trance (en′ trəns) gate or door; way to get into a building or area

en trust ed (en trust′ əd) given into someone's care

es tab lish (es tab′ lish) to set up

es ti mate (es′ tə mit) opinion; judgment

E trus can (i trus′ kən) of the civilization of the Etruscans, an ancient people who lived in Italy

ex ag ger ate (eg zaj′ r āt) to say something is bigger or better than it really is

ex cur sion (eks kėr′ zhən) pleasure trip

ex per i ment (eks per′ ə mənt) to make tests in order to find out something or to prove a theory

ex plo ra tion (eks′ plə rā′ shən) travel into an unknown place to discover what it is like

ex press (eks pres′) fastest possible means of transporting something; non-stop or having few stops

fan tas tic (fan tas′ tik) very odd; unreal; strange

fas ci nat ed (fas′ ə nāt əd) very interested in something

fa thom (faᴛʜ′ m) unit equal to six feet, used for measuring the depth of water

fau na (fôn′ ə) all the animal life in an area

fes ti val (fes′ tə vəl) special time of rejoicing; celebration; big party

fes tooned (fes tünd′) decorated

feud (fūd) quarrel that lasts for a long time

fire place (fīr′ plās′) framed opening in a stone or brick wall to hold a fire

flap jack (flap′ jak′) kind of pancake

flat boat (flat′ bōt′) flat-bottomed large boat used on rivers, similar to a barge

fledg ling (flej′ ling) baby bird

Flem ish (flem′ ish) of Flanders, a region in Belgium

flex i ble (flek′ sə bl) able to be bent without breaking; able to move in all directions; usable for many purposes

flo ra (flôr′ ə) all the plant life of an area

flo res (flōr′ es) Spanish: flowers

flut ter (flut′ r) to flap back and forth; to wave

for est ry (fôr′ is trē) the care of trees and forests; the care of woodlands

fran ti cal ly (fran′ tik lē) with great excitement; with panic

freight er (frāt′ r) ship that carries products, not passengers

French (french) **1.** language spoken by natives of France and parts of Canada and Africa. **2.** having to do with France

fric tion (frik′ shən) rubbing of one thing against another; heat or resistance caused by the rubbing

fron tier (frun tēr′) border between the settled part of a country and the wilds

fu ner al (fūn′ r l) ceremony held after a person has died

fu ri ous (fūr′ ē əs) very angry

Gal lau det (gal' ə det') Thomas Hopkins (tom' əs hop' kənz)

gal ley (gal' ē) **1.** type of ancient ship having oars and sails **2.** kitchen of a ship

gan der (gan' dər) male goose

Gas pé (gas pā') peninsula on the Atlantic coast of Canada at the mouth of the St. Lawrence River

ga zelle (gə zel') small swift antelope of Africa or Asia

gec ko (gek' ō) small tropical lizard that lives on insects

gen er a tor (jen' r ā tər) machine that produces electricity by moving wires very quickly between several magnets

Ger man (jèr' mən) **1.** language spoken by natives of Germany, Austria, and parts of Switzerland. **2.** a native of Germany

ghast ly (gast' lē) horrible; awful

gi gan tic (jī gan' tik) very large; big as a giant

gin ger ly (jin' jər lē) very carefully, so as not to break something

Glack ens (glak' ənz) William James

globe (glōb) the earth; anything shaped like a ball

gor geous (gôr' jəs) extremely beautiful; splendid

gos ling (goz' ling) baby goose

grad u a tion (graj' ù ā' shən) ceremony held when one has completed a certain number of courses in school

Greaves (grēvz) Walter

Greek (grēk) language spoken by natives of Greece

gris ly (griz' lē) frightful; horrible

gua va (gwä' və) sweet yellow tropical fruit

guin ea pig (gin' ē pig) small furry tailless animal, kept as a pet and often used for scientific experiments

Gulf of Guin ea (gulf' uv gin' ē) part of the Atlantic Ocean along the west coast of Africa

Ham burg (ham' bèrg) port city in West Germany

har poon (här pün') barbed spear attached to a rope, used for catching whales

hau (hou) Hawaiian plant used for making string

ha ven (hā' vən) safe place

heave (hēv) strong upwards or sideways movement

He brew (hēb' rü) language in which the Old Testament of the Bible was written; the official language of Israel

Hemp stead cart (hem' sted kärt) very light two-wheeled cart made of natural wood, used for carrying passengers

Her nán dez (hár nän' dez)

hin drance (hin' drəns) something that gets in the way; something that creates a difficulty

Ho ku sai (hō' kü sī') Katsushika (kät' sü shē' kä)

hop scotch (hop' skoch') children's game in which one player throws a stone into a design marked on the ground and then hops and jumps over the lines to get it

Hum boldt Cur rent (hum' bōlt kèr' ənt) current in the Pacific Ocean that flows north along the west coast of South America

ice land (īs' land') land covered with ice during all or most of the year

---

hat, āge, cãre, fär; let, bē, tèrm; it, īce; hot, gō, ôrder; oil, out; cup, pùt, rüle, ūse; ch, child; ng, long; th, thin; ᴛʜ, then; zh, measure; ə represents *a* in about, *e* in taken, *i* in April, *o* in lemon, *u* in circus.

i den ti fy (ī den′ tə fī) **1.** to mark a person or thing as separate from others. **2.** to find out what something is

ig nore (ig nôr′) to pay no attention to

ig nor ing (ig nôr′ ing) paying no attention to

Il ler (il′ ėr) river in Germany

im per i ous (im pēr′ ē əs) as proud as a king

im ple ment (im′ plə mənt) tool

im press (im pres′) to make others have good thoughts about something

in cu ba tor (in′ kyə bā′ tər) heated box used for hatching eggs

in di cate (in′ də kāt) to mark; to point out

in dig nant (in dig′ nənt) angry at something unfair

in gre di ent (in grēd′ ē ənt) part of a mixture: *Sugar is an ingredient of candy.*

in hab it ed (in hab′ it id) lived in; occupied

i ni tial (i nish′ l) first letter of a word or name

Inn (in) river in Germany

in sert (in sėrt′) to put in

in spec tor (in spek′ tər) one whose job is to examine something to see that it is right

in spi ra tion (in′ spə rā′ shən) strong influence; something that causes thoughts or actions

in stall (in stôl′) to put something into place for use: *The mechanic had to install a new battery in the car.*

in stinct (in′ stingkt) natural untaught ability or knowledge

in stinc tive (in stingk′ tiv) known without having been taught; inborn knowledge: *Fish have an instinctive ability to swim.*

in struc tions (in struk′ shənz) directions telling how to do something

in ter na tion al (in′ tər na′ shən l) having to do with more than one country

in ter rupt (in′ tə rupt′) to break in on a speech or activity

in ves ti gate (in ves′ tə gāt) to look into closely; to study

in vis i ble (in viz′ ə bl) impossible to be seen; not visible

Isar (ē′ zär) river in Germany

I sha ju (ē shä′ jü)

Isle of Skye (īl uv skī) island west of Scotland

I tal ian (i tal′ yən) **1.** language spoken by natives of Italy. **2.** a native of Italy

Iya Ilu (ē′ yä ē′ lü)

jeal ous (jel′ əs) wishing to have something that someone else has

jeal ousy (jel′ əs ē) feeling of anger caused by someone seeming to have an advantage; envy

jeer (jēr) to laugh at; to make fun of

jel ly fish (jel′ ē fish′) transparent sea animal with long tentacles and no skeleton

John son (jon′ sən) Eastman (ēst′ mən)

jung le (jung′ gəl) land in a hot damp climate, completely covered with bushes, trees, vines, etc.

jut (jut) to stick out

Ka na lo a (kä nä lō′ ä) Hawaiian god of healing

Ka nan go (kä näng′ gō)

Kane (kä′ nā) a Hawaiian god

ka ty did (kā′ tē did) large grasshopper that produces a shrill sound

Kaye (kā) Danny

Ke (kā)

Klee (klā) Paul

Knize (nīz) Lili (lil′ ē)

koa (kō′ ä) a Hawaiian wood

Ku (kü) Hawaiian god of the forests

Kwa ku (kwä′ kü) African title similar to Mister

lab o ra to ry (lab′ ə rə tô′ rē) place where scientists work

land mark (land′ märk′) some familiar object used as a guide

Las caux (läs kō′) site in central France of famous caves

Lat in (lat′ n) language of the ancient Romans

Lech (lek) river in Germany

le mur (lē′ mər) small furry animal, related to the monkey family, that lives in trees

lib ro (lēb′ rō) Spanish: book

life- span (līf′ span′) length of time that something is apt to live

light house
(līt′ hous′) tower with a revolving bright light on top that warns ships of dangerous waters

lip read ing (lip′ rēd′ ing) understanding someone's speech by watching his lips move

lo cust (lōk′ əst) short-horned grasshopper that often swarms and travels in large groups

loom ing (lüm′ ing) appearing from nowhere; appearing mysteriously

lub ber grass hop per (lub′ r gras′ hop′ r) large stout grasshopper common to the Southwest

lu mi nous (lüm′ i nəs) giving off light; shining

ma ca da mia (ma kə dām′ ē ə) large tropical plant that produces an edible nut

Ma de moi selle (mad′ ə mə zel′) French: Miss

mag nif i cent (mag nif′ ə sənt) very rich; grand

main sail (mān′ səl) largest sail of a ship

ma lar ia (mə lãr′ ē ə) serious mosquito-carried disease that causes chills, fever, and sweating

mam mal (mam′ l) warm-blooded animal that feeds its young on milk: *Mice, rabbits, cats, dogs, cows, and elephants are mammals.*

Man dan (man′ dan) tribe of Sioux Indians of North Dakota

man tel piece
(man′ təl pēs′) shelf over a fireplace

mar i ner (mar′ ə nər) sailor

mar i o nette (mar′ ē ə net′) string-operated puppet

marsh land (märsh′ land′) land partly covered by water; swampland

mar vel ous (mär′ vəl əs) very good; surprising; wonderful

May flow er (mā′ flou′ r) ship in which the Pilgrims sailed to America in 1620

me chan i cal (mə kan′ ə kəl) having to do with or like a machine

med i cal (med′ ə kəl) having to do with medicine or doctors

mi cro scope
(mīk′ rə skōp) small device with a lens or several lenses that makes it possible for people to see things too small to be seen with the naked eye

Mi de wi win (mi dā′ wə win) secret group of medicine men among the Ojibwa Indians

mi grate (mī′ grāt) to move from one place to another

mi ra cu lous (mə rak′ yə ləs) marvelous; wonderful; going against the laws of nature

mis er a ble (miz′ ə rə bl *or* miz′ rə bl) very unhappy; very poor

mis pro nounce (mis′ prə nouns′) to pronounce wrong

mod i fy (mod′ ə fī) to change partly

Mo gul (mō′ gul) civilization in India that began in Turkey

mon grel (mong′ grəl) dog of mixed breeding; mutt

---

hat, āge, cãre, fär; let, bē, tėrm; it, īce; hot, gō, ôrder; oil, out; cup, pùt, rüle, ūse; ch, child; ng, long; th, thin; ᵀH, then; zh, measure; ə represents *a* in about, *e* in taken, *i* in April, *o* in lemon, *u* in circus.

Mon sieur (mə syə′) French: Mister

mon strous (mon′ strəs) very big; huge; like a monster

mon u ment (mon′ yə mənt) something such as a statue or a plaque set up to make people aware of the importance of a person, event, etc.

moor (mủr) wild grassy land with no trees, similar to a marshland

mor ti fi ca tion (môr′ tə fə kā′ shən) extreme shame

mous tache (mus′ tash) hair on a man's upper lip

mu cha cho (mü chä′ chō) Spanish: boy

mur mur (mèr′ mər) to speak softly and indistinctly

mu tu al (mū′ chủ l) felt or done equally by both people involved; in common

mys te ri ous (mis tēr′ ē əs) hard to understand; secret; not able to be explained

mys tery (mis′ tə rē) something that is not known; something that is extremely puzzling

nat u ral ist (nach′ ə rəl ist) one who studies animals and plants in their natural state

nav i gate (nav′ ə gāt) to sail; to figure out and steer a ship on course

nav i ga tion (nav′ ə gā′ shən) art of figuring out how to get from one place to another; steering a ship on course

nudge (nuj) to poke or push to catch someone's attention

Oba (ō′ bä) Nigerian ruler

ob serve (əb zèrv′) to look at closely; to study

ob vi ous (ob′ vē əs) clear; easily seen or understood

O jib wa (ō jib′ wä) tribe of Indians in the northern United States and Canada

O ni ko yi (ō nē kō′ yē)

op er at or (op′ r ā tər) one who runs a machine

o pin ion (ə pin′ yən) belief; feeling that something is true or likely

or di nar y (ôrd′ n er′ ē) average; usual; like most others of the same kind

or ga ni za tion (ôr′ gən ə zā′ shən) group of people who work together

o rig i nal (ə rij′ ə nəl) not like anyone or anything else; the first of its kind

or ni thol og ist (ôr′ ni thol′ ə jist) scientist who studies birds

O sage (ō sāj′) Indian tribe that lives in Missouri and Oklahoma

out rig ger (out′ rig′ r) float attached to the side of a canoe to keep it from turning over; canoe with such an attachment

pad dock (pad′ ək) pen for horses; corral

pa pa ya (pə pä′ yə) yellow tropical fruit that looks like a melon

par a chute (par′ ə shüt) large cloth shaped like an umbrella, used to bring people or things down safely from great heights

par ra keet (par′ ə kēt) small brightly colored bird kept as a pet

par tic u lar (pər tik′ yə lər) separate or different from others; unusual and distinct

pa se o (pä sā′ ō) Spanish: walk

pea cock (pē′ kok′) blue and green male bird with a beautiful tail made of very long feathers that can stand up like a fan

pen du lum (pen′ jə ləm) hanging weight that swings back and forth, often used to keep large clocks running

per ish (per′ ish) to die; to exist no longer

phil har mon ic (fil här mon′ ik) a musical organization such as a symphony orchestra; related to an orchestra

phrase (frāz) group of words

phys i ol o gy (fiz' ē ol' ə jē) study of the bodies of people and animals

Pi cas so (pi kä' sō) Pablo (päb' lō)

pi lot age (pīl' ə təj) art of steering a ship using landmarks as guides

pin cers (pin' sərz) tool for gripping and holding something, similar in shape to scissors and pliers

pipes (pīps) bagpipes

Pol y ne sia (pol' ə nē' zhə) group of islands in the southern Pacific

pome gran ate (pom' gran' it) red fruit having many seeds, which are covered with edible pulp

por cu pine (pôr' kyə pīn) animal covered with long spines or quills

por poise (pôr' pəs) large sea mammal that looks like and is related to a small species of whale

por tion (pôr' shən) part of a whole; amount; share

poul tice (pōl' tis) soft medicinelike salve that is put on a cut or wound

prat tle (prat' l) to talk on and on without making sense; to babble

pre fer (pri fèr') to like one thing better than another; to choose

pre his tor ic (prē' his tôr' ik) of the time before any known history

pres ence (prez' əns) way of acting; bearing; appearance

pre serve (pri zèrv') to keep; to fix so that it will last

pres to (pres' tō) quickly; right away

pre tend (pri tend') to make believe

pre vail (pri vāl') to triumph; to win

pri ma bal ler ina (prē' mə ba' lə rēn' ə) most important female dancer in a ballet company; ballet star

pri va teer (prī və tēr') privately owned ship allowed to attack and capture ships of enemy governments

pro long (prə lông') to make longer; to stretch out

pro pel ler (prə pel' r) revolving fanlike group of blades that moves an airplane, a boat, or some other motor-driven vehicle

puck er (puk' r) to form into wrinkles or folds

py thon (pī' thon) large African snake that kills animals by crushing them

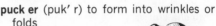

raf ter (raf' tər) beam of a roof or ceiling; large heavy piece of wood that runs across a ceiling

rare (rãr) unusual; not common

rec i pe (res' ə pē) set of directions for cooking something to eat

reck on ing (rek' n ing) calculation

re clin ing (ri klīn' ing) leaning back; lying back

re flec tion (ri flek' shən) careful thought

rep re sent a tive (rep' ri zen' tə tiv) person who speaks or acts for others

re search (ri sèrch') to hunt for facts about something

re sem ble (ri zem' bl) to be like; to look like

res er va tion (rez' èr vā' shən) place set aside for some purpose such as for Indian tribes

rip ple (rip' l) very small wave; sound of a small wave

Roo se velt (rōz' ə velt) last name of leading American family that has produced two Presidents

Rous seau (rü sō') Henri (än rē')

---

hat, āge, cãre, fär; let, bē, tèrm; it, īce; hot, gō, ôrder; oil, out; cup, pùt, rüle; ūse; ch, child; ng, long; th, thin; ŦH, then; zh, measure; ə represents *a* in about, *e* in taken, *i* in April, *o* in lemon, *u* in circus.

roy al (roi′ l) belonging to or like a king or his family

Ruiz (rü ēs′)

rum ble (rum′ bl) to make a low heavy noise

ru mor (rüm′ r) story that people pass along as news without knowing or caring whether or not it is true

rus set ap ple (rus′ ət ap′ l) kind of winter apple with rough skin

rus ty (rus′ tē) covered with rust, the reddish substance that forms when certain metals get wet

St. Law rence Riv er (sānt lôr′ əns riv′ r) river in Canada flowing northeast from Lake Ontario to the Atlantic

sal a man der
(sal′ ə man′ dər) moist-skinned animal shaped like a lizard

Satch mo (sach′ mō) nickname for Louis Armstrong

sat el lite (sat′ l īt) something that revolves around a large heavenly body, either a planet, a moon, or a man-made object that has been put into orbit

sat is fy (sat′ is fī) to give what is needed; to please

sa vor (sāv′ r) to taste slowly and with pleasure

Scan di na vi an (skan′ di nāv′ ē n) **1.** any of the group of languages of Denmark, Iceland, Norway, and Sweden. **2.** a native of Scandinavia

scare crow (skãr′ krō′) stick figure of a person, dressed in old clothes, put in a field to scare birds

schoo ner (skün′ r) sailing ship with two or more masts

scone (skōn) kind of bread made from oatmeal or barley flour

scrump tious (skrum′ shəs) very delicious; good to eat

scru tin ize (skrüt′ in īz) to look at closely and carefully; to study

sculpt (skulpt) to carve something from stone or other hard substance

sec tor (sek′ tər) part or piece

sen sa tion (sen sā′ shən) something that causes great excitement or very strong feeling

sen si ble (sen′ sə bl) showing good judgment; wise

se quoia (si kwoi′ ə) extremely tall evergreen tree that grows in California; also called redwood

shark (shärk) large rough-skinned fish that eats other fish

sher bet (shèr′ bət) fruit-flavored ice made with milk

shriek (shrēk) to scream loudly and sharply

shrug (shrug) to raise one's shoulders to show lack of knowledge or care

shuf fle (shuf′ l) to drag or push one's feet along the floor

sí (sē) Spanish: yes

Si a mese (sī ə mēz′) from Thailand, which used to be called Siam

sim mer (sim′ r) to cook at a heat just below the boiling point

sit u a tion (sich′ ü ā′ shən) the way things are; state of affairs

slime (slīm) soft sticky wet substance; ooze

slith er (sliŦH′ r) to move smoothly; glide like a snake

slot (slot) narrow opening

snore (snôr) to make a loud harsh sound while sleeping

sol i tude (sol′ ə tüd) state of being alone

sor cer er (sôr′ sər r) person who works magic; evil magician; witch

Span ish (span′ ish) language spoken in Spain and most of South and Central America and Puerto Rico

spe cies (spē′ shēz) kind; type; group of living things that are alike and closely related

sprout (sprout) to start to grow

squawk (skwôk) loud harsh cry

squirm (skwerm) to wiggle; to twist

stare (stãr) to look directly at for a long time

star fish (stär′ fish′) sea animal with five or more arms shaped like a star

stev e dore (stēv′ ə dôr) one who loads and unloads ships

stink bug (stingk′ bug′) insect that gives off an unpleasant smell

stool (stül) backless chair, symbol of an African chief's power

straight a way (strāt′ ə wā′) at once; immediately; without pause

stren u ous ly (stren′ ū əs lē) strongly; with much energy

struc ture (struk′ chər) arrangement of the parts of something

stu di o (stüd′ ē ō) room where an artist or writer works

sub mit (səb mit′) to yield without resistance; to surrender

sub stance (sub′ stəns) stuff; matter; what a thing is made of

sug ar cane (shúg′ r kān′) tall grass with a hard stem, from which a sweet sap is taken and made into sugar

Sung Dy nas ty (súng dīn′ əs tē) period of Chinese history from 960–1280

sur name (sèr′ nām′) family name; last name

sus pi cion (səs pi′ shən) feeling that someone has done something bad; belief that someone is guilty of wrongdoing

swoop (swüp) to bring down suddenly; to come down suddenly

sym pho ny (sim′ fə nē) long musical work played by an entire orchestra: *A symphony orchestra is made up of violins,* clarinets, *flutes, cornets, trombones, drums, etc.*

Ta bas co (tə bas′ kō) hot pepper sauce

Tall chief (tôl′ chēf) Maria (mə rē′ ə)

tap es try (tap′ is trē) heavy cloth material with a woven design or picture, usually used as a wall hanging

tee ter (tēt′ r) to rock back and forth

tel e graph (tel′ ə graf) way to send messages, usually in Morse code, by electrical wires

tem ple (tem′ pəl) building used for religious purposes

ten ta cle (ten′ tə kəl) long slender part or growth used to propel an animal or to feel or pick up objects

Ter Borch (tər bôrk′) Gerhard (gär′ härd)

ter ri fy (ter′ ə fī) to scare; to frighten greatly; to cause terror

Thai land (tī′ land) country in Southeast Asia, formerly called Siam

the a ter (thē′ ə tər) place where shows are put on

the o ry (thē′ ə rē) explanation; probable reason for something

thong (thông) thin strip of leather

throne (thrōn) fancy chair, like the one a king sits on

tilt (tilt) to slant; to lean

todo (tō′ dō) Spanish: all, every

tram ple (tram′ pəl) to crush; to step on heavily

trans form (trans fôrm′) to change form or appearance; to turn into something else

trib u tary (trib′ yə tèr′ ē) small river or stream that flows into a larger river; branch of a river

UNICEF (ū′ nə sef) acronym for United Nations Children's Fund

---

hat, āge, cãre, fär; let, bē, tèrm; it, īce; hot, gō, ôrder; oil, out; cup, pút, rüle, ūse; ch, child; ng, long; th, thin; ₮H, then; zh, measure; ə represents *a* in about, *e* in taken, *i* in April, *o* in lemon, *u* in circus.

uni corn (ūn′ ə kôrn) imaginary animal that looks like a horse but has one horn coming out of the middle of its forehead

uni ver sal (ū′ nə vèr′ səl) belonging to or true for everyone or everything; having to do with the universe

uni verse (ūn′ ə vèrs) everything that is; all things that exist everywhere and anywhere

uni ver si ty (ū′ nə vèr′ sə tē) most advanced school; highest place of study; large college

vac cine (vak sēn′) medicine given by mouth or needle to keep someone from getting a certain disease

van ish (van′ ish) to disappear; to become invisible

va ri e ty (və rī′ ə tē) 1. number of different things. 2. a change or difference

vary (vār′ ē) to differ; to be different

ven ture (ven′ chər) to dare; to explore or go forward

ven ture some (ven′ chər səm) daring; adventurous

ve ran da (və ran′ də) large porch

Ver di (vār′ dē) nineteenth-century Italian composer

vet er i nar i an (vet′ r ə när′ ē n) animal doctor

vig or ous (vig′ r əs) strong; full of energy

vo cab u lary (vō kab′ yə ler′ ē) all the words known by a person: *He has a large vocabulary and can make his meaning clear.*

vol un teer (vol′ n tēr′) to offer to do something for nothing

weav er (wēv′ r) one who weaves; one who makes cloth

white cap (hwīt′ kap′ *or* wīt′ kap′) white foam at top of a breaking wave

whoo zis (hüz′ is) someone; a person whose name is not remembered

wi li wi li (wē′ lē′ wē′ lē′) Hawaiian tree, the wood of which is used for making canoes

wist ful ly (wist′ fə lē) longingly; with a feeling of mild sadness

wiz ened (wiz′ ənd) dried up; wrinkled

wob ble (wob′ l) to move back and forth unsteadily

wreck er (rek′ r) worker or large machine that tears down buildings

writhe (wrīᴛʜ) to twist with pain

Wy eth (wī′ eth) Andrew (an′ drü)

yam (yam) edible root, such as a sweet potato

yearn (yèrn) to want something very much; to long for

yon der (yon′ dər) at or in a distant place pointed to

Yo ru ba (yôr′ ü bə) a language spoken in West Africa

Yo sem i te (yō sem′ ə tē)

yuc ca (yuk′ ə) large desert plant with white flowers

zuc chi ni (zü kēn′ ē) green squash that looks like a cucumber